INCLUSIVE SCIENCE STRATEGIES

Greg Stefanich—Editor

ISBN 978-0-7575-4560-3

This material is based upon work supported by the National Science Foundation under Grant No. NSF-HRD-0533197. Any opinions, findings, and conclusions or recommendations expressed in this material are those of the author(s) and do not necessarily reflect the views of the National Science Foundation. Permission is granted to copy these materials for noncommercial purposes provided the source is acknowledged.

Printed in the United States of America

1 2 3 4 5 6 7 8 9 10 12 11 10 09 08 07

Contributing Authors

Rather than being an original composition, this book is a synthesis of work rewritten and edited from professional papers, and activity ideas. The structure of the activity sequences are modifications of materials from programs developed through National Science Foundation Supported Curriculum Development Projects in the 1960s and 70s. A significant amount of the material was gleaned from the work of students attending the University of Northern Iowa. In addition, I drew from other professionals who possess similar goals towards educational equity for all students particularly Dr. Edward Keller, Jr. from the University of West Virginia and Ms. Linda McCartney from the University of Northern Iowa.

Table of Contents

List of Tables

List of Figures

Preface

The material in this book should be of interest to everyone who is concerned about creating an educational setting where every child can be a successful learner. The book is an effort to incorporate new insights about how information drawn from research and educational practice can be used to address the everyday problems of teaching. In schools all over the United States there are students of widely ranging abilities, many different cultural backgrounds, and often several languages are spoken. The book contains models and strategies specific to science instruction to help teachers structure their classroom so that all students have an opportunity to learn. Students need an environment where they can be active participants and contributing members of the learning community.

In Chapter 1, the rationale for inclusive education is presented, along with its benefits for students with and without disabilities alike. The challenge to teachers and schools is explored, particularly in terms of various categories of disabilities.

Chapter 2 presents a model for organizing instructional practice and managing students in an inclusive classroom. Well-organized classrooms with effective instructional practices reduce the number of management interventions for all students. Effective teachers support students in their learning and have clearly defined expectations and limits. However, students with disabilities often have unique learning needs and sometimes engage in behaviors that interfere with learning and instruction. Suggestions for adaptations are shared. An evaluation tool, the Cascade Model Management Profile, (Appendices A and B) is aligned with the chapter.

Chapter 3 presents five proven models of effective instructional practice in the science classroom. Heightening the awareness of these models provides teachers with an improved arsenal of tools to vary instructional practice based on desired learner outcomes. Applications of each model are presented in Chapters 5-9.

Chapter 4 shares special accommodations for students who have unique learning needs. Real experience in science is critical for any learner. Locating and utilizing resources, making accommodations, and structuring the learning environment so that all students can learn is an essential teacher responsibility. The chapter provides specific suggestions by disability category for classroom instruction, in science laboratories, and special accommodations in field settings.

Chapter 5 contains an activity sequence on Skeletal Systems applying **Mastery Teaching**, a model popularized at the UCLA Laboratory School and credited to Madeline Hunter (1982). The strategy is particularly effective in providing learning alternatives for students through skill enhancement activities and small-group instruction.

Chapter 6 contains an activity sequence on the Suffocating Candle applying a convergent strategy **Direct Instruction** where student learning is directed toward behavioral outcomes determined and communicated to the students in advance. It reflects a business-like approach to education. The materials and activities in this sequence were specifically selected with consideration to the educational needs of students with disabilities. Handling glassware of different sizes and working around fire important experiences for all youth because they are frequently encountered in adult living. Without proper experiences the likelihood of accidents with major consequences increases. Yet outside of school many children are "protected" from these experiences by adults and guardians, making in-school experiences even more critical. The framework presented in this sequence is intended to provide a template for lesson development.

Chapter 7 contains a sequence that combines exploration, convergent instruction, and divergent reasoning into a single strategy, called **Guided Discovery**. The strategy is highly popular in contemporary science curriculum materials in the format of a 5-part learning cycle called the 5-E's (Expose, Explore, Explain, Extend and Evaluate). The conceptual scheme of Energy is addressed in the instructional sequence.

Chapter 8 contains a series of activities consisting of discrepant events in a strategy called **Inquiry Teaching**. It is an approach used to determine if students can demonstrate an understanding of a concept by challenging them with an unfamiliar task or discrepant event. The concept of Density is developed through a series of activities.

Chapter 9 contains two activity sequences that allow a teacher to facilitate student learning through **Exploratory Learning**. The approach helps students develop confidence in their ability to learn and reason in a supportive and non-threatening environment. The approach may be particularly valuable for students with disabilities and others who are not confident and who frequently experience frustration and a lack of success in other learning tasks such as basic skills. Puzzling Powders provides an introductory exposure to analytical chemistry. The second sequence involves investigating electricity.

Acknowledgements

I wish to acknowledge a few of the many people who provided assistance and support over the past thirty years. The publication is a result of accumulated information from many conferences and workshops, and my work with students. Contributions came from scientists and engineers with disabilities, science educators, teachers at all levels, and many university students. I wish to acknowledge some who are most noteworthy. I thank the students at the University of Northern Iowa for their patience, tolerance, and support as I worked to infuse and try out ideas in my courses. Their contributions, through assignments and oral discourse, have always been helpful. Worthy of special note is Dr. Ed Keller at the University of West Virginia who spearheaded efforts to improve science instruction for students with disabilities for four decades. Many of the suggested accommodations were gleaned from his pioneering work. Courtney Ihde, as a student worker, provided secretarial and technical support on every aspect of the project. Appreciation is expressed to Carole Yates, Cheryl Smith and Joyce Broell, who provided editing and technical assistance.

Many professional organizations provided support. The Directors of the Human Resource Development Program at the National Science Foundation, who provided insight and ongoing encouragement for these efforts. I have appreciated collegial support from the American Association for the Advancement of Science, the National Science Teachers Association, the Association for Science Teacher Education and the Science Education for Students with Disabilities Association. Most recently I wish to express appreciation from other members of the Alliance for Students with Disabilities, the DO-IT Program at the University of Washington, RASEM at New Mexico State University, and EAST at the University of Southern Maine.

This material is based upon work supported by the National Science Foundation under Grant No. NSF-HRD-0533197. Any opinions, findings, and conclusions or recommendations expressed in this material are those of the author(s) and do not necessarily reflect the views of the National Science Foundation.

Chapter 1
On the Outside Looking In

This publication blends research, theory, and practice to guide the classroom teacher in using teaching strategies that serve all students. It is designed as a resource book for preservice and inservice teachers. The primary goals are: a) to instill in every teacher the patience, optimism, and generosity to bring out the best in his or her students, b) to encourage a commitment to make every child feel important and appreciated, and c) to provide suggestions and checklists for self-analysis and reflection to assist any teacher seeking ideas in science teaching.

If American education is devoted to offering opportunities for *all* students to gain sufficient schooling to help them make life choices and become productive members of society, then *all teachers* must have the knowledge to make appropriate adaptations so that every student, regardless of ability or disability, can become an active participant in the learning process. This basic statement brings to the forefront the complex nature of the issues of teaching science to students with disabilities. Because of that complexity, there is a great need to educate teachers to help them learn to make needed adaptations.

In education curricula, science and social studies present special problems. They promote special opportunities for developing resources, but they are both broad fields with an extensive and rapidly expanding knowledge base. Teachers will never agree on which segments of that knowledge base are of the greatest value for learners and future citizens. However, we do know that teaching the processes (tools of the scientist) is critical to having students develop the logic structures they need to understand the concepts in these disciplines.

Often, when it comes to educating all students the attitude today in a large majority of classrooms is "equal treatment is fair treatment," particularly for students who demonstrate academic achievement at acceptable levels. Many times, the students most seriously shortchanged are those with disabilities who have average or above-average academic performance. The only services they receive relate to general accommodations (like translators, assistive access devices, and interpreters). They receive little or no accommodations in science classrooms or laboratories. They are expected to be the "observers" or, if they wish to participate, to become "experts" in providing their own suggestions for accommodation. Fair treatment isn't about equal treatment; it is about giving all students what they need to have a successful learning experience. Yet, the perception of "equal treatment" persists. School personnel, the families of school children, and even the students themselves generally believe:

- Students are responsible for their own learning.
- When students don't learn, there is something wrong with them.
- Schools need to determine what's wrong, with as much precision as possible, so students can be directed to the tracks, curricula, teachers, and classrooms that match their learning profiles.

These attitudes and beliefs must change. This publication is devoted to helping educators examine their roles and responsibilities in serving the needs of all students in our schools and to focusing on an awareness of unique conditions and needs of students with disabilities. Consider the few elements listed below as needed shifts in current educational practice to more inclusive education for all:

- A shift away from bureaucratic schools structured and organized according to ability, and a shift toward schools structured around student diversity with an instructional program that includes many different ways of organizing students for learning.
- A shift away from teaching approaches that emphasize the teacher as the one who disseminates content that students must retain, and a shift toward teaching approaches that emphasize the role

of the learner in creating knowledge, competence, and the ability to pursue further learning.

- A shift away from the school's role of providing educational services, and a shift toward a role of providing educational supports for learning.
- A shift away from trying to change or diminish a diverse school culture, and a shift toward valuing diversity.

Why Inclusive Education?

Most people's conditioning comes from a multitude of experiences with family and peers, plus observing and interacting with others in a variety of settings. Interpersonal communication skills are reflected in a person's ability to transmit and receive information from others. But the life experiences for most persons with disabilities are significantly different from those of the general population. Their opportunities to experience and fully adjust to the mores of the majority culture are usually much more limited. In cases of sensory and/or processing deficits, the disabled person may not process experiences in the same way as the general population. The nuances of interpersonal communication are highly sophisticated, and even small deviations can transform feelings of trust and confidence to feelings of skepticism and avoidance.

Many elements of day-to-day social integration may present special challenges for students with disabilities. In the case of congenital disabilities, the relationship with the mother and family may have been disruptive due to the uniqueness of the situation. Interactions with the extended family may also be influenced. During early childhood, the quality and extent of interactions with other children and with the greater community outside the family may be significantly affected. During later childhood, group games and team activities are critical for effective social development. But students with disabilities are often excluded because accommodations are necessary to participate as a team member at the same rate or pace of others in the group. Adolescence has some special challenges as individuals investigate interactions involving intimate relationships with a member of the opposite sex. These settings are where adolescents discover interactions that are bonding, interactions that create negative perceptions, and interactions that create appropriate steps to move a relationship from one of acquaintance to one of love and caring. Yet students with disabilities are often excluded from the gatherings and parties where these interactions are played out.

Some things are changing. The personal computer has dramatically increased participation for persons with disabilities as new adaptations emerge from improved technology and engineering. This has allowed many persons with disabilities to greatly improve their receptive and expressive communication, providing more opportunities for frequent daily interactions with other people. However, many of these adaptations are expensive, particularly subject-specific adaptations in the science classroom or laboratory. Non-disabled individuals with narrow views on civil and human rights may perceive this expense as being unfair or detracting from the needs of the general population.

Because of the special challenges of social integration for people with disabilities, the educational environment is an ideal setting to blend persons with physical, cultural, emotional, and intellectual diversity into a cohesive, mutually supportive group. Group synergism can become more powerful than the collective output of each person acting independently. In a democracy, this is what society is searching for and what businesses seek in their employees. Why shouldn't it be the essence of what we wish to accomplish in schooling? To accomplish these outcomes, the talents and abilities of *everyone* must be considered. The environment and interactions must be adjusted and modified to meet the capabilities and potentials of each individual.

Signature Feelings

To begin understanding how a school setting can become a supportive, inclusive learning community for all students, educators need insight into why their students feel/react as they do. Signature feelings are one major element of everyone's personal abilities to set and reach goals and to feel part of a community.

Signature feelings are inclinations, often unconscious, that have a significant effect on decisions individuals make about relationships. These feelings are often imprints from one comment or one episode that influence choices concerning interactions. These feelings often result in stereotypes (e.g. "you can't trust..., ...has problems with alcohol") and inappropriate generalizations. They affect personal decisions (e.g. the comment overheard from your mother in a telephone conversation with your aunt—"...is a nice girl but she is not very good in mathematics") regarding career choices and goal setting. These signature feelings become carried out in everyday life. They relate to those you greet on the street or whom you interact with in social situations, and they relate to your academic dispositions (e.g. "I shouldn't take advanced algebra; I'm not very good in math"). Signature feelings affect both academic and social choices, it is important for educators to have this awareness in interacting with students.

Persons with disabilities experience many challenges and disappointments resulting from the signature feelings they get from others. This often narrows their opportunities in interpersonal relationships, influences their choices of independence over interdependence, and limits their personal and professional lives.

Consistency is critical in nurturing social behaviors. However, persons with disabilities frequently experience inconsistency because adults and even peers often vary their interactions based on prejudices and attitudes in a social context. To perceive trust but experience avoidance can be a debilitating interaction for an individual. The result of inconsistent social overtures often creates signature feelings such as not trusting your dispositions of acceptance, or expecting the pain of avoidance if a social context changes. The long-term result often becomes to play relationships "close to the heart" rather than confidently reaching out toward collaborative opportunities. Yet skills of confidence and trust are the exact skills that enable people to advance professionally and move through the management hierarchy.

The role of educators is critical in nurturing the interpersonal development of students with disabilities. Professionals in each educational context need to work vigorously to refocus their signature feelings about students with disabilities to become more inclusive and more accepting in their teaching.

Meeting the social-emotional needs of all students is difficult, and some may perceive it as being outside the arena of appropriate educational services. To address these needs, one must consider not only the generally accepted norms of mutual cooperation and respect, but also other elements such as etiquette and cultural values. Many students with disabilities (particularly those with physical disabilities, learning disabilities, and attention deficit disorders) have an input deficit or a processing deficit that affects their ability to understand the subtle, and sometimes the obvious, messages in an interaction. Individuals with social-emotional anomalies are also more likely to experience inconsistencies in feedback concerning relationships. So, having an opportunity to engage in private interactions can be where those with limited social experiences gain the capacity to feel comfortable and secure in other informal social settings. The social context of the school should be safe and secure for all those present, and assistance should be provided to help those who experience social anxieties.

The social and emotional diversity among students with disabilities closely parallels that of the general population. Sometimes there's an inclination to cluster people to describe common characteristics, but this can present some particularly difficult circumstances for persons with low-incidence disabilities. Are some persons with disabilities bubbly and expressive while others are reserved? Do some seek ways to avoid work while others are responsible and remain persistent? Do some avoid uncertain circumstances while others seem to be overanxious risk-takers? Yes, all are true for persons with disabilities just like for the general population.

In fact, many persons with disabilities are not pleased with events like "disability awareness day," just as many would be displeased with something like "obesity awareness day." These platforms tend to overlook the uniqueness and dignity of the individual. Most individuals know the challenges and inconveniences they must face, and with appropriate accommodations, probably prefer to address them in a private manner. Inappropriate treatment by adults is a common daily experience for many persons with disabilities. Whether it is overt discomfort, being ignored or avoided, being the target of lower expectations and/or contributions, each experience has a way of saying "you don't belong." Perhaps one of the highest levels of courage are persons with disabilities who, in spite of constant bombardment with rejection signals and being undervalued, wake up in the morning and say inside "I will try again today." A large percentage of persons who have special life challenges avoid social contexts where their disabilities will affect their interactions. No one appreciates being rejected, and these dispositions are frequently transmitted in group situations, particularly when significant numbers of the people are unfamiliar with each other. Social experiences are frequently much more traumatic and have more long-lasting avoidance responses (many times physical) than physical challenges related to disability accommodations.

In general, persons with obvious physical disabilities receive fewer negative reactions than those with "invisible disabilities." In fact, it is not unusual to hear people privately discuss what they may call "advantaged disabilities." Some people consider "advantaged disabilities" to be deviate maneuvers by guardians or the individuals themselves to use a disability label to leverage additional services or preferential employment conditions. In fact, people usually react with surprise, and often disbelief, when they are told that persons with disabilities are not a "protected class" in the workplace as are females and minorities. The Individuals with Disabilities Education Act (IDEA) (1990) and Americans with Disabilities Act (ADA) (1999) essentially extend equal opportunity for those with disabilities so they can experience the same services and opportunities that have always been accessible to the general population. They are not receiving something extra; they are gaining access to what the general population has taken for granted as being universally available. American schools purport to provide an appropriate and challenging assortment of educational opportunities for all citizens. In the case of students with disabilities, this may often result in a substantive expense, just as medical or legal expenses are accrued if a person encounters an illness, accident, or a miscarriage of justice. Even so, everyone should have a right to pursue happiness and to fully experience the resources made available to the general citizenry.

Likewise, the ability to use language and numbers to acquire information and make decisions is a tremendous advantage in modern society. The purpose of education in America is to develop these abilities in *all* youth, not only those who fit the general norms. Extending special services to those who are not fully developing these skills in a traditional delivery system should be as natural as changing your walking path when there is an obstacle ahead. The essence of decision making is to modify and adjust in order to obtain a positive outcome.

Teaching Science to Students with Disabilities: Where We Are and Where We Need to Go

Numbers of Students Served

The United States Department of Education's National Center for Educational Statistics (2004) reported that 13.8% of all students in 2003-04 had a disabling condition, reflecting a population of 6,633,000 individuals receiving special services in schools.

- Learning disabilities, including attention deficit disorders (42.7%)
- speech and language impairments (21.7%)
- mental retardation (8.9%)
- serious emotional disturbances (7.4%)

Approximately 8.2% of school-age students had a physical disability or health impairment. The U.S. Department of Education (2004) reported the following number of students with disabilities:

- speech or language impaired - 2.3% (1,022,000)
- hard of hearing and deaf – 1.2 % (79,000)
- motor/orthopedic impaired - .2% (77,000)
- other health impaired – 1.0% (464,000)
- visually impaired - .1% (28,000)
- multi-disabled -.3% (140,000)

In addition, other identified conditions eligible for special education services include:

- learning disabled – 5.9% (2,831,000);
- mentally impaired – 1.2% (593,000); and
- seriously emotionally disturbed – 1.0% (489,000).

There is enormous variation in these impairments. They can assume many forms, and each requires some specific and unique accommodations for instruction. These impairments, particularly in the case of health impairments, may require many different adaptations day-to-day depending upon the effects of the disability itself (i.e. acute occurrences, progressive diseases, or incapacitating conditions), the effects of the medication used to treat the disability, and the changing conditions of the learning environment. A frequently neglected group consists of the most talented students with physical disabilities. Over 500,000 gifted students with disabilities receive little accommodation because they are achieving "on grade level," or get special help from persons without the content knowledge to fully understand their academic needs.

Based on the total population of students with disabilities, it is apparent that there is a significant discrepancy between expected performance and student proficiency as measured in reference to a norm population. Data specific to science is lacking because there is not a consistent framework for defining and/or measuring core knowledge. However reading and mathematics do provide such a reference base. Table 1 provides a summary of the discrepancy between grade level norms on standardized tests and the grade level they are attending in reading and mathematics by disability category for 17-year-old students in American schools. The data reveals that, as a group, students with disabilities are 3.6 grade levels below the norm population in both reading and mathematics. Furthermore only about 1 in 8 students are at or above grade level. Around 20% are 1 to 2.9 grade levels behind, about 40% are 3 to 4.9 grade levels behind, and over 25% are 5 or more grade levels behind their peers. One could argue that the data exists because in some disability categories, such as learning disabilities or developmental delays, the data offers evidence of student inability or inattentiveness to successfully compete in academic tasks with their peers. However when one looks at physical disabilities (orthopedic impairments, visual impairments, other health impairments, and hearing impairments), the data reflects the same major discrepancies.

Table 1.

Discrepancy between Tested and Actual Grade Levels in Reading and Mathematics of Students with Disabilities

	Reading	Mathematics
Mean grade-level discrepancy between students' tested and actual grade levels	-3.6	-3.6
Percentage of students whose abilities are:		
Above grade level, at grade level, or less than 1 grade level behind	12.4	12.8
1 to 2.9 grade levels behind	20.9	20.7
3 to 4.9 grade levels behind	40.8	40.2
5 or more grade levels behind	26.0	26.4

From "The Academic Performance of Secondary School Students with Disabilities," by J. Blackorby, M. Chorost, N. Garza, A. Guzman, 2003, in *The Achievements of Youth with Disabilities During Secondary School. A Report from the National Longitudinal Transition Studies-2 (NLTS2)* by M. Wagner, C. Marder, J. Blackorby, R. Camato, P. Newman, P. Levine, E. Davies-Mercier, et al. Copyright 2003 by the National Longitudinal Transition Studies-2.

More specific data related to student performance disaggregated by disability category is presented in Table 2. From that data it is clear that large numbers of students with disabilities are not receiving an education that enables them to fully participate in educational experiences that are at an appropriate level to challenge their thinking. The cumulative effect of being marginalized in an educational setting is clearly evidenced in the secondary school data. A consistent research base, recently iterated in the work of Kati Haycock (2001) and supported by decades of prior research on student achievement, shows that teachers matter a lot. What teachers do to help all students succeed is often critical, especially for students represented in the "achievement gap" including minority students, students with disabilities, and socio-economically disadvantaged students. All students must have a challenging curriculum with standards to meet and any extra help needed.

Exceptional teachers do extra things, they make sure the learning opportunities are accessible to all students and they provide support and encouragement to all learners. Saunders and Rivers (1996) sum it up when they reported some of the classrooms showing the greatest achievement gains were filled with low-income students. They stated, "It is not the students after all; something is going on with the teaching." A report from the Boston Public Schools (1998) showed that in one academic year, when compared, the upper one-third of teachers produced six times as much learning growth as the bottom one-third of teachers.

In classrooms across our nation, teachers must have the skills and resources to engage each and every student under their tutelage. Melvin Levine (2002), in the book, *Mind at a Time*, concluded that teachers can generate ideas about how to teach through the personal ways that students learn when they commit themselves to acquiring the background knowledge. A challenge is to educate and engage science teachers about their responsibilities and to provide support so they gain a sense of accomplishment and satisfaction for their efforts. Linda Albert (1996), in *Cooperative Discipline*, noted three C's: Capable, Connect, and Contribute. Students need adults who can convince them that they are capable whatever their native abilities. Teachers need to work with each student on aspects of socialization that develop a connection between life in the classroom, the student's life, and the lives of fellow students. Teachers must look at the abilities of each individual and construct an environment where each learner can contribute.

Many students with disabilities are not able to acquire the desired learning outcomes as quickly as other students. Just as there is considerable variation in the ability of an individual to bounce and shoot a basketball, we must understand that equal variation exists with all other aspects of learning and performance. Mark Cooper (2005), in his book *Bound and Determined*, described the word **compensation** as an effective way to help students develop this mental and emotional armor. He stated this can only be accomplished if the learner learns to accept two very important personal characteristics -- deficits and strengths. He believes that children who learn to accept their deficits learn not only that there is something to overcome, but also that they can go beyond their present level of functioning. In discussing his own learning disabilities and challenges in the classroom Cooper noted that recognizing your deficits is not enough. It is learning what to do with the deficits that is essential. The learner must develop tenacity and persistence. He further said that because school provides so many reminders of their deficits, it is typically much harder for struggling learners to embrace their strengths.

There are times when strengths can emerge from natural abilities such as the expressive arts or athletics. However, other strengths exist in the inner realm and must require more in-depth cultivation. Cooper (2005) listed some of the strengths as tenacity, determination, delayed gratification, resisting temptation, patience, persistence, perseverance, and risk-taking. Although a few students may possess these abilities, Cooper said in most cases they need to be brought forth if the individual is to survive the tribulations of learning problems. This often requires that parents and teachers devote an extraordinary amount of time to encourage and support such attitudes and behaviors (p. 88-89). Cooper listed several leading educators who note these attitudes and behaviors as core dispositions (Boyer, 1995; Devine, Seuk and Wilson, 2001; Rich, 1992; Goleman, 1995). It is these traits, Cooper noted, that enable the students' to struggle through the obstacles they will inevitably face. He stated educators must label, describe, demonstrate, rehearse, monitor, and reinforce these success skills with students who have disabilities. Without these tools for success in their arsenal, academics for students with disabilities are seen as insurmountable tasks; apathy and frustration inevitably dominate their lives in school.

Table 2.

Discrepancy between Tested and Actual Grade Levels in Reading and Mathematics, by Disability Category

	Learning Disability	Speech/ Language Impairment	Developme ntal Delay	Emotional Disturbance	Hearing Impairment	Visual Impairment	Orthopedic Impairment	Other Health Impairment	Autism	Traumatic Brain Injury	Multiple Disabilities	Deaf-Blindness
Reading												
Mean discrepancy in years between tested and actual grade level	-3.4	-3.2	-6.3	-2.2	-3.6	-2.6	-2.8	-2.4	-4.2	-4.6	-5.8	-5.3
Percentage of students with test scores:												
Above grade level, at grade level, or less than 1 grade level behind,	10.8	13.1	.5	28.6	19.4	28.5	29.5	25.1	18.8	8.7	3.6	12.6
1 to 2.9 grade levels behind,	23.3	24.0	2.7	25.6	13.1	20.2	20.4	28.4	11.4	16.8	5.8	6.2
3 to 4.9 grade levels behind,	45.1	42.8	32.4	31.3	34.9	36.2	25.4	30.7	25.9	26.9	33.0	25.6
5 or more grade levels behind	20.8	20.0	64.4	14.5	32.6	15.2	24.7	15.8	44.0	47.6	57.6	55.7
Mathematics												
Mean discrepancy in years between tested and actual grade level.	-3.2	-3.4	-6.1	-2.9	-3.0	-2.7	-3.4	-2.9	-4.9	-4.4	-5.9	-4.6
Percentage of students with test scores:												
Above grade level, at grade level, or less than 1 grade level behind,	13.6	15.2	2.4	14.7	21.7	24.4	23.6	20.1	13.4	9.6	3.2	17.3
1 to 2.9 grade levels behind,	22.8	16.6	4.6	29.0	17.6	26.8	16.0	23.7	9.8	13.7	6.8	15.2
3 to 4.9 grade levels behind,	43.9	50.4	24.8	37.0	37.8	29.3	28.2	37.7	24.8	35.4	35.0	23.2
5 or more grade levels behind	19.7	17.8	68.3	19.3	22.9	19.5	32.2	18.5	52.0	41.3	54.9	44.3

From "The Academic Performance of Secondary School Students with Disabilities," by J. Blackorby, M. Chorost, N. Garza, A. Guzman, 2003, in *The Achievements of Youth with Disabilities During Secondary School. A Report from the National Longitudinal Transition Studies-2 (NLTS2)* by M. Wagner, C. Marder, J. Blackorby, R. Camato, P. Newman, P. Levine, E. Davies-Mercier, et al. Copyright 2003 by the National Longitudinal Transition Studies-2.

The Challenge for Teachers and Schools

Legislation from PL 94-142, SB 504, ADA, and IDEA (1990, 1997, 2004) are all initiatives to provide equal opportunities for persons with disabilities to experience the same full and independent life available to the general population. Over 30 years ago the Education of All Handicapped Children Act (PL 94-142) was enacted. But are general classroom teachers better educated to serve students with special needs today? Do our teacher preparation programs provide more than an awareness of types and characteristics of exceptionality? Do teachers entering the profession receive adequate preparation on assistance, training, and services to meet the needs of all exceptional learners? And, are these services and resources available in our schools? A first and foremost preparation challenge is to familiarize science educators and practicing science teachers with educational practices that will allow students with disabilities an opportunity to experience a program in science that is challenging and rewarding commensurate with their capabilities.

All science teachers must develop proficiency in how to make appropriate adaptations in curriculum content, teaching materials, physical settings, instructional strategies, and assessment instruments for students with disabilities. The challenge for educators is not only to improve teaching, but also to put in place mechanisms that elicit student participation and responsibility. This must be characterized by clear vision and coordinated, consistent, and purposeful actions (Stefanich, 1994). Cawley (1994) reported that science teachers generally have little training or experience working with students with disabilities, and in general, special educators have little or no exposure to science. Patton, Polloway, and Cronin (1990) in a survey of special education teachers found (a) 42% of special education teachers received no training in science; (b) 38% of children in self-contained special education classes did not receive any instruction in science; (c) among special educators who did teach science, nearly half devoted less than 60 minutes a week to science, and nearly 90% of the teachers surveyed depended upon a textbook for science instruction. Ysseldyke, Thurlow, Christenson, and Weiss (1987) reported that for students with mild disabilities, approximately 200 minutes of reading instruction was received for one minute of science instruction.

Research in education has indicated a continuing lack of responsiveness by science teachers to adjust the learning environment so students with disabilities feel a sense of success and accomplishment. In an examination of science grades for over 400 students with mild disabilities in grades 9-12 , Cawley, Kahn, and Tedesco (1989) reported 50-60% of the grades were Ds or Fs. Donahoe and Zigmond (1988) reported 69% of the science grades for ninth grade students with learning disabilities were D or below. Jones's (1992) research indicated students with learning disabilities demonstrated a reduced sense of control in all aspects of their lives as compared with non-disabled peers. She stated: "They often fail to develop efficient and effective strategies for learning. They do not know how to control and direct their thinking to learn, to gain more knowledge, or how to remember what they learn" (p. 136).

The best index of an effective school for all students is how the adults interact with other adults. Adults may think they teach students how to behave by managing behavior, or teach them responsibility by holding them responsible. But these are actions of control and power demonstrating dominance by an adult over someone who is lesser, either in strength or ability. Children don't learn to talk like adults through direct interaction with adults. Rather, they learn to talk by watching and listening to adults talk. Much work is needed in the school community to have the adults model the types of actions towards students with disabilities that they would like their students to exhibit as adults. It begins when students leave for school. All adults, including bus drivers, teacher associates, custodial staff, teachers, and administrators need guidance on greeting all people in ways that make them feel important and appreciated. Students need to see this every day and experience consistency. They can learn the importance and value of a positive disposition, but only if there is strong modeling by adults.

Another challenge for teachers is knowing how to adapt and modify. Significant differences can be seen between teachers who teach groups of students and those who look at the uniqueness of each individual. Communication and understanding are needed for all students, but especially for those with disabilities. They do make the life of teachers more difficult and challenging because standard instructional materials are often not appropriate. The type and time of modification must reflect the context of the student's needs. American education has a long-standing history of low expectations for students with disabilities. These expectations influence (a) the amount of time students with disabilities spend learning science and the amount of time they are actively engaged in investigation in the science laboratory, (b) the academic focus and quality of objectives, (c) the sequence and depth of the learning opportunities afforded to students, (d) access to knowledge and resources, (e) homework expectations, and (f) curriculum alignment. A common danger students with disabilities encounter is the cumulative effects of sympathy and low expectations. A convenient teaching action is just to expect less from those who don't perform well on common group assignments. Similar low expectations occur by having the student with disabilities only be an observer during science experiments or by providing peer assistance in activities that require writing or fine motor coordination.

When students realize low expectations, it may be the result of teacher decisions that sustain mediocrity in students. Teachers must make hundreds of decisions every day. In trying to cope with the intensity of multiple inputs, decisions are often made quickly, carried out, and forgotten. Ask yourself if your reactions and actions often become so automatic that you are unaware of your own thinking processes.

In much the same way, students often just start doing an assignment when it is made without reflecting on previous learning. They do not think about why they are doing the assignment, and they seldom reflect on the thinking skills and strategies after they are done such patterns of carelessness are reinforced consistently in the traditional educational system. Papers are turned in, graded, and returned. The same students always get the As, and the same students always get the lower grades. Papers that reflect substandard efforts are not returned to the students to be redone; quality standards are not met through a series of refinements; and complaints are expressed about the quality of student work. Educators too often fit this operational definition of insanity: "repeating the same thing and expecting different results." The same complaints from teachers have been common for centuries, yet examinations of professional practice indicate little change in teaching methods concerning testing, grading, and expectations for all students.

A major thread common to meeting expectations, performing successfully, and advancing in the adult world is the effective use of language. Therefore, throughout the year, extra effort should be devoted to the process of contextual language instruction in an atmosphere of support, acceptance, and refinement for all students. Communication skills require rigor and repetition. Proofreading, refining, and precision in an accepting environment are essential skills in developing a growing, conscientious attitude about clarity and effective communication. Science teachers can model the importance of the language arts and mathematics as essential process skills for clear and articulate communication.

On the other hand, expecting too much of students can be equally devastating. Many physical disabilities place a strain on a student's endurance and time. The student probably needs more rest, may take longer to get ready for school or to get set up for homework, and may find activities physically challenging that are routine for most students. Much depends upon the relationship between the student and the teacher in establishing an appropriate balance.

Teachers also need skills as effective coaches who have the ability to enlist support, cooperation, and responsibility from all players. They develop a team synergism that accomplishes more than each individual alone using all members' unique skills and responsibilities that will help bring about success. This is exactly what effective teachers also do. Their ability to instill in each child his or her worth and importance as a learner and to develop a class cohesiveness are critical teaching skills. These teaching skills help students remain persistent because they all feel important and appreciated. Effective schools have structure and order, a business-like environment. Students in the school should have a place to be and a meaningful responsibility that is appropriate and challenging from the time they enter until the time they leave. Nurturing a positive climate, sharing responsibility to assist students in the development of basic skills, and helping with management and routines should not rest with certain individuals. All professionals must perceive these elements as joint and collective responsibilities.

If you perceive yourself only as a science teacher, you are meeting just a part of your responsibility as an educator. Highly effective teachers address student socialization as well as academic instruction. Time and attention should be devoted every day to helping an isolated child become a part of the class and school community. However, teachers must be aware that not all students carry the same perception of what it means to be included. There are those who are more comfortable being quiet, and these behaviors must be respected as well. By getting to know each student, most teachers will be able to distinguish whether school relationships are healthy or need improvement. If there are difficulties, teachers can help bring everyone into the community of scholars who work together and celebrate the accomplishments of each other. Good schools value and support the healthy generation and socialization of *everyone* present.

Making Accommodations

Physical disabilities

Physical adaptations and emotional adaptations have a permeating importance for all settings and all individuals. In addition to making the curriculum more accessible, they communicate to everyone that all individuals are important, and we have different needs depending upon personal circumstances.

Opportunities to expand awareness of science come in many forms. A beetle is brought in from the preschool playground during outdoor play. An elementary teacher introduces the science process of predicting by using bouncing balls. A middle-level teacher takes the class on a trip to the seashore. A high school chemistry lab uses acids and bases in titration. These events and many more every day offer an opportunity for all students to expand their awareness of science.

However, in many cases the student with disabilities does not get to handle things because of teacher inconvenience, unwillingness to make adaptations, or the teacher's overall lack of awareness and sensitivity. Early experiences, extending throughout the school-age years, often instill in disabled students the idea that their role is one of a "passive observer" in an active learning setting. As a result, students with disabilities often become passive observers in activity-centered settings because their unique needs are not considered with sufficient positive regard. It is not surprising that a lack of exploratory experiences in childhood and adolescence becomes a barrier to later learning, particularly when the primary means of instruction are expository, verbal, or through print materials.

Robert Rehwoldt, a paraplegic chemist, described the lack of sufficient consideration given to providing a physical environment in which the disabled can participate. He stated:

> Most high school science laboratories are not constructed so that the student with orthopedic disabilities can participate in experiments. Limited resources and a lack of imagination may have actually prevented high school students with disabilities from experiencing science in a positive and constructively challenging fashion. (As cited in Rehwoldt & Samoff, 1978, p. 132)

In studies on the instruction of deaf students, Lang (1994) stated that the majority of science instruction deaf students receive is by teachers with inadequate content preparation in the discipline. Less than 5% of teachers of deaf children reported a major in the physical sciences. He concluded, "Although 86% of deaf students report liking science, their academic preparation is inadequate for post-secondary education" (p. 148).

Often, simple teacher initiatives to make students with disabilities feel important and appreciated can pay rich dividends in student cooperation and initiative. Consider the following reflections from an individual who experienced a mild bout with polio at age 12.

> I consider myself fortunate to have been raised in a small community with very limited services. Shared responsibility for chores and membership in a large family tended to prevent any tendencies for a sedentary lifestyle. The greatest difficulties encountered were emotional and social, feeling insecure in my ability to establish friendships or caring relationships. My major physical barriers were a lack of coordination and limited endurance. There were no special education services in the community other than a traveling speech therapist who served several districts in the county. My physical rehabilitation program required frequent absences from school during junior high school because the closest rehabilitation services were 30 miles away. Academic accommodations rested largely upon the sensitivity and willingness of individual teachers to modify and adapt instruction. (Stefanich et al., 2001, p. 10)

Many educators might consider the most successful modifications made for this student to be inappropriate. For example, an English teacher discussed assignments individually and allowed the student to make oral presentations before the start of school rather than in front of the class; an algebra teacher waived homework assignments and gave a grade based just on test scores; and an English teacher modified and adapted writing assignments for each student, not only those with disabilities, in a high school of 90 students. Most important of all was the non-verbal communication from teachers, some who showed encouragement and acceptance. However, others created a sense of isolation and rejection because they felt modifications interfered with the standard academic program being presented. If students with disabilities can constantly count on those who care and are willing to accommodate, they can cope with those who are less considerate of their needs. The impact of a single teacher can have a profound effect on the development of any student, but this is especially true for a student with special needs. As a teacher, it is your choice. Are you willing to put yourself into the minds of children and make accommodations that will promote their healthy development? One teacher, in one setting, can make a world of difference.

A publication of the American Chemical Society titled *Working Chemists with Disabilities* (Blumenkopf, Stern, Swanson, & Wohlers, 1996) contains annotations from the careers of practicing chemists and descriptions of accommodations that make their professional work more successful. The following paragraphs present commentary drawn from the descriptions, which will enlighten teachers of students with disabilities.

The biographies indicate the most serious barriers are attitudinal rather than physical. Anne Swanson, an emeritus dean of the School of Natural Sciences at Sonoma State University, was described by the obstetrician at birth as “a hopeless case involving profound mental retardation who will never function in society” (Blumenkopf et al., 1996, p. 51). Todd Blumenkopf, a research chemist at Pfizer, was taken aside by a school administrator at age 14 and told, "You don't want to go to regular school. You'd really rather be with your own kind" (p. 34). Judy Summers-Gates, a chemist with the Food and Drug Administration in Philadelphia has impaired vision, multiple sclerosis, and select hand movement because of carpal tunnel syndrome. She said, "I had to fight my parents, the school, teachers, guidance counselor, and the state vocational rehabilitation agency. Everyone thought it was crazy for a kid, almost blind, to major in chemistry" (p. 16).

These barriers also exist within the individual and in society. Del Robinson is a senior development consultant for UOP and has progressive multiple sclerosis. UOP is a leading industrial supplier to refineries, petrochemical, and gas-processing industries. He stated:

> If you think you are disabled, you are. Everyone has handicaps. Some are physical. Some are mental. Some are emotional. Some, I suppose, are spiritual. Everyone has problems. I've never gotten to know anyone very well at all without realizing that I wouldn't want to trade my problems for theirs! My disability is no worse than anybody else's—it's just different. (Blumenkopf et al., 1996, p. 9)

William Zoller was afflicted with a traumatic brain injury and profound memory loss. After rehabilitation, he became the most highly rated teacher in the Chemistry Department of the University of Washington (Blumenkopf et al., 1996, p. 14). Thomas Doyle, a profoundly deaf internationally known organic chemist, indicated that for deaf persons willing to pursue a degree in chemistry, "Most of the physical, technical barriers are gone." Society's negative attitudes are probably the major remaining barrier to getting more young people with disabilities into science careers (p. 30).Many of the adaptations are not expensive. Doyle is responsible for U.S. Food & Drug Administration laboratory research on the analysis of chiral drugs. The field studies the effects and side effects of medications. Doyle explained one of low cost adaptation he himself offered, after the departmental head received a seven-hundred dollar bid to modify an exhaust hood with a light to indicate the exhaust hood was working. His accommodation involved taping a strip of tissue paper to an exhaust hood opening to observe if it is working and/or functioning properly. Many common laboratory accommodations are modifications in the workstation to make the equipment and supplies accessible. Other important accommodations are safety devices like eyewashes, showers, evacuation procedures in case of an emergency, and modified signal devices such as fire alarms. Dorothy Miner, a part-time extension associate with the North Carolina Cooperative Extension Service at North Carolina State University, suffers from cervical vertebrae damage, chronic migraines, and severe pain if she lifts heavy objects or engages in repeated arm movements. She stated that flexible work hours are her most important accommodation (p. 21).

Safety comes up constantly as an unwarranted concern. Summers-Gates said that concerns about safety are exaggerated. "I simply took extra care and extra time in setting up and using apparatus" (Blumenkopf et al., 1996, p. 16). William Skawinski, a blind chemist with retinitis pigmentosa, is a professor at the New Jersey Institute of Technology. He said that a visual impairment imposes an extraordinary sense of orderliness and neatness on the individual. Neatness and orderliness are the cardinal rules of safety (p. 58). An extensive study of safety conducted by Anne Swanson and Norman Steere found persons with disabilities pose no greater safety hazard in the classroom, laboratory, or workplace than their able-bodied peers (p. 4).

Todd Blumenkopf, a senior research investigator, spends much of his time in the laboratory. He discussed several safety precautions that he has long used to accommodate chemistry in a seated position. "You learn to think the experiment through ahead of time and wear appropriate protective gear that might be a little different from what a standing scientist might choose to wear" (Blumenkopf et al., 1996, p.). For instance, Blumenkopf's face is closer to the apparatus and reacting chemicals than a chemist who is standing; thus, he chooses to wear a full-face safety shield rather than safety glasses at times, probably more often than most other chemists. He wears a heavy rubber apron to protect against injury if an acid or corrosive chemical should spill into his lap, and he keeps a lightweight fire extinguisher by his work area. Blumenkopf uses extra-heavy heat-resistant gloves for carrying hot objects. He grips objects harder when wheeling his chair, and sometimes he uses the gloves to rest a hot object safely on his lap. Blumenkopf must use nonlatex products, especially nonlatex gloves. Like half of those born with spina bifida, and like an increasing number of laboratory workers, he is allergic to latex. The Pfizer Health Center is aware of his allergy in the unlikely event that he must be treated in an emergency (pp. 37-38).

Blumenkopf (1996) acknowledged that many modifications "don't come cheap, but they benefit the more able-bodied users along with those with disabilities" (p. 37). Ron Nieman has Kugelberg-Welander disease, a form of muscular dystrophy. He also serves as the director of the Nuclear Magnetic Resonance

Laboratory at Arizona State University. He encourages employees to seek out persons with disabilities. He stated, "A person with a disability seeking employment is likely to be very successful, creative in solving problems, and competent in ways that you seldom find in other job applicants" (p. 59). He added that they are more likely to be persistent and inventive in overcoming obstacles, where others are likely to become frustrated and disillusioned.

Gail Pickut, a high school chemistry teacher, utilizes an aide to help with physical accommodations. Principal Richard Thorbahn said, "Ms. Pickut is a genius as an educator. . . Everyone benefited, especially the students." (Blumenkopf et al., 1996, p. 39). Pickut explained, "As long as you have your mental facilities, why should physical problems be a barrier? You don't need to be an athlete to coach. If you love to teach and love kids, then just find a way to do it" (p. 41). Tod Waldrop is an incomplete quadriplegic who is paralyzed from just below the arms and has limited hand movement. He stated, "Most of my problems and frustrations are the same as my able-bodied co-workers. They have nothing to do with the disability" (p. 50).

The importance of affective factors on learning cannot be overemphasized. Creating a classroom environment that promotes student interdependence instills an appreciation of human diversity and brings out within the student a sense of feeling important. This idea is strongly supported in educational research (Biklen, 1992; Villa, Thousand, Stainback, & Stainback, 1992). The effective teacher is willing to devote time to establish a sense of trust and confidence from every student. Student motivation is affected by trust in the teacher, a perceived commitment of the teacher to help the student experience success as a learner, and a perceived interest that the teacher wants to know the student as a person. Community involvement has also been found to contribute significantly to reducing the number of students who are at risk (Brookover & Lezotte, 1979). Teachers who spend the time to involve and communicate with parents, to welcome and respect their input, find this often provides large dividends. In addition, Lacey (1991) recommended involving the community by finding volunteers to serve as mentors who provide surrogate support to students with disabilities. These individuals keep in close communication with the child's parents, the school, and the teachers.

Emotional disabilities

Many students with disabilities have encountered traumatic life experiences. These may have major effects on students in the classroom. One emerging biomedical theory, the biogenic amine theory, holds that stress or trauma can create abnormalities in postsynaptic (receiving) neurons, creating too many receptors. The individual feels "starved" for "mood sweetener" hormones such as norepinephrine, serotonin, or dopamine and, as a result, has feelings of depression, compulsiveness, or anxiety (Kramer, 1993).

Regulation becomes extremely difficult. If drugs are used to provide adequate amounts of the biogenic amines, the cell becomes over stimulated and reduces the number of receptors by drawing them back into the cell membrane where they become inactive (Kramer, 1993, pp. 130-133). Kramer stated, "and the neural-transmitter pathways that are out of kilter in each of these symptom complexes appear to be similar whether the illness is depression or compulsivity, or addiction, and whether the animal under study is rat, rhesus, or man" (p. 130).

One observable influence of people affected by traumatic experiences is a high degree of vulnerability to stress. The influences of strong social supports are critical in helping the individual function well in an educational setting. Kramer (1993) presented cognitive therapy to create a supportive environment to help reframe environmental stimuli, redefining what is perceived as rejection so that sensitive or anxious individuals avert their functionally autonomous responses (p. 128).

From a school perspective, this biomedical theory indicates that students will work harder to receive support and encouragement than to avoid negative consequences. Threats, punishment, and negative comments are almost always harmful to motivation and affect. Teachers can make a difference by demonstrating enthusiasm in posture, voice, mobility, and excitement. The manner of teaching can bring out science as a fascinating topic of study that helps us understand the world around us.

Students' emotionality and ability to develop a sense of trust are so important that science teachers must be willing to serve an active role in assisting student socialization along with academic instruction. Science teachers who are warm and receptive to individual student needs are necessary if we are to improve student and public perceptions toward science. In many cases, science teachers with an elitist attitude have contributed to a public perception that anything beyond general science and biology is appropriate only for those who plan to go to college, and anything beyond a third year of high school science is appropriate only for those seeking careers in scientific or related fields.

Being able to detect the feelings and emotional states in students' oral and body language, being accepting of alternative points of view, being able to accurately express another person's feelings, and being able to help a child express ideas are characteristics all great teachers share. In a classroom setting where another person's ideas are laughed at or ridiculed, morale quickly declines, questions are not asked, and problems are not posed for fear of displaying ignorance or experiencing embarrassment. An accepting teacher can help students resolve their internal conflicts, using anger management and conflict resolution to help them deal more effectively with their school environment. Teachers will never succeed by confronting the confrontational student. In many cases, this disposition has developed during the child's first year of life, and the student perceives yielding to confrontation as a threat to the basic fabric of survival.

Teacher modeling is probably the greatest influence on student behavior. Overt modeling involves demonstrating a skill or activity by performing it. However, indirect actions and mannerisms associated with stereotypical attitudes often have a great influence on classroom atmosphere and the acceptance level of the students. Rosenshine (1979), in a research summary, reported that effective teachers are warm, concerned, flexible, and allow students more freedom to move within the classroom. These actions send powerful messages -- being receptive to the expressions of each student, maintaining a posture of encouragement, recognizing the responsibilities of each student, being responsive to a student's unique strengths and limitations, designing class activities so every student feels included, and modifying instruction so each student feels challenged and successful. These messages are reflected in the classroom and in the school and will influence decisions and attitudes the students will hold throughout their lives.

At-risk students with disabilities

Working with students with disabilities who are also at risk is demanding and often emotionally draining. Many of the reasons why students are at risk come from factors outside of the school environment and, in many cases, are not perceived by public constituents as areas of school responsibility. Yet, if not addressed, these external factors make efforts toward student success almost hopeless.

The following actions are found to be effective for all students, but particularly, for students who are at-risk. Keep in mind that at-risk students expect confrontation and will often engage in inappropriate actions to validate the label they have been given. In this way, they can generate an affirmation that they do not belong, thereby justifying their denial of identification with the institution and the authority figures within it.

Many at risk students have developed a belief that inevitably they will fail. Often they have instilled within themselves an attitude that adults cannot be trusted and that adults will act out against them if they make a mistake. This perception probably has built up over time and will only be alleviated over time. Successes in teaching at-risk students cannot be measured in daily or even weekly performance; significant change often takes months. Regression often occurs particularly when students feel helpless or sense a threat to their relationships.

Counseling intervention can help students sort out problems and reduce many at-risk factors. Social services staff can often gain easier access to the family to help make adjustments for the child outside of school. Tutoring has proven to be an effective aid, and the use of parent volunteers, or more capable peer helpers, can be a successful, low-cost strategy (Earle, 1990). Offering additional help, often outside of the regular school day, in homework enhancement, study skills, life skills, and job skills has shown favorable outcomes (Benedict, Snell, & Miller, 1987).

The school administrator can help at-risk students by carefully selecting teachers and providing extra support to assist in meeting the special needs of the student with disabilities. Encouraging and recognizing teachers' special efforts can make them feel important and appreciated.

Some time each day should be devoted to reflection and, when possible, collaboration in teacher work with at-risk students with disabilities. During this time, teachers can initiate, implement, and evaluate a strategy that addresses a problem that needs improvement. They can think about what is known and what additional information would help produce a better decision. They can determine if the plan is working or should be discarded, reflect on the plan, and make a judgment to determine if an alternative approach would be more humane and/or more efficient.

At the same time, we've learned what doesn't work with at-risk students with disabilities. The traditional structures of a common course of study predicated on equal treatment being fair treatment fail to provide the necessary structure and support needed for students at risk. Many of the solutions in common practice today do, in fact, aggravate the problem. Those practices generally consist of remediation, grade retention, ability grouping or tracking, and sometimes suspension (Quinn, 1991, p. 81).

If we are to successfully educate students at risk and prepare them for a productive life, our educational system must respond to the internal and external factors that placed these students at risk. We can design programs to meet students' needs and reduce the components of risk.

Learned helplessness

Schools (educators) appear to be losing large numbers of students who disengage from the educational process and are inclined to become apathetic. The theory of learned helplessness provides some insights into this phenomenon. The phrase was first introduced by Seligman and Maier (1967) and Overmier and Seligman (1967) who reported responses of dogs whose failure experience was an unavoidable shock. This research has been replicated in school settings by Butkowsky and Willows (1980), Dweck (1975), Fowler and Peterson (1981), and Gentile and Monaco (1986, 1988).

Gentile and Monaco (1988) have described learned helplessness as a group of behaviors commonly observed after exposure to uncontrollable failure experiences. They stated:

> After initial exposure to such trauma, the subject tends to increase movement, to increase emotionality as adrenaline increases with the stress associated with discomfort, and to increase motivation to search for solutions which will bring relief. As repeated attempts to gain control do not produce the desired alleviation of suffering, subjects come to believe that the situation is uncontrollable: their fate is unrelated to their behavior. Should such subjects subsequently be placed

in a different situation in which their responses might be instrumental in controlling outcomes, they nevertheless cannot perceive the possibility of gaining control due to their past history. (pp. 16-17)

It is likely that learned helplessness may be influenced by changes in the individual's physiology or vice versa. Studies of rats and humans who have experienced high stress, show there are higher than normal levels of cortisol and enlarged adrenal glands. The stimulated brain can produce a cascade of hormones, each influencing specific centers of the brain that can signal physical responses in body organs. One hormone produced in the brain is called corticotrophin-releasing factor (CRF), which stimulates the adrenals to produce cortisol. When released into the bloodstream, the body's own cortisol affects mood, food intake, the sleep-wake cycle, and level of locomotor activity. Furthermore, hormonal stimulation can affect receptor cells and thereby alter the neural architecture—the hard wiring—of the brain (Kramer, 1993, pp. 115-117).

Teachers' and parents' lack of understanding of learned helplessness leads to untold suffering by many students afflicted with this condition. These students feel less competent, which results in performance deficits unrelated to actual skill deficits (Butkowsky & Willows, 1980, p. 411). Seligman and Maier (1967) noted further that learned helplessness has been found to be debilitating to individuals to the point of obstructing their performance in school, social settings, and later in life.

From a constructivist point of view, the notion of learned helplessness becomes more meaningful, indeed, for what really matters is what learners bring to the classroom. And what they bring is not only their prior ideas about how the natural world works, but also their fears, anxieties, hopes, and expectations. It is all these that make the difference between failure and success and not just what students believe about electric current, action and reaction, or the greenhouse effect. Teachers should bear in mind that the central idea of the theory of personal constructs is that the individual "is neither the prisoner of his environment nor the victim of his biography" (Kelly, 1955, p. 560).

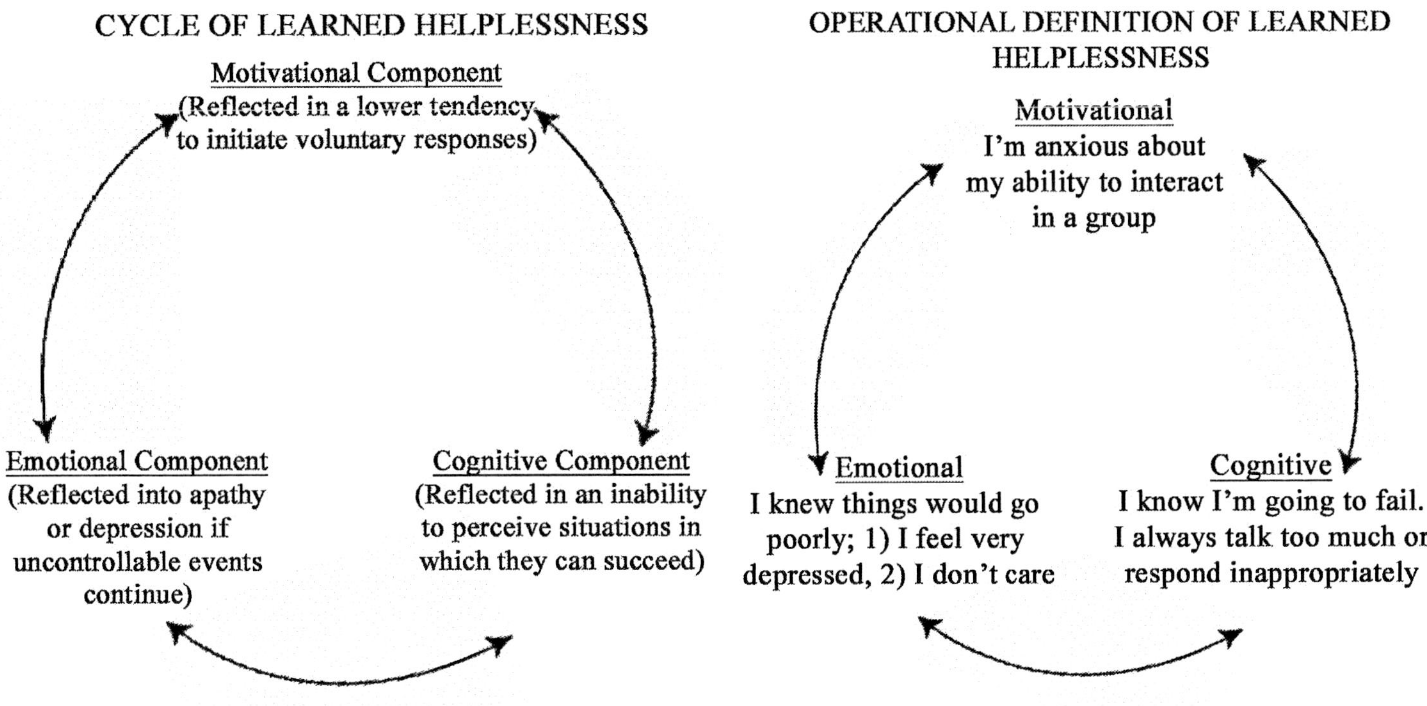

Figure 1. Cycle of Learned Helplessness

Figure 2. Operational Definition of Learned Helplessness

Figure 1 displays the components reflected in the cycle of learned helplessness. An example of how this may be reflected in the behavior of an individual is shown in **Figure 2**. This leads to the apathy and depression so often found among these students.

What can we do to help? Twelve suggestions follow:

1. Rigidity causes problems for students afflicted with learned helplessness. The process of visualizing an activity and providing advanced organizers is often helpful.

2. Students afflicted with learned helplessness often have difficulty with verbal instructions. Providing each student with a written sequence of steps accompanied with verbal directions can be effective.

3. Limit the number of new vocabulary terms and provide sufficient context clues for students. Employ strategies that show multiple exposures to new terms (Wood, 1990).

4. In helping students acquire a better sense of self-worth, present assignments that allow a number of refinements with teacher feedback. Provide frequent opportunities for assistance and work on short-term deadlines (Cheatham, 1989).

5. Work collectively with other teachers in interdisciplinary teams. Share ideas and develop uniform strategies for working with students who are reluctant learners. Develop interdisciplinary units to help students recognize the relationships among subjects. Presenting instruction in an integrated manner helps develop a schema as a multidisciplinary concept.

6. Use formative rather than summative evaluation. Avoid closing a topic with a test. Instead, after testing, provide students with a high-interest culminating activity.

7. Try to find a creative outlet that the student can use without criticism. This will relieve stress and may lead to a locus of positive association.

8. Develop the ability to laugh at one's mistakes. Laughter is therapeutic both physically and psychologically.

9. Bibliotherapy is an effective method for helping students learn more about themselves. Students who experience learned helplessness are often coping with dysfunctional relationships. They can also associate with others who are experiencing difficulty with academic, physical, and social-emotional adjustment.

10. Help students develop skills of self-regulation and self-direction. Making a videotape of students who are not responding to learning tasks during independent or group work provides an excellent vehicle for engaging in conversation that will foster higher levels of self-regulation. We must continue to nurture students toward developing an internal locus of control. Don't only provide opportunities for students; expect responsibility from them.

11. Be less than perfect yourself. Make a conscious decision to seek help in those areas in which you lack sufficient skill. Solicit assistance of students in meeting a desired goal.

12. When possible, structure learning experiences based on cooperation rather than competition. Students afflicted with learned helplessness are often unwilling to try because they expect failure (Tyrell, 1990).

Current Promising Practices for Teaching Students with Disabilities

The use of adapted materials has been reported as being effective with mainstreamed students (Hoover, 1990). If we are to improve instruction for students with disabilities, and probably for all students, science teachers will need to become oriented to multi-modality teaching. They must be willing to accommodate instruction and adjust the learning environment so *all* students can achieve success and *all* students can be active participants in the learning process. They must become accustomed to teaching fewer concepts with richer insights, deeper understanding, greater attention to application, and more relationships. Instructors of science methods must model appropriate strategies in their classes if we are to bring about change in current practices.

The following adage contains an appropriate warning for teachers: "If you don't know where you are going you are never lost." The majority of decisions that teachers make relate to instructional context. Teachers generally assume the information contained in the print material the students use is appropriate and give little thought to content accommodation. Rosenshine and Stevens (1986), in a meta-analysis of studies on direct instruction, found that more effective teachers maintained a strong academic focus and spent less time on non-academic activities.

Specifically, Olarewaju (1988) found seventh grade students had a better attitude toward an integrated science program in classes guided by instructional objectives. Brophy and Good (1986) reported teachers who plan and organize on a daily basis prior to instruction produce higher levels of student achievement. Prior planning is essential in preparing students for learning. Ausubel (1968) proposed the idea of advanced organizers to help students prepare for learning. By aligning objectives to prior knowledge and experiences, students have a greater opportunity to make personal meaning of the facts and concepts presented in instruction. Shostak (1990) recommended planning the first 5 minutes as "entry" into the lesson. This would include clarification of expectations, reflection using an advanced organizer, and introduction of the lesson topic. In a similar fashion, the last 5 minutes of the lesson should be directed to "closure" to reinforce the key points of the lesson and transfer learning by bringing in applications that relate to age-appropriate experiences.

Instruction

Research provides support for using a variety of methods to deliver instruction. Brophy and Good (1986), in a review of research on instructional methods, reported that the systematic use of a variety of techniques leads to higher levels of student performance than heavy reliance on one technique (p. 342). This is particularly important for instruction directed to students with disabilities. In many cases a teacher cannot discern the limitations of an impairment. Through a variety of instructional approaches, the student is able to bring input from learning experiences in an area of strength to compensate and fill in learning missed because of processing difficulty.

Multi-modality instruction is especially critical in helping students with disabilities become familiar with the content material. Scruggs, Mastropieri, Bakken, and Brigham (1993), in presenting suggestions for teaching science lessons to students with disabilities, have stated that students with disabilities are likely to encounter far fewer problems when participating in activity-oriented approaches to science education. The use of multi-modality approaches both in teaching and in assessment has shown positive effects (Cheney, 1989). An example of the importance of direct experience is well illustrated in a study by Recht and Leslie (1988). The researchers identified junior high school students on the basis of their knowledge of baseball and their reading ability. They determined four categories of students: good readers/high baseball knowledge, good readers/low baseball knowledge, poor readers/high baseball knowledge, and poor readers/low baseball knowledge. Poor readers who knew baseball remembered more than good readers with low baseball knowledge and almost as much as good readers with good baseball knowledge. Poor readers with low baseball knowledge remembered the least about what they read. What the study clearly indicates is that having familiarity with the material is often more important than one's ability to assimilate and remember information.

Wood (1990) noted that strategies that lend multiple exposures to new terms and concepts enhance opportunities for student mastery. Actual examples or models are especially helpful to students with disabilities. In many cases, these individuals do not have as many experiences as those with greater mobility who constantly receive a variety of exposures to the world by being able to visit places in a community.

Adjusting the length of assignments and acquiring alternative resources with different levels of reading ability also improve student success rates (Lawrence, 1988). To maximize the efficiency of the educational program, all teachers must provide students with assistance in basic skills (Brookover & Lezotte, 1979). If a teacher is to have standards of quality, students must be guided to meet the standard. This is going to typically require the students to revise and resubmit an assignment until it reflects the desired quality. For example, in preparing a laboratory report following an experiment, if students are to produce a report of high quality, they will need a process of refinement that requires careful planning with a scope and sequence. The teacher may begin with organization of the collected data, followed by data analysis and establishing inferences and generalizations. Checking arithmetic calculations and organizing the data may require several refinements. Developing a quality narrative demands that the science teacher has a good command of the mechanics of written expression; it may require collaboration with other teachers. Writing refinement may begin with capitalization, then progress to putting a subject and verb in every sentence, and then to syntax and clarity of expression. The challenge offered to the student should be attainable. Guidance and encouragement must be provided. Having high expectations does not mean demanding higher standards; it means earning the higher standards by guiding students through the learning process in steps students can master.

Evaluation

Student evaluations in various forms determine progress and performance by making value judgments on the quality of students' work. Formative evaluation primarily provides feedback to students and guides them in their learning. Effective formative evaluation helps students correct misconceptions, gives the teacher feedback on the effectiveness of instruction and the appropriateness of the curriculum, and helps the teacher match instructional decisions with a student's instructional needs. A type of formative evaluation, immediate feedback, is the most helpful to learners. It refers directly to a behavior or assignment that may challenge the students but is a task possible to perform. Using immediate feedback, teachers can check on clarity through observation and questioning, help students unscramble confusion, and help them examine their understanding by performing authentic tasks.

Many students with disabilities will be unable to demonstrate their true level of understanding under traditional testing conditions. Although tests and quizzes are one means of evaluation, they should not be the dominant tool used in evaluation. In many instances, the added difficulty of needing to focus to a large extent on carrying out the mechanics of the response can hinder student performance. Assessment strategies in which students are allowed to share what they know are often more effective. For instance, students with disabilities must be allowed to take examinations in a comfortable setting and on a timetable that enables them to share what they have learned.

A teacher's willingness to examine students' work to ascertain where problems are occurring has been shown to significantly improve student learning. A teacher's improved diagnostic ability results in improved student performance. The use of portfolios and/or exhibitions allows students to accumulate samples of their work. The portfolio should reflect student participation in selecting the contents, student knowledge criteria for judging merit, and elements of student self-reflection. Through an anecdotal reflection, students can share what they know and what they can do. Other evaluations can be used in a science class. Conducting a science investigation that a teacher monitors is an excellent means of assessing student abilities to use science processes. Operational definitions allow students to indicate an understanding of a concept by relating examples or sharing thoughts on how something works.

Summative evaluation is also an important component in meeting professional responsibilities as a teacher, but must be utilized with discretion. Summative evaluation can provide valuable feedback on how much information the students have learned and retained. The results of summative evaluation are often used to make placement decisions, to certify students as being competent in a field of knowledge, or to norm and compare students. These measures can provide valuable information, but are generally of little value in helping students' learning. Research has shown that student performance decreases when teachers emphasize an evaluation system based on a comparison of classmates' achievements (Brookover & Lezotte, 1979). Evidence has also indicated that increased student absenteeism and higher dropout rates occur in classrooms with a higher percentage of lower grades, a competitive atmosphere, and arbitrarily high standards (Moos & Moos, 1978; Trickett & Moos, 1974).

The following suggestions are for teachers who wish to maintain high standards and, at the same time, avoid the negative effects of competitive evaluation frameworks.

- Keep expectations high; reward effort and perseverance.
- Don't give praise or rewards that are not deserved.
- Don't single out a student more than necessary, and do actively seek opportunities that provide positive socialization experiences with peers.
- Reflect on instructional techniques and provide sufficient time for independent work when special needs can be accommodated if necessary.
- Use formative evaluation and become aware of "critical features" of concepts if the student is unable to master all of the objectives.
- Be cautious about the use of the results from standardized assessment tests.

In regard to the latter point, the use and interpretation of evaluation instruments is a fundamental concern in student identification for special services. Indeed, the validity and reliability of tests used for classification and placement has been repeatedly challenged (Gartner & Lipsky, 1987; Stainback, Stainback, & Bunch, 1989; Wang & Wahlberg, 1988). Gartner and Lipsky (1987) described these tests as "barely more accurate than a flip of the coin" (p. 372). Addressing the relative permanence of such classifications, Gartner and Lipsky have stated that less than 5% of students are declassified and returned to the mainstream of regular education. Wolfensberger and Thomas (1983) have argued that a great deal of unfair treatment of clients is from professionals who unconsciously devalue the people they are trying to serve.

Chapter 2
The Cascade Model for Managing Students with Disabilities in Science Classrooms

Increasing numbers of students with disabilities have made the science teacher's responsibility of managing the classroom far more challenging than it used to be. Over 6 million students are identified with special needs in our nation's schools. More than 70% of those students represent the least severe impairments for which pull-out programs are a disservice to their educational needs. Under NCLB essentially all students must be included in assessments relating to the regular curriculum. A science teacher must work to build truly inclusive classrooms where children work and learn together. Students with disabilities must not be marginalized; they should be valued and respected. That means the science teacher must create a caring, positive learning environment by modeling sensitivity to differences and using a variety of instructional approaches and interaction styles. The question is not whether to teach students with disabilities, but how to teach them.

Criticisms of ability grouping and tracking have resulted in more academically heterogeneous classrooms. Efforts have been made to address the needs of children with disabilities in the regular education context. One such effort is the Cascade Model, which stresses the need to create a positive learning environment in which all students are respected and have opportunities to learn. IDEA, SEC 614 (Individuals with Disabilities Education Act), and NCLB legislate that placement of students with disabilities in regular classrooms is mandatory unless it is specified that the general curriculum is not appropriate. Regular classroom teachers must be a part of a student's Individual Education Plan (IEP), and evaluation measures must take into account the goals and objectives of the regular curriculum.

The proactive and reactive teaching practices described in the Cascade Model are appropriate for all teachers, including science teachers, who have students with disabilities in their classrooms. This chapter relates the four steps of the Cascade Model to science teaching and reviews the underlying principles of the discipline plan. It then emphasizes procedures a teacher should follow to help students with disabilities successfully learn science with their nondisabled peers.

The Cascade Model = A Dynamic Approach

The Cascade Model can be likened to a journey in a raft moving down a cascading stream (the K-12 curriculum) to the sea (entrance to adulthood). The group about to take the classroom journey consists of the students and their science teacher. Just as there are four important aspects to consider in taking a raft trip, so there are four main steps to this model (see Figure 3.)

1.

2.

3.

4

Figure 3. Steps in the Cascade Model

Step 1 – Preventive Measures

Before a raft journey begins, it's important for the guide to plan ahead and prepare for it. Preparation includes becoming familiar with the territory and the route to be traveled, as well as collecting and arranging for adequate equipment and supplies, planning a schedule, informing the raft participants of the plans and expectations, and working out the "minor details." These preparations will prevent many unnecessary complications and make for a nicer trip.

Similarly, the first step of the Cascade Model is Preventive Measures. During this phase, the science teacher must plan and prepare to prevent discipline problems from occurring. He or she arranges the learning environment, decides on materials and strategies appropriate to students' needs and abilities, and plans schedules and routines. Then the routines, expectations, and lesson information are clearly communicated to students. Advanced preparation and clear communication can prevent many problems from occurring.

Step 2 – Supportive Measures

Once everyone is situated in the raft and the raft is moving in the water, the guide tries to help everyone choose to follow the specified behaviors. The guide acknowledges the productive efforts of the participants in order to maintain and increase the desired behaviors.

Likewise, the need to recognize and support students who demonstrate positive behaviors carries over to the science classroom. The second phase of the Cascade Model is Supportive Measures. During this phase it is important that the science teacher becomes a vibrant figure in the classroom, one who is in close contact with the students throughout the school day and into the extended day when reasonable. A teacher can use questions and various types of rewards to recognize positive behaviors and express a genuine interest in the students' personal growth and development. When students feel that their needs and efforts are acknowledged, desired behaviors toward self-discipline will increase.

Step 3 – Corrective Measures

Sometimes, regardless of the preparations and proactive measures taken, Corrective Measures must be taken to maintain a desired course. These reactive measures may include assessing the situation at hand, slowing down or backing up, speeding ahead, and in some cases, redefining the original planned route.

In the same manner, the third step of the Cascade Model, Corrective Measures, emphasizes the need to sometimes react to correct inappropriate behaviors. Some students need defined limits of behaviors that include explicit rules and consequences. Each science teacher should have the skill and power to stop misbehaviors when they occur. Clarity is critical, and consequences should be consistently applied. The teacher's action to stop disruptive behavior should be at the lowest level of intervention possible, while at the same time making an effort to sustain classroom learning.

Step 4 – Adaptive Measures

A final aspect to consider when planning a raft journey is to have definite procedures for emergency situations. What should be done when circumstances include a major disruption or event? If so, what kind of a lifeline or procedure should be followed to assure the safety of the overboard person as well as the other participants on board? The guide has to adapt to the situation and follow a procedure that will help ensure the safety and welfare of the participants.

The final level of the Cascade Model, Adaptive Measures, relates to situations in which a student does not (for whatever reasons) function within the defined limits of the science classroom. The rights of the students are considered and positive negotiations, such as conferences and contracts, may be implemented. But sometimes the teacher needs the power to remove a source of conflict that interferes with the delivery of positive learning experiences for those who are attending school to learn.

Just as the flow of a cascading stream changes with various conditions, the Cascade Model looks at an effective discipline plan along a continuum. Each science teacher and each classroom requires adaptations that best fit the needs of the students and teacher at a specific place and point in time. The model ascribes to the view that a discipline plan must be dynamic, reflect the human condition, and continually adapt to the environment. The underlying principles of the Cascade Model are summarized in Figure 4.

I. Principles of Students

- Students must have a clear awareness of what adults consider to be appropriate conduct.
- Human contact is necessary for human development and growth.
- Students should have a say in the management system.

II. Principles of Teachers & Teaching

- Teachers are models for students
- Variety is appropriate and desirable.
- Equal is not always fair.
- Consistency is important to relationships.
- It's difficult getting people to do something they don't wish to do.
- Good teaching reduces discipline problems.

III. Principles of Discipline

- Schools should mirror cultural realities.
- Discipline is not a disease with a cure.
- A discipline plan is not always good because it works.
- Effective discipline requires high, but reasonable expectations for all.
- Effective discipline elicits student responsibility.
- Effective discipline isn't static.

Figure 4. Underlying management principles of the Cascade Model

Planning for Success

It is not unusual for regular classroom teachers to feel they lack the professional preparation necessary to help students with disabilities (Semmel, Abernathy, Butera, & Lesar, 1991), but often the teaching behaviors associated with outstanding achievement gains for students with disabilities are similar to the behaviors effective with all students (Slavin, 1989). The underlying principles of the Cascade Model are appropriate for teaching science to all students. Yet because the model is dynamic and reflects the human condition, science teachers should follow some procedures when working with students with disabilities.

Fine-Tune Your Language

Within past years some debate has occurred over the most appropriate expressions to use when referring to students with disabilities. Physicians and psychologists have greatly influenced education terminology with terms such as "physically handicapped," "mentally retarded," and "emotionally disturbed." These expressions represent a medical model and are used by professionals who tend to view problems as existing within the person (Borich & Tombari, 1997). The first major piece of education law, PL 94-142, used such terms and was named the Education for All Handicapped Children Act of 1975 (EAHCA).

More recently, many advocates of learners with disabilities believe that classifications encourage stereotypic thinking and may stigmatize learners (Wang, Walberg, & Reynolds, 1992). In 1990, amendments to PL 94-142 renamed it the Individuals with Disabilities Education Act (IDEA). The phrase "handicapped children" was changed to "children with disabilities," and other phrases like "learners with developmental delays" and "children with attention-deficit disorder" were used. Using such phrases was to enhance the image of children with disabilities and affirm that they are "people first, who incidentally have certain physical, cognitive, or emotional characteristics" (Borich & Tambari, 1997, p. 475).

To enhance the image of children in the science classroom, teachers must refine their language. Most students, including those with disabilities, think of themselves as "normal," so when referring to the fact that a student is not disabled, the term "nondisabled" (rather than "normal") should be used. The majority of students with disabilities experience no more sickness than other students, so they are not patients who need sympathy. Students with disabilities need acceptance and respect for their abilities and talents, and the terms "brave," "inspirational," and "courageous" should be used only when appropriate (AAAS, 1991a). The science teacher should emphasize the students (rather than the disabilities) and carefully choose words with nonjudgmental connotations.

Mostakas (1967) stated that at an early age children are taught to perceive in a certain way - not in their way, but in the way adults perceive things. Compliant children learn through repetitive conditioning that the adult, who possesses authority, perceives correctly (Kamii as cited in Martin, Sexton, Wagner & Gerlouich, 1997). Gradually, individuals begin to act in standard ways without being aware of conforming; they begin to base their reasoning on the standards and expectations of others.

Noncompliant children learn, through repetitive punishment, that they do not belong. They often become agents of disruption both individually and through interactions with peers who have similar signature feelings. The role of the school becomes clear – to stamp out the inappropriate behaviors and to bring the students into compliance. However, both the teachers and the students learn that teachers and administrators have neither the power nor the authority to carry out their threats. Therefore, schools often become battlegrounds with the nonconforming students pitted against powerless authorities, each manipulating the ineffective weapons in its arsenal. One group challenges the system and the other group seeks ways to suppress the challenges to the institutional mores. The school becomes not an institution of learning, but an institution of conditioning to the mores and beliefs of the adults who make up the staff and administration of the school. Laotzu (cited in Bynner, 1944, p.) characterizes the degeneration of independent thinking in the following poem:

> Losing the way of life, men rely first on their fitness;
> Losing fitness, they turn to kindness;
> Losing kindness, they turn to justness;
> Losing justness, they turn to convention.
> Conventions are reality and honesty gone to waste,
> They are the entrances of disorder.
> False teachers of life use flowery words,
> And start nonsense.
> The man of stamina stays with the root
> Below the tapering,

Stays with the fruit,
Beyond the flowering;
He has his no and he has his yes.

Students must learn to develop confidence in their ability to reason through logical relationships. Rowe (1973, pp. 278-302), in her discussion of fate control, iterates the importance of instilling in children a belief in their ability to conceptualize based on their own skill and ingenuity. This, in turn, implies that students need experiences in which they will have a reasonably good chance of developing a logical understanding.

Plan a PreCourse Visit

Before the school year or semester begins, the science teacher should consult privately with a student who may need some accommodations. Privacy is important because the student may find it difficult to tell the teacher about his or her limitations and may feel embarrassed about requesting an adaptation. The student can learn what accommodations are available and find out more about the teacher and science activities that will be expected. In addition, a visit to the science classroom before classes begin can enable a student with a visual impairment to explore the lab and learn the locations of furniture, materials, and equipment. For a person in a wheelchair or with a physical impairment, concerns relating to trafficking, materials access, and materials handling can be addressed before they become problems during class or after school starts, when it becomes much more disruptive and difficult to make accommodations.

A teacher should not make preliminary assumptions about a student with a disability because not all students with disabilities need adaptations. Adaptations vary from person to person, and the best way to learn about an individual is to meet and consult with him or her about possible adaptations. A precourse visit helps the student with a disability know that the teacher is concerned, and it benefits the teacher by learning about the disability and getting an early start on any lesson plan modifications that should be made (Weld, 1990).

In some instances, a student with a disability may not wish to be identified as such. For various reasons, a person may try to hide the disability. It may be helpful for the science teacher to make an announcement at the beginning of the term inviting students with special needs to set up a private meeting. Although it is the student's responsibility to initiate a discussion, if a disability is apparent the teacher may consider bringing up the topic (AAAS, 1991c). But the teacher must remember that some students with disabilities may not wish or need any special accommodations.

Adapt the Environment and Materials

The design of the science laboratory is important to the success of students with disabilities. Aisles should be wide so that people using wheelchairs, crutches, or canes can easily move around tables. Lower mountings of chalkboards, water faucets, electrical outlets, and storage cabinets and higher lab tables can also benefit students in wheelchairs. Lighting is important, and there should be an unflickering light source that easily shows the teacher's facial expressions and lip movements. The science teacher must understand that building noises, mechanical equipment (fans, heaters, and buzzing lights), moving chairs, and group work that involves several people talking at one time can greatly interfere with the ability to understand speech (Birch, 1975).

Many science materials can be adapted or substituted with more appropriate materials. Students in wheelchairs can use special snap-on trays to transport equipment and microscopes with angled occulars to examine slides. Electronic balances with auditory output, braille rulers, and audible timers can be made available. In addition, braille, large print, taped materials, talking calculators, clocks, thermometers, probes, raised-line drawings, computers, and videotapes with Descriptive Video Service (DNS) can be used (AAAS, 1991b). Captioned films and videos, microphones, and assistive technology that includes computers and provides for "real-life" captioning of lectures (AAAS, 1991b) could be made available to students who are hearing impaired or deaf.

The effective science teacher must "play carpenter, interior designer, and adaptive technician" (Weld, 1990, p. 36). Students with disabilities must be encouraged to take part as much as possible in science activities. Even "minor" adaptations, such as wrapping tape around a handle or knob to enlarge it or providing a counter armrest to steady hand-held objects, can do much to help students with disabilities develop confidence and independence. Once students with disabilities know that the science classroom is free of obstacles to learning, "inhibitions disappear, and they are free to focus on scientific, rather than logistic problem solving" (Weld, 1990, p. 36).

Prepare Positive Lessons

Learners with disabilities deserve more than just being placed in a science lab with their nondisabled peers and some modified equipment; they need to be included socially as well as physically. The science teacher must work to build a positive community of learners. Silence, ignorance, fear, separateness, and shunning/avoidance should be replaced with attention, importance, identification, dependence, and appreciation (Schlossberg, 1989). Students with disabilities should feel that others (teachers as well as students) are interested in and care about them, depend on them, and appreciate their contributions.

Students without identified disabilities should be given opportunities to understand the nature of disabling conditions. Instructional units and simulation activities (Wood & Reeves, 1989) can be used before students with disabilities begin working in regular science classrooms. If students with disabilities or their family members feel comfortable entertaining questions, perhaps a "getting to know you" question-and-answer lesson can be planned. It's important that special efforts are made to help students feel comfortable with each other before they are asked to work cooperatively on science activities.

When nondisabled students and students with disabilities work together, positive relationships are promoted. Science concepts can very effectively be taught and learned where all students have abundant opportunities to benefit from multisensory stimulation in cooperative settings. Pairing students as lab partners can be helpful to a student with disabilities, provided one student doesn't end up doing all the work. A student who has taken the class previously and is familiar with concepts, terminology, and equipment, can be an excellent laboratory assistant. When working in small groups, with partners or assistants, everyone should be involved in planning, monitoring, organizing, analyzing, and concluding (AAAS, 1991c). All should share in thinking and discovery.

As previously mentioned, the teaching practices appropriate for nondisabled learners are often effective for learners with disabilities. The National Science Education Standards of 1996 recommend that there be less emphasis on competition, whole-group instruction, and recitation of acquired knowledge. Instead, effective science education should emphasize cooperation and shared responsibility, active inquiry, discussion and debate, and various forms of assessment (NSF, 1997). The learning of all students can be strengthened when students in science classrooms are given opportunities to work together, understand how different people approach different situations, and share responsibility for their learning.

Have High, Reasonable Expectations of Discipline

Nothing hurts the chances of success for a student with disabilities as much as the attitude, "Oh well, he (she) has a disability. I can't expect him (her) to do that." Children with disabilities are too often the victims of low expectations. Sometimes, in an effort to be sympathetic and understanding, the science teacher waters down the curriculum and sets "ceilings" rather than floors (Good & Brophy, 1994). Far too frequently students in special education are students of small expectations, not great ones. Little is expected and little is demanded. Gradually, these children – no matter their IQ level – learn to be cozy in the category of being "special." They learn to be less than they are (Granger & Granger, 1986, pp. 26-27).

Some science teachers dealing with students with disabilities for the first time feel that the presence of these students will inevitably mean a "softening" of their approach to teaching as well as their disciplinary requirements. This idea equates "disabled" with "inferior" and "inept" and gives the message that students with disabilities are incapable of understanding and keeping pace. Students may be placed in safe environments where they are not asked to do things "we know they can't do," and inappropriate behaviors may be forgiven because "they can't help it." Then, when students with disabilities do not learn or act inappropriately, the beliefs about them seem justified (Gartner & Lipsky, 1987).

The advocates of PL 94-142 did not want students with disabilities to be treated with kid gloves – especially in regards to discipline. Dr. Edwin W. Martin, Jr., principal framer of the Education for All Handicapped Children Act, said that the intent of the act was not to give students with disabilities special rights, but it was to give them the same rights that had always been available to those without disabilities. "What disabled students have a right to expect is the same fairness, firmness, and compassion that would be given to any other student" (NAESP, 1983, p. 1).

Special education was never intended to focus on general education failings. It was an effort to focus on individual need. Special education is to serve the unique requirements of students with disabilities who are in danger of being handicapped by their disabilities unless they receive some form of accommodations or assistance.

The science teacher has the responsibility to clearly communicate classroom procedures to every child in the class. High standards must be set and enforced, and children must understand that there are consequences for misbehaviors. Disruptions should not be ignored. If a student with a disability acts inappropriately, he or she should be held accountable. As long as appropriate procedures are followed, even the most extreme aspects of school discipline, suspensions and expulsions, are allowed for students with disabilities. If a child is removed from the classroom, then appropriate special education services must still be provided.

For many people, discipline is associated solely with punishment. However, the word "discipline" has an origin close to the word "disciple," which is "one who learns from a leader" (Carpenter & Craig, 1991). A disciplinarian can be thought of as a leader (teacher), and discipline as a set of behaviors and attitudes that the leader (teacher) hopes the followers (students) will acquire. In the science classroom, effective discipline is an attempt to teach attitudes and behaviors that the teacher hopes the students will acquire and demonstrate even when the teacher is not present. The focus of effective discipline is not just the enforcement of rules and consequences; it is a focus on developing a self-controlled and self-disciplined person. The science teacher must have high, reasonable expectations of discipline for all students, including those with disabilities.

Increasing diversity has made the science teacher's responsibility of managing the classroom far more challenging than it used to be. Yet many of the effective practices for homogeneous groups of students can be effective with heterogeneous groups. The proactive measures (preventive and supportive) and the reactive measures (corrective and adaptive) of the Cascade Model can be implemented in any science classroom. It's important that teachers should use appropriate language and have high, reasonable expectations of discipline for all students as they work with appropriate materials and learn science through cooperative, inquiry-based lessons.

The primary tools for the implementation of the principles included in the Cascade Model are the Management Profile contained in Appendix A and Point Total Summary contained in Appendix B. The subsections in the following pages of this chapter provide suggestions, research, and documentation relating to the scientific suggestions and assessments noted in the Management Profile.

Preventive Management

Creating a Positive Learning Environment

The key to successful management is advanced planning and organizing an environment that meets the needs, interests, and abilities of individual students. An attractive classroom, good lesson preparation, fair rules, and an enthusiastic, caring teacher are major ingredients in preventing discipline problems. An effectively managed classroom provides exciting, dynamic learning experiences for students and teachers. This involves managing space, time, materials, lessons, and people so that students are highly involved and use instructional time efficiently. On-task, involved students spend their energies learning and are rarely discipline problems.

Preventive approaches to discipline encourage learning as a lifelong process. Learning becomes more enjoyable for students when the teacher expends little time maintaining order. A fair, consistent method of management and discipline mixed with caring and understanding goes far in preventing most discipline problems. A well-managed classroom is a task-oriented, predictable environment where students know what is expected of them and how to succeed. Establishing such an environment requires the classroom to be effectively organized.

Organizing the Classroom

The classroom setting, which includes room arrangement and room preparation, has an impact on the students. Appropriate lighting, noise levels, bulletin boards, and seating arrangements can help to create attractive classrooms that are places where students learn. Classroom organization is an important precursor to effective classroom management. Before the students arrive, think through your instructional strategies and the movement of students and materials. Then arrange the classroom accordingly, with special attention to providing access to any students with physical impairments. An attractive classroom can provide a student with a place to learn and feel a sense of belonging. A well-arranged classroom is one in which learning resources are easy to access and use. Clean and neat storage areas are important safety considerations. An area where a student can work without interruption provides greater flexibility for accommodating difficult student learning needs.

Careful consideration should be given to the selection of desks, tables, and furniture. The color, size, comfort, and type of physical surroundings can facilitate or limit materials flow and traffic patterns in the classroom, as well as influence how the students perceive the classroom. The principles of universal accommodation should apply to all decisions. Accessible classroom environments serve all students well, in addition to providing an independent-learner environment for students with disabilities.

A classroom arrangement can be evaluated by answering the following questions:

1. Can the teacher see all of the students from any place in the room?
2. Does congestion occur in any particular area?
3. Do any students disturb others around them?
4. Can students easily access all or the appropriate resources; e.g., supplies, materials for experiments, computer sites, books, and nonprint resources?

If all students are able to access the materials without help from the teacher, there will be fewer disruptions and students will be able to spend more time learning. Materials should be counted out and ready for distribution before students enter the room so that work can begin promptly.

Routines and Procedures

Permissive teaching is not humanistic teaching. It is difficult for students to adjust to a classroom in which there is not a certain level of predictability and stability that includes routines and procedures to direct behavior. It is necessary in managing a classroom to spend sufficient time developing and implementing a workable set of performance standards. Effective classroom managers have clear expectations. Students know the limits of acceptable behavior and exactly what is expected of them.

Although there is no one "correct" belief regarding what is acceptable behavior, teachers need to delineate limits that are consistent with their educational philosophy and instructional style. Students must realize that standards of conduct may change between classrooms because teachers are individuals with different philosophies and styles. Just as there are different traffic regulations with different speed limits, students should understand that different teachers have different regulations and limits.

Procedures for special needs students who need accommodations should be clarified and practiced. These procedures should address the dignity and primary needs of the student. Relevant school policies and instructions for student behavior in emergencies should be clearly explained. Times when students are allowed to leave their seats and when they are expected to remain seated should be defined. There should be established routines for passing out and returning materials to students. Taking a little time during the first week to practice and refine classroom routines in order to improve efficiency can be a big time-saver throughout the year.

Good managers clearly denote procedures to students during the first few weeks of school and give feedback to the students when inappropriate behavior occurs. They begin the year by explaining that order is needed for a classroom to function efficiently. Then they give specific instructions about the expectations, routines, and procedures that are to be followed in their classroom.

Effective teachers are explicit about what is desirable behavior and use these standards when giving feedback to their students. Students are knowledgeable of procedures for emergencies, moving about the classroom, and entering a learning classroom environment. The routines for materials traffic such as turning in assignments or picking up equipment and supplies are clearly outlined. Meta-cognitive expectations are reviewed relating to student self-monitoring and self-responsibility. The routines and procedures for asking questions, working within the lesson and limits of behavior outside of regular instruction are clear to all students. It is important that, whenever possible, the teacher should model behaviors consistent with those expected of the students.

Most students prefer firm teachers to overly permissive ones. Effective teachers maintain discipline in their classrooms without punishing students because their students understand expectations and live within the limits of appropriate behaviors. Yet this does not mean that a firm teacher cannot be warm and supportive.

The following items list areas where expectations should be explicitly defined for students:

1. Beginning the period
2. Grading policies
3. Communication regarding assignments
    a. Procedures for turning in written assignments
    b. Procedures for returning assignments to students
    c. Procedures for makeup work
    d. Procedures for group work
    e. Consequences of assignments that are not completed
    f. Procedures for work that is not done in a satisfactory manner
4. Proper behavior for teacher-led instruction
5. Proper behavior for group work
6. Proper behavior for seat work
7. Course requirements
8. Planning of class activities
9. Ending the period

Instruction

Students have ideas about how teachers should teach and direct effective instruction. A ninth grader generalizes that

> some teachers lecture for an entire period and will not let up. Others never lecture. There should be a compromise somewhere, allowing the student to understand the lesson by presenting the material in an interesting way. We have a really neat teacher! He's neat because he challenges you. He has all sorts of things up his sleeve. He challenges you because you have to dig for information. (Stefanich & Bell, 1987, p. 13)

This student cites the necessity for a teacher to use a variety of teaching techniques to prevent boredom and lead to more on-task behavior. These techniques include emphasis on multimodality instruction and using semiconcrete mediums such as computer simulations, pictures, videos, and films when direct interaction is not possible. Prior planning in instruction is an important aspect of classroom management. Utilize diagnostic assessments to determine what the students already know. Provide students with advanced organizers and communicate the expected learning outcomes in advance. Limit expository instructional practices and provide students with multimodality learning opportunities whenever possible. Consider opportunities for cooperative learning and peer collaboration; these practices are strongly supported by research or teaching and learning. Independent work and homework should be meaningful and tailored to the learning needs of the individual student.

The needs and abilities of each student should be considered when choosing various materials. Special consideration should be taken to provide high interest material at the students' instructional level. Selecting appropriate texts and other reading materials can be especially challenging. In the typical seventh grade classroom, the range of reading abilities spans eight years. It should be remembered that what is preferable and reinforcing for one student may not be for another. Instruction that includes a variety of teaching methods and materials based on student needs, abilities, and interest can help a lesson be effective. A well-taught and effective lesson is a strong deterrent to disruptive classroom behavior.

An effective mnemonic tool when reflecting on instruction can be looking at the thumb and fingers of an open hand. The thumb represents what you teach, your goals, objectives and desired student outcomes. The first finger represents when you teach, it is the scope and sequence used in framing instruction. The middle finger represents how you teach, it consists of the variety of methods employed when teaching. The fourth finger represents how you know what students have learned, it consists of the assessment and evaluation measures employed in instruction. The little finger represents what happens when a student(s) doesn't learn, and it consists of the adaptive practices involving modifications and alternative methods employed for those who do not achieve the outcomes desired in the instructional sequence (C.M. May, personal communication, October 15, 2006).

The teacher should work to vary instruction. There's a time for whole class instruction, group instruction, and individual instruction. Regardless of class size, every instruction period should include student discussion and questions. Discussions give students a legitimate reason for talking and a chance to clarify their ideas. When the teacher asks questions, he or she should wait at least three seconds before rephrasing the question or moving on. A longer wait-time encourages students to think before responding. The four-quarter paradigm is a good framework for reflective thought. After a week of teaching, consider the following as a general goal: ¼ of the time is teacher talk, ¼ of the time is spent in cooperative work groups, ¼ of the time is discussions and sharing in class, and ¼ of the time is spent in independent work suited to the student's individual needs.

Managing the classroom well includes creating a positive learning environment by paying attention to individual differences among students. Some students misbehave because the teacher has not considered what the individual students are able to do, and instruction is not at their performance level. Frustrating students by giving them very difficult assignments causes disruptive behavior that can surface in a variety of forms. Sometimes students try to gain attention by acting like class clowns to cover up their feelings of being "dumb." It is essential that academic work be in tune with students' ability levels so that all get positive reinforcement for what they are able to do.

All students must be challenged. It is just as important to provide material at an appropriate level for gifted students as it is for students of limited abilities. Providing challenging, successful experiences offers students a positive means of gaining recognition and helps them build positive self-concepts. Just as teachers can reinforce students with limited abilities by providing short assignments and recognizing the completion of each task, they should provide learning tasks and activities that challenge and "stretch" the thinking processes of the most able students. Giving every student the same homework assignment is not fair treatment. Effective teachers tailor homework for students in ways that respect their abilities and have equivalent expectations relating to the amount of time necessary to complete the homework.

Physical factors often affect student performance. A hungry or tired student is often unwilling to do school work because food or a rest is necessary. Sometimes an overactive learner cannot sit still for long. It may be that the overactive student may be a kinesthetic learner who needs frequent movement. These comments made by a junior high school student are worth considering:

> I think that it is important for teachers to try to understand how their students feel. They shouldn't favor one student over another. I also think that teachers should know that most of us enjoy school. The thing most of us don't like is busy work. I think that if we are going to spend time working, it ought to be on worthwhile things. Another thing I have noticed some teachers doing is humiliating or embarrassing us to get us to learn. A better approach is to try to tell us all how to do things correctly. Adults don't like to be embarrassed in front of their friends, and neither do students. It is important for us to get to know all of our teachers as people and not just as teachers. One way to do this is to tell us about yourself and also about the way you feel about certain things. Also try seeing your students as you would see the people you work with and not just as children.

As this student points out, good teachers are concerned about each student and express this concern by being available to talk to students about their problems and build trust relationships. A caring teacher can help students reach their fullest potential as total human beings by encouraging them to be the best possible people they can be and by modeling behavior the students should exhibit. By treating students with respect and showing them feelings of love and self-worth, the teacher demonstrates care and concern for students. The students, in turn, will treat the teacher with respect, admiration, and trust.

Personalized Instruction

The teacher's expectations for students also play an important role in determining student behavior. A teacher who makes students feel capable can have a significant impact on the students' academic performance. The teacher should let the students know his/her expectations and the learning outcomes should serve as an appropriate challenge for the student. Students who are expected to do their best work and act in a proper manner will learn to evaluate their own work and to take the responsibility for their own learning. As students develop a sense of pride in themselves, their feelings of self-worth will improve as well.

Enthusiasm is as important as expectations. It is contagious, and a positive, enthusiastic teacher will go far in instilling the desire to learn in students. Students tend to imitate behaviors they observe. Just as sarcasm breeds sarcasm, so enthusiasm breeds enthusiasm. The saying "he who kindles others must first glow" is true especially in education. Every effort should be made to help the learner identify with the importance and value of responsible behavior. Adapt the instruction so every student who is putting forth effort and initiative can gain a sense of success and accomplishment. Provide sufficient flexibility to allow students who have mastered the basic concepts opportunities for enrichment. Enthusiasm is important and the disposition of an enthusiastic teacher rubs off on students. Frequent communication with parents and guardians improves classroom and school-wide climate and effectiveness.

Caring, enthusiastic teachers with high expectations know themselves and build a positive learning climate. The classroom environment should reflect the teacher's educational philosophy, teaching style, and personality. As a facilitator and catalyst in the learning process, the teacher must be flexible, willing to change to improve teaching techniques, and give students a sense of belonging and personal responsibility to the school. Students can be given opportunities to perform tasks like watering the plants, arranging books, decorating the room, pinning up bulletin boards, or even planting trees and shrubs in the schoolyard. The school needs to be a safe, secure place to which students eagerly come, where they are excited by what they learn. As students develop pride in their classroom and school, acts of vandalism will diminish because students are reluctant to destroy their own work.

The following suggestions, written by students to teachers, sum up the essence of creating a positive learning environment.

1. Be considerate of others' feelings.
2. Listen actively to what students have to say.
3. Find out their interests.
4. Be courteous.
5. Radiate genuine enthusiasm.
6. Be positive at all times—even among peers.
7. Make the classroom an exciting place to be.
8. Treat students in ways you would like to be treated.

Time on Task

An appropriate, well-planned, interesting lesson with fast, smooth transitions and challenging assignments sets students up for a high rate of success and little or no time for negative behavior and time off task. Teachers can do many things to stress the importance of their role. The learning environment is enhanced when instructional time is protected and used efficiently. Having materials ready, modeling punctuality, and developing consistent procedures are important facets of teacher performance. Learning is enhanced when assignments are returned promptly. Many students need monitoring to stay on task, and it is important that the teacher move around the classroom and become involved with assisting students during independent work.

The teacher should come to class each day ready to use every minute of every period. If worksheets are used, they should reinforce what is being learned rather than provide busywork. Students like to know what will happen next, so the schedule should be posted somewhere in the classroom. Routines help students know how the period will begin and end, where finished work is to be placed, and procedures for asking questions, sharpening pencils, and visiting the restroom. Structure helps reduce anxiety and provides for a smoother-running classroom.

The amount of time allocated for instruction may be quite different from academically engaged time. Allocated time refers to the amount of time provided in the school calendar or time limited to instruction by the teacher, while academically engaged time denotes time in which the students are actually engaged in learning activities or instruction. A study conducted through Northwest Laboratories in Denver, Colorado, found that in comparing 50 math classrooms with 250 minutes of allocated time per week, engaged time ranged from 244 minutes to 100 minutes. Consider this: If just 5 minutes are lost from each 50-minute period, an entire school day would be lost in just two weeks! Time spent in getting students ready for learning, materials traffic, cleanup, and waiting all reduce available learning time and consume allocated time. Classes that begin and end on time help students to spend more effort on academic tasks. Starting and ending late, discussing irrelevant material, and taking considerable time to pass out materials all erode time students could be on task.

Another element more difficult to measure is time-on-task. This is the period of time each individual student is engaged in meaningful equilibration. This requires a shared responsibility. First is the accommodation of the instructional tasks so students can be an active participant, and second is the enlistment of student responsibility for engagement and commitment to the learning tasks.

Among the most noteworthy of the preventive techniques employed by successful teachers are demonstrated abilities to do the following:

- Effectively pace instruction without distraction, inactivity, or interruptions.
- Establish routines that enable students to engage in a smooth transition from one learning task to the next without interrupting others or waiting for others to finish.
- Assign different learning alternatives within a class in the normal course of classroom instruction.
- Use a variety of techniques to keep students attentive and active. Take prompt action to control disruptions unobtrusively when they first occur, rather than waiting to correct misbehavior.
- Use interactive techniques that provide the teacher with frequent feedback and active monitoring of student performance.

- Use techniques and statements that have a ripple effect of stimulating motivation and on-task behavior by others in the classroom so that the group becomes a collective support system.

Supportive Discipline
Reinforcing Desirable Behavior

It is important that teachers become vibrant figures in the lives of their students. Teachers should frequently employ both direct and indirect methods of expression to communicate to all students that they are caring adults. They must express a genuine interest in the personal growth and development of each individual student.

A positive classroom atmosphere must be created for supportive techniques to be most effective. Students should develop respect for the worth and dignity of individuals. They should feel free to communicate ideas and feelings without fear or hesitation. A positive atmosphere lets students develop self-discipline as rapidly as possible so that they can make their own decisions rather than rely on teachers. The principle of accepting minority views while supporting majority decisions is an essential element of a democratic society.

Two techniques used to help students achieve desirable behaviors are "shaping" and "modeling." Shaping involves reinforcing behavior that is close to the desired behavior. As each level of behavior is attained, the criterion for reinforcement is raised until the ultimate behavior is achieved. Modeling is the teacher demonstrating appropriate behavior in all interactions, including teacher-administrator, teacher-teacher, teacher-staffer, and teacher-student, so that students will see the expected behavior and follow it.

Recognizing Positive Behaviors

Teacher dispositions have a great influence on the context of learning. There is perhaps no more powerful method for teaching than modeling. When the behaviors you want students to demonstrate are consistently reflected in the behaviors of the teacher, schools will improve. Students need to feel important and appreciated. Students need to feel that teachers want them to succeed and expect them to be successful.

Careful consideration should be given to how a teacher praises students. The praise should share information that can be used to direct student learning. When delivering praise, speak to specific behaviors rather than forwarding a general comment. Specific praises as, "Your use of the analytical balance is excellent," or "I can visualize a model of the solar system as you describe it," relate to the behavior and not the student. General praise, such as "You're a great student," does not share information that can be used for the student to direct further learning.

Rewards

Everyone in a school environment deserves to be treated with dignity and respect. Students need to feel the freedom to communicate without fear or hesitation. The teacher must be aware of classroom influences affecting communication and must search for ways to nurture a positive climate. Many times discipline is easier to manage when students have a sense of ownership. Therefore, when appropriate, allow for student input and dialogue about how things are done and why. Acknowledgment, through praise and reinforcement, is important and necessary for many students.

For some students, concrete rewards are often effective in reinforcing desirable behavior. Younger students often appreciate tokens, happy faces, and/or treats. Many students of all ages like to receive positive written notes and comments. Rewards can be certificates awarded during assemblies and recognition communicated through school newspapers or the local news media. To older students, the manner in which the reward is given as well as the perceived source of the reward may be more significant in determining the student response than the reward itself. Reinforcers that are usually effective with middle-level students include praise, recognition, opportunities to participate in unusual events, and opportunities to engage in conversation with peers. At the high school level the most prevalent positive consequences are intrinsic student satisfaction resulting from success, accomplishment, good grades, social approval, and recognition. Concrete rewards can work well as additional motivators particularly when coupled with recognition (e.g., pins or school letters).

Different students have different needs and expectations. Get to know each student and determine reinforcers that bring out desirable behaviors. Although you are always seeking self-motivation and intrinsic stimulation through success, many students have not reached desired levels of self-actualization. What is more important is to get responsive student behaviors. Once a pattern of participation is established, the frequency and extent of rewards can be reduced. Communication is the key; decisions should be reached through conversation and dialog whenever possible. This allows all parties to have a part in the process.

In using praise, rewards, or positive nonverbal communication, it is important to remember that what works as a reinforcer for one student won't necessarily work for another. One student may feel that receiving tokens is highly reinforcing, and another student may feel that receiving those same tokens is very degrading. Teachers should allow students to suggest meaningful methods of reinforcing. Then they should vary praise by using a variety of remarks and differing delivery styles that take into account individual feelings.

The students are important, the reinforcers are important, and the teacher is equally important during this supportive discipline phase. If the teacher is skillful in motivating students to a level that ensures real interest, student performance and good grades will help to promote good behavior.

In Evertson, Emmer, Clements, Sarford, and Warsham's (1981) study of teachers' classroom management, more effective managers were rated higher than less effective managers on several variables. These included clarity in giving directions and information, stating desired attitudes and behavior more frequently, providing activities and assignments with higher levels of student success, presenting clear expectations for work standards, and consistency of response to appropriate and inappropriate behavior. Effective teacher managers were rated higher on use of listening skills and maintaining eye contact (Emmer et al., 1980).

Teachers should continually communicate with guardians to enlist their support. There should be a two-way flow of information between the home and school because parents need to understand what their child's teacher is trying to accomplish. Parents need to know how they can assist and support the teacher at home, and teachers need to understand what's going on in the home.

One approach to parental communication can be through support reports such as the one presented below, phone calls that show an accomplishment or proctor behavior, and written newsletters. The teacher should always think ahead and find something positive and true to say about each student in beginning the conversation with a parent or guardian.

Reasons for This Report

ABILITY
_____ Good aptitude in subject
_____ Conscientious preparation in subject
_____ Effective motivation

ATTITUDE
_____ Good attendance
_____ Ample preparation for class
_____ Serious approach to studies
_____ Homework turned in regularly

PERFORMANCE
_____ Satisfactory test scores
_____ Excellent written homework
_____ Exemplary participation in class discussions

Comments ____
____
____

Sincerely,

____
Your child's teacher

Figure 5. Support report

Questions

Questioning skills are valuable tools in a teacher's arsenal. They should be structured in a manner that encourages all students to respond. It is important for teachers to improve the time they wait for a student reply. Increasing wait time to three seconds improves the depth of student responses.

Teachers must work toward developing higher order questions such as analysis and application rather than questions that focus on knowledge and simple comprehension. Encourage students to ask questions. Lastly, encourage dialog where questions are exchanged between all participants.

A strategy to support desirable classroom behavior for both younger and older students is to have regularly scheduled meetings during class time to discuss positive events and problems. Encourage students to provide their input into how the problems can be solved. The students can role-play problem situations to clarify and solve their problems.

The meetings or discussion should be well-planned and conducted using a prepared parliamentary procedure or discussion format. An important part of effective supportive discipline is respect for academic learning time. Therefore, the effective use of time in sharing sessions is equally as important as when engaging in academic instruction.

A variety of nonverbal signals can be used to communicate approval and appreciation for an appropriate behavior. These include a smile, a nod, a handshake, or just a twinkle of the eyes. The teacher's closeness or proximity to the student can show interest and concern and serve as an additional reinforcer. Proximity can frequently be used to focus student attention or bring students back on task.

Self-Discipline

There is a wealth of literature on developing self-discipline in students. However, reflective self-discipline for teachers and other adults is frequently overlooked. Manners, tone of voice, choice of words, and dispositions send significant messages to students. Consistency, fairness, and patience characterize teachers who are perceived positively by students. Many students do not often see adults interact in positive ways. The manner in which you communicate with other adults can be an important influence in school climate. Life is happier when the environment is supportive and reassuring. All educators must work to improve not only the disposition of school climate but also life outside of school.

Using positive regard, teachers reward students for desirable behavior. Verbal, nonverbal praise, and specific rewards are all part of the process. Students are encouraged to take pride in their school endeavors. Self-control and love of learning are the desired outcomes. A supportive teacher combined with a positive classroom environment will ensure that maximum learning will take place under the most desirable circumstances.

Communication

Communication can be a valuable tool. Send introductory notes and thank-you notes to parents. Use support reports to help bring about desired interactions between parents and their children, make efforts and encourage parent participation and involvement in their child's work and/or school activities. Seek out parent input relating to school, and utilize their input to improve your school and/or classroom.

In implementing elements of supportive discipline into your school discipline plan, consider the following:

- Utilize student comments and parental input. An effective supportive model cannot be left totally to school personnel.

- Parents must consistently support the premise that students have responsibilities as well as rights, and schools have an obligation to insist on both.

- The primary responsibility of the school, which is to direct academic learning, cannot be achieved efficiently if a disproportionate amount of time and resources must be expended to maintain order or facilities.

- No one is ever taught anything. The school environment is intended to facilitate the learning process. Active cognitive participation on the part of the learner is essential for learning to take place.

- If you do things for students that they can do for themselves, you are robbing them of self-respect and responsibility.

- Be both kind and firm. Kindness refers to your manner, and firmness refers to your follow-through behavior.

- Talk less; act more.

- Be patient.

- A good place is one where people are courteous, especially the adults.

- A good place is one where laughter is frequently heard, not because of frivolous activity but because of genuine joy brought about by involvement with caring people engaged in relevant work.

- A good place is one where communication is practiced and not preached.

- A good place is one that has reasonable rules, rules that everyone agrees on because they are beneficial to the individual and the group, and rules that everyone has a democratic stake in because everyone has a say in making and changing the rules as needs arise.

- A good place is one where the administrators actively support and participate in an approach to discipline that teaches self-responsibility.

Corrective Strategies

Despite measures taken to prevent discipline problems, inevitably some students will choose to misbehave or fail to respond to the academic opportunities provided in the school environment. Disruptive students may be verbally and physically aggressive or noncompliant. These behaviors consist of interrupting the class frequently, leaving seats without permission, provoking other students, or refusing to become involved in school work. An eighth grade student stated:

> I feel that discipline is a very important thing in school. If students are acting up, they should be reprimanded, but it shouldn't be held against them for the rest of the year. On the other hand, if students are acting up and they don't get reprimanded, they will continue to disrupt the class. This is unfair to other students.

Conferences

It may seem somewhat unusual to begin a section on corrective strategies with suggestions for student conferences. However, this technique is especially important in the context of inclusive classrooms--and probably all classrooms. Some students elect to misbehave and others are naturally confrontational. In both cases students expect controlling adult responses and have developed coping mechanisms that work for them. Conferencing with the student is a strategy that can often serve to make an uncomfortable situation more manageable.

At the beginning of the conference it is important to indicate the desire to be a helpful and supportive adult. You need to communicate that the difficulty relates to the behavior choices the student is making, not the student as a person. Discuss good qualities, and at the same time indicate a firm intolerance of specific unacceptable behaviors. If there are a multitude of inappropriate behaviors, it might be best to focus on one or two of the most important. Be flexible and discuss circumstances that could be altered that might alleviate the problem. Once a strategy is established, work toward having the student chart his or her own progress. When appropriate, enlist parental cooperation and support.

Withdrawn, shy students who retreat into their own world of daydreaming are too often overlooked but need to be brought into the mainstream of the class. Many teachers indicate that the most troublesome of all behaviors they face is not misbehavior, but rather student apathy and lack of motivation. Teachers must approach passive students with a vigor equivalent to that of the disruptive students. They must clearly communicate to each student that the consequences of passive, resistant, or disruptive behavior are serious enough to make on-task behavior a more desirable choice.

Formulating Rules

At the corrective level of the Cascade Model, student support is enlisted to develop rules. These rules are designed to establish norms and limits of students' behavior. In addition, consequences are established to clearly communicate to students that misbehavior will not be tolerated and to provide the classroom teacher with a consistent format for dealing with noncompliant behavior.

The importance of defining routines and expectations was mentioned at the preventive level. Some may argue that the differences between these terms and rules are simply a matter of semantics. However, the differences are significant in how the classroom teacher deals with them and in the way they are communicated to the students. Unfortunately in a pluralistic society, perceptions of right and wrong are often unclear. Therefore, rules need to be established to define appropriate behaviors and reasonable limits.

Rules defined at the corrective level of classroom discipline reflect clearly defined expectations with the imposition of consequences if they are not adhered to and respected. Student responses to the rules are monitored and supervised by the instructional and administrative staff in the school. Routines and expectations are defined in order to provide mechanisms for smooth traffic flow within the classroom whether it concerns papers, supplies, equipment, or working in groups. In most instances teachers should be open to discussing classroom rules and why consistency of behavior is important. The right of all students to learn and study in an environment that is comfortable to everyone can build a sound base of credibility. The rules should be clear and explicit enough so that all parties understand them.

The process of rule formulation requires reflection on the part of the classroom teacher prior to talking with students. The teacher needs to decide what the tolerable limits of the classroom will be and the extent of student involvement in selecting rules. A good starting point in preplanning is to reflect on the following questions:

1. What behaviors do I wish to increase?
2. What behaviors do I wish to decrease?
3. What are some likely consequences for inappropriate behavior?
4. What are some effective rewards for reinforcing appropriate behavior?

It is much easier to start with a management plan that is overly firm than it is to revise a discipline policy that isn't working effectively. Proactive decision-making is critical with a careful review of the limits of students' choices. It is easy to loosen up classroom limits, but to impose more severe limits often erodes the potential for gaining cooperative student support for the new policies. The teacher should state rules in positive terms. An example might be "Students are to be in their seats and ready to learn when the bell rings." The rule should be stated in terms of observable student behavior using a vocabulary that students clearly understand. When formulating rules, try to keep the number below 10. Rules should be understandable to the students and stated in positive terms. Good rules are flexible and should be reviewed from time to time to determine if they are necessary and if they are accomplishing the desired effect.

Younger students and students of limited abilities should have rules appropriate to their capabilities and development. Extreme care must be taken to ensure that everyone will be able to abide by the student-generated rules. If necessary, instructional time should be allocated to ensure that all students are familiar with the rules and capable of interpreting them based on their own behaviors. Some time should be allowed for the rules to be tested to ensure that they produce the desired student behaviors and are consistent with school policy.

Implementing Rules

After the rules are clearly understood and students have established a pattern of expected behaviors, it is appropriate to introduce the consequences for those who choose to break the rules. Difficulties often occur because there are multiple perceptions of fair treatment. Many subscribe to a most basic belief that fair treatment is equal treatment. This differs from a profound statement attributed to Arthur Combs, "There is nothing so unequal as equal treatment of unequals."

Whenever possible, use logical consequences that will result in the student learning the skill or concepts missed in the process of implementing the consequences. The consequence could also be a restriction that logically relates back to the behavior. Procedures should be established for students that comply with the imposed consequence(s). For students with special needs, consequences should be consistent with the IEP. This provides greater assurance that actions will be supported up the chain of command.

Consequences should be periodically reviewed to ensure they are affecting desired student outcomes and are appropriate for the future development of the individual. Communication with parents and guardians is also important. Ask for suggestions, seek support, and show them respect and support for their initiatives.

Formulating Consequences

When considering consequences, be sure that student dignity is respected. Consequences should be enforced consistently and immediately after the undesired behavior. In instances when a warning is appropriate, eye contact and proximity control are often effective. If the behavior distracts other students from learning, develop a plan for refocusing class attention to the learning task. Consequences should be periodically reviewed to assess their effectiveness in producing the desired outcomes.

Students need to see the relationship between their actions and the consequences of their actions. Natural consequences are more effective than punishment because they teach the student what should be done. This helps them understand that consequences are a natural outgrowth of breaking the rules and that positive behavior is more conducive to successful learning than negative behavior. Each consequence should be fair but firm. In violating a rule, the student must accept the responsibility for the inappropriate behavior and the consequences of this act.

Allowing students to have input into developing consequences gives them the opportunity to express their feelings and have some effect on the functioning of the classroom. This is essential if the classroom is to become their classroom. However, teachers must reserve the right to veto any consequences that they determine to be inappropriate or ineffective with a student or group of students.

Implementing Consequences

Any effective management plan has to respect student diversity and provide accommodations for students with special needs. Adaptive management practices involve making modifications to ensure that all students can have an opportunity to learn in environments that are appropriate to their needs.

Most inappropriate classroom behavior is not seriously disruptive and can be managed by addressing the individual and avoiding escalation. The classroom teacher must immediately address minor misbehaviors such as prolonged inattention, failure to follow instructions, incessant whispering or talking, and/or movement about the classroom. Whenever possible, the behavior should be unobtrusively addressed without disrupting the instructional activity. Some suggestions are given below.

- Use proximity control and move toward the offending student.
- Use eye contact, a nod of the head, or some other nonverbal signal.
- Pass the student a written reminder.
- Provide a short verbal cue.
- Redirect the student by stating what the student should be doing and, if applicable, cite the proper procedure or rule.

If several students are involved in misbehavior, the best strategy may be to refocus the class attention to the assigned learning task. The teacher might say, "I would like everyone to address their attention to the transparency and focus on the illustration. What are some physical features that complicated the building of a canal through the Isthmus of Panama?" The purpose of the redirection is to create a behavior that is incompatible with the disruptive behavior.

Good classroom managers do not ignore deviations of classroom rules. Students expect discipline procedures to be fair, with consequences that are enforced consistently, not according to how the teacher feels at the moment. When a problem occurs, whenever possible the student should be addressed in private. For many students with disabilities, confrontational teacher actions in public will escalate rather than moderate appropriate behaviors. The teacher should explain to the student that there is a choice: abide by the rules or accept the consequences.

As little time as possible should be spent on disruptive behavior. Teachers should let the student know the rule that has been broken and then move on with the lesson. They should mean what they say and follow through with it. At a later time, the teacher can discuss with the student what occurred. In effective schools, teachers handle most discipline problems themselves and rarely send students to the principal's office.

If discipline problems occur, students need to know what to expect. They need to be aware of what is acceptable and unacceptable behavior and that consequences will be imposed if they engage in a pattern of inappropriate behavior. Discipline should be prompt, appropriate, and private. To correct discipline problems, the teacher must begin by being a good listener. The good disciplinarian is emotionally mature and professionally competent. Such a teacher must express empathy and develop rapport with students, but also must establish limits and carry out consequences if students go beyond these limits. Providing for the disruptive student takes patience and understanding.

Discipline should be developed from a human relations perspective with emphasis upon communicating in a democratic way. The teacher should communicate beliefs and feelings by letting students know expectations. The teacher should encourage student dialogue in addressing the problem or concern by listening to what students are saying and by communicating care and concern.

Yet sometimes angry conditions occur that can possibly lead to power struggles. Angry feelings are natural, but under angry conditions, judgment is impaired and perceptions are inaccurate. Resulting arguments become emotional encounters that create ill will for all concerned. If a teacher gets drawn into a power struggle with a student, a no-win situation ensues.

When angry feelings are present, there should be a "cooling off" period before the problem is tackled. The student should be told that the problem will be discussed later, during a private conference. Teachers should make a conscious effort to put some space between themselves and the student. Listed below are 12 suggestions for the teacher to consider when dealing with discipline problems:

- Do not allow students to remain passive in a classroom setting.
- Do not allow excuses. Instead, focus on appropriate future behaviors.
- Determine a course of action to deal with small problems. Try proximity control, that is, move closer to the child who is misbehaving or move the child closer to you. If you must take action to stop a behavior, try to establish an unobtrusive signal to alert the student without disrupting instruction. A glance, a frown, or a shake of your head is often sufficient.
- Avoid challenges. If you dare students to misbehave, they will more than likely take you up on it.
- Avoid extracting confessions. The accused may lie just to have the situation over with. It is better to tell students you know what they did and that you don't want it to happen again. Then drop the matter.
- Avoid confrontations in front of others. Whenever possible, handle a confrontation by postponing it until later when it may be handled in private.
- If you feel you must threaten, be certain you can carry out your threat.
- When you reprimand, do it privately whenever possible.
- Avoid humiliating a student. Ridicule and sarcasm make students resentful and may turn the entire class against the teacher. Treat students with respect.
- Know your students. A trip to the office may be just what a student wants at that moment so the individual can get out of a difficult situation.
- Beware of mass punishment. If a child misbehaves, that child should bear the responsibility, not the whole class. In most cases, if you don't know who did it, it is better to drop the matter rather than accuse the whole class.
- If behavior problems cannot be solved in the classroom, seek the help of counselors and administrators.

Means of administering consequences. There are two ways to use consequences. One is to have consequences that are the same for each rule. These are carried out in sequential order regardless of the past history of the individual involved. A list of consequences carried out in this manner might be as follows:

1. Warning
2. Time-out in the classroom (for 5 minutes)
3. Detention (for 30 minutes)
4. Contact parents and detention (1 hour)
5. In-school suspension (for 1-3 days)

When disruptive behavior occurs, the rule is stated and the consequence implemented. ("Robert, you called out without raising your hand. Go to the time-out area for 5 minutes.") Another way is to post a class roster and communicate to the student by placing a check after the student's name when an infraction occurs.

An alternative approach to implementing consequences is to provide a range of alternatives for each rule and to select the consequences that best meet the needs and past history of the individual student. For the rule "Use appropriate language," the consequences of using foul language might consist of the following:

1. Detention (30 minutes)
2. Write a 300-word paper on the proper use of oral expression.
3. Ask the student to leave and come back when he or she is ready.
4. Meet with parents, teacher, and student.
5. In-school suspension.

The means of implementing consequences should be decided by the teacher and explained to the students. One teacher may feel that consequences should be implemented in sequential order, regardless of the particular student involved. Another may feel that a consequence should be selected that fits a particular student's needs. In this manner, the uniqueness of each student is addressed and individual needs are met.

Having a range of alternative consequences allows the teacher greater flexibility in dealing with misbehavior and greater opportunity to provide a consequence, if necessary, that is most likely to arrest the negative behavior for the individual student. To help students accept differential treatment, let them know why a particular consequence is selected. Explain that not everything in life is equal because no two people are alike. If necessary, engage in a discussion related to the statement, "There is nothing so unequal as the equal treatment of unequals."

On the other hand, with individual treatment there is a greater risk of generating student perceptions that the teacher plays favorites or is punitive toward certain individuals. It is common for students to establish attitudes concerning the fairness of a teacher. It's important to reexamine rules and consequences at regular intervals to ensure that they are having the desired effect. If a discipline problem occurs that threatens the teacher's or students' safety, the disruptive student must be removed from the classroom immediately. Plans should be made ahead of time for procedures to be used in the event of violent student behavior. If an intercom button is available, it can be pressed to call for assistance. If not, the teacher should identify another person who can help or have a cell phone accessible.

Time-outs. Time-out is useful in helping students correct disruptive behavior. Placement in a time-out area in the classroom isolates students by setting them apart from peers in a nonreinforcing situation. This provides individuals with a chance to gain control and organize themselves. It is based on the premise that being a part of the class is more desirable than sitting in the time-out area.

Since time-out calls for the student to be removed from an environment within the regular part of the classroom, care must be taken to ensure that the regular classroom is more reinforcing than the time-out area. The location of the time-out area should allow the teacher to observe the student as well as the student's impact on the rest of the class. Time-out is not effective for all disruptive behaviors. Behaviors such as daydreaming or rocking can be performed in the time-out area, and the frequency of these behaviors may increase rather than decrease.

To determine if time-out is effective in decreasing a particular behavior, a baseline count of the disruptive behavior may be taken prior to and after using time-out. The baseline data should be taken over a 1-2 week period. This allows the teacher to determine if a change is the disruptive behavior has taken place after time-out has been implemented.

Prior to using this procedure, consider possible problems and determine how they could be handled. What will you do if:

1. The student refuses to go to the time-out area?
2. The student has to go to the bathroom during time-out?
3. The student engages in behavior that could injure himself or herself while in time-out?

If the student refuses to go to the time-out area, have a backup plan, such as after-school detention or in-school suspension. If using time-out does not solve the problem for a particular student, other strategies may be needed.

Time-out is useful in managing disruptive behavior. If properly applied, it allows the student to stop receiving reinforcement for inappropriate behavior.

Notification sheets. An approach found to be effective in classrooms is to hand a disruptive or off-task student a notification sheet. Three examples are noted below. Example 1 gives an illustration of a first notification sheet given to a disruptive student. Example 2 shows an illustration of a first notification sheet given to a student engaged in an off-task behavior. Example 3 shows an illustration of a second notification sheet.

Example 1. Notification sheet: Warning to disruptive student.

I perhaps do not realize it, but I am interrupting the classroom lesson by my behavior. It is rude and unfair to the rest of my classmates. I will cease my inappropriate behavior immediately or realize I may have to engage in an alternative learning task to demonstrate that I have mastered the concepts included in this lesson and provide evidence of self-responsibility and self-control.

Example 2. Notification sheet: Warning for off-task behavior.

I perhaps do not realize it, but I am engaging in a behavior that is not in my best interest. The teacher has the responsibility to provide opportunities for me to learn and to expect achievement from me. I will pay attention to the assigned task immediately.

Example 3. Notification sheet: Action.

I have chosen to ignore the written warning of the first notification sheet. Disregard for the first warning shows rudeness that will not be tolerated. Therefore, I will bring this paper to my teacher at the end of the class period, or earlier if appropriate, so that he or she can identify a consequence for my action.

1. An additional assignment of ______________________
2. Meeting with teacher before or after school
3. Written plan of how I will improve my behavior and why improvement is necessary
4. Conference with my teacher and guardians on ____________(date) and ______________(time)

Signature ____________________________

Punishment versus logical consequences. Punishment usually stops disruptive behavior only temporarily. It is designed to get even with students and alleviates the teacher's need to seek release from anger and stress. It does not teach students what they should be doing and is the least effective means of dealing with disruptive behavior. Punishment tends to create further discipline problems rather than correct them. It often encompasses a strong dislike for the punished and can have a negative effect on learning. When teachers punish a learner, they are encouraging hate, fear, or withdrawal. The student wants to avoid contact with the teacher and whatever is being taught. Punishment induces violence rather than acceptable behavior.

Instead of punishment, logical consequences that are related to the misbehavior can be used. If students are late for class, asking them to remain after school to make up the work that has been missed is a logical consequence. Requiring students to write "I must not be late" 100 times is a punishment. A consequence is logical if it helps the violator learn acceptable behavior. Here are several differences between punishment and logical consequences:

- Punishment expresses the power of personal authority. Logical consequences express the impersonal reality of social order.
- Punishment is rarely related to misbehavior. Logical consequences are logically related to misbehavior.
- Punishment tells the individual he or she is bad. Logical consequences imply no element of moral judgment.
- Punishment focuses on what is past. Logical consequences are concerned with present and future behavior.
- Punishment is associated with a threat, either open or concealed. Logical consequences are based on goodwill, not on regulation.
- Punishment demands obedience. Logical consequences permit choice.

Detention, depending upon the manner in which it is handled, can be perceived either as a logical consequence or as a punishment. Whenever possible, it should be communicated as a logical consequence for inappropriate use of time during the instructional day. Students should be expected and provided opportunities to engage in productive learning efforts during detention periods, and resources should be available whenever possible.

If there are no logical consequences, the teacher may withdraw privileges. If students break a rule, they may lose the privilege that may consist of free time to pursue a desired activity, play an educational game, or go to recess on time. The essence of discipline is finding effective alternatives to punishment. To punish a child is to enrage him and make him uneducable (Ginott, 1972).

Parental involvement. One consequence for a broken rule may be to have students call their parents and explain what has happened and why they must remain after school. When students make the phone call, the teacher should be there to be certain they are telling what actually happened. This may be sufficient to stop the disruptive behavior.

If behavior problems continue, enlist parental help. Call the parents to let them know what is happening and ask for suggestions regarding possible management strategies. Continue communicating with the parents regarding student class progress. Call home, send notes, and have periodic conferences. Parents may be able to offer the support needed to motivate students to change their behavior.

If parents say that it is difficult for them to manage behavior at home, suggest getting help from a professional guidance counselor or psychologist. Meet as a team on a regular basis to try out strategies at home and at school and determine those that seem to work best for the particular student.

In-school suspension. The most restrictive consequence to be suggested at the corrective level is in-school suspension. Students are assigned to a special room set up for this purpose. While there, students must keep up with their regular classroom assignments. This offers a means through which the misbehaving student may be dismissed temporarily from the regular classroom. The plan is designed to keep students in school. Assignments are given by the student's teacher(s) commensurate with that of their classmates. The in-school suspension teacher assists the student if there are questions about the assigned work.

The student is assigned to in-school suspension for one to three days. Parents are notified immediately. While under this plan, students are restricted to the in-school suspension room for the entire day with only brief trips to the bathroom. Lunch is eaten individually, and contact with other students is strictly limited. In using this procedure, care should be taken that suspensions are being administered consistently and fairly.

Teachers, as instructional leaders, are the authority in the classroom and must conduct themselves accordingly. If misbehavior is not addressed, one can expect the incidences to increase.

Among the most important elements in the discipline process are (a) a feeling of trust that your decisions are for the good of the individual and the group, and not capricious or arbitrary, (b) a feeling of confidence from the members of the group so that they know what to expect, and yourself (c) acceptance of you as the person responsible for learning in the classroom and the confidence that each day will provide meaningful learning.

The general plan is to establish rules by which the school and classroom must operate. These rules are directed toward observable student behavior and are clearly communicated to the students. Consequences are developed that are imposed on students who break the rules, with the severity of the consequence increasing if rule violations are repeated. This aspect of the management plan is designed to control undesirable behavior and to clearly communicate to students specific unacceptable behaviors.

Effective disciplinarians are good listeners and express empathy with students but also establish limits and carry out consequences. They avoid power struggles and punishment and, if necessary, are consistent in using time-out, notification sheets, logical consequences, and in-school suspension.

Adaptive Measures

Adaptive measures take two forms. One is the accommodation of the educational environment for those students who have special physical, emotional, or learning needs. The importance of the teachers' role cannot be overemphasized in presenting all students with a learning environment in which they can have a successful learning experience if they give forth a full-scale effort. Although absolute attainment cannot always be accomplished, it is important that students feel a sense of growth when engaging in the learning process. Keep in mind that persistence in adults results through high levels of perceived success in childhood.

Students who cannot function productively within the previous three levels in the Cascade Model sometimes need an adaptive management plan. During this phase the teacher pinpoints a disruptive behavior the student exhibits, collects and examines data about that behavior, and has a conference with the student. During the conference, the teacher shows the student the data representing the frequency of the undesired behavior, discusses and decides on a more desirable behavior, and writes and signs a contract specifying a reward system for achieving the more desired behavior.

The goal of adaptive techniques is to have students gradually assume responsibility for their own behavior. As students find benefits and pleasures derived from learning, they can be weaned from extrinsic reinforcements. The student whose reading ability improves will begin to enjoy reading and will no longer need to be rewarded for completing a reading assignment. The student who begins to feel good about participation in a discussion will no longer need check marks to encourage that participation. The student who receives reinforcement from both the teacher and peers for conforming behavior will discontinue attention-getting comments.

In using these adaptive techniques, persistence is important. The teacher shouldn't give up too easily. Remember that the student probably has had these problems for a long time, and it may take a few months to see any positive changes. If the student doesn't succeed at first, the teacher should keep trying. Since all else has failed in the past, there's nothing to lose.

Student Contracts

We have become more quantitative in performance expectations, and there are increasing expectations and responsibility to produce evidence that students are learning. Contracts can be a mechanism for such conversation and documentation. They can serve in a variety of ways -- to help students in their learning, to communicate expectations and performance outcomes to a larger audience, and to provide documentation to guide students. They can also be used as a basis to restrict behavior when necessary. Ideally, any intervention should be constructive, building toward improved efficiency and self-responsibility from the student. On the other hand, there are times when contracts are needed to provide a baseline or foundation for an alternative placement, such as in-school suspension or assignment to a residential school.

Despite using the techniques suggested within the previous levels in the Cascade Model, teachers will find that a few students will continue to be consistently disruptive and frequently break classroom rules. Students with intensive behavioral problems, particularly highly aggressive ones, require an individualized discipline plan with intensive monitoring.

Adaptive discipline emphasizes individualizing the corrective process for students when all other techniques have failed. It includes a process of incremental steps using behavior management techniques, contracts, and tangible rewards to reinforce desirable behavior. This procedure is used with students who choose to engage in deviant behavior or those students who need special support to help them acquire an acceptable behavior pattern at school. It utilizes a reinforcement system drawing heavily from behavioral psychology and is highly structured with a carefully designed, systematic plan for dealing with disruptive classroom behavior or refusal to participate in learning activities.

In any plan the importance of becoming familiar with a process, thinking it through, and then enlisting the support of the learner is critical in the adaptive management process. The following steps can be used as a guide:

- Identify the behavior pattern(s) you want to encourage and any behaviors that you perceive as debilitating to the learning process for the student and/or others in the classroom.

- Talk with the student to develop a value judgment about the behaviors and a plan to eliminate the negative behaviors and increase the positive behaviors.

- Obtain the student's commitment and offer a reinforcement if a certain success level is met. Establish easily attainable levels at first and increase expectations after the student has had several successful outcomes.

- Do not tolerate excuses. Simply replan and readjust if necessary; do not punish or impose consequences.

The role of the teacher is to provide a context of learning in which there is a high likelihood that the student can achieve success, to work with the student to generate a commitment, and to encourage and support the student when good choices are made.

The baseline period. This process begins with the teacher determining the target behavior. Questions like "What do you want the student to change?" and "Why is this change necessary?" should be examined. It is important that the target behavior focus on the need to remediate a behavior, not on an inadequacy within an individual. Only one or two behaviors should be concentrated on at a time to prevent frustration and rebellion.

When choosing a behavior to focus on, the teacher should choose one with a high likelihood of success for modification. Success is necessary because at the earliest stage gaining student compliance is most important. The primary goal is to obtain a sense of self-responsibility on the student's part. To build this attitude, success is essential. Success builds confidence, generates trust, and improves self-concept.

Some specific disruptive behaviors that can be modified are listed below.

- Not being seated (when students are supposed to be)
- Whispering (when everyone is to be quiet)
- Laughing or snickering at people
- Talking out of turn or using unacceptable language
- Excessively loud coughing, hiccupping, burping, mumbling, or knuckle cracking

It's also important for a teacher to consider some of the passive and/or resistive behaviors that can be modified. Students should learn self-responsibility for their own growth as well as considering the needs of others. Among some passive and resistive behaviors that can be modified are the following:

- Not completing assignments
- Forgetting supplies and/or homework
- Excessive daydreaming
- Not following directions

After the teacher determines the targeted behavior(s), the teacher should take a baseline count to measure the number of times the behavior occurs. This baseline data can be collected in several ways depending on a teacher's preference. It should be collected for at least a week to determine the actual frequency of the behavior.

The conference. Holding a private conference allows the student to save face. The teacher's role during the conference is to talk with the student and indicate a concern and a desire to be a helpful, supportive adult. The teacher attempts to develop a trust relationship by emphasizing the good qualities and worth of the individual while demonstrating a firm intolerance of specific undesired behaviors. The focus is on the present and how unacceptable behavior can be altered.

Positive confrontations are provided as the teacher and student discuss the problem. Students are allowed to express themselves without being blamed for the inappropriate behavior. However, students are encouraged to realize that they must take the responsibility for their own behavior in class and in the learning process. It's important for the teacher to let students know what is acceptable behavior. The teacher should discuss behaviors, not feelings, and force a value judgment of appropriate and inappropriate behaviors.

The following items should be discussed during the conference:

1. What behavior should be changed?
2. Why is this change necessary?
3. What does the baseline data show about the frequency of the behavior?
4. What are the expected, appropriate behaviors?
5. What will happen if the student behaves in the expected, appropriate way (the reward)?

Developing a contract. Once the appropriate behavior has been delineated, the teacher should plan a written contract with the student, using specific rewards. Students are asked to offer information about what they would like to do. Perhaps they would like free time to pursue an area of interest or receive tangible items such as a poster. Care must be taken to assure that the event or item selected is reinforcing to the student. These free-time activities or tangible items are used to reward the student for using the appropriate behavior instead of the targeted disruptive behavior. Figure 6 is an example of a student contract.

I, Mike Brown, do hereby agree on this 9th day of February to the following terms: I will receive 1 point for each 15-minute period in which I don't interrupt. For every 20 points I earn, I will receive 5 minutes of free time on my computer. Points are earned for not interrupting.

Signed: ____________________	Signed: ________________________
Teacher	Student

Figure 6. Student contract.

Using a contract puts the responsibility of the behavior on the student while promoting self-confidence. Students are responsible for their own behavior as they make choices to behave appropriately or inappropriately and must accept the consequences of their choices. In using rewards, it is hoped that tangible items and reinforcing events will give way to the satisfaction derived from succeeding and that learning will become self-rewarding.

The sample contract offered here is a performance agreement between the student and the teacher and is directed toward improving the targeted behavior. The student is involved in how it will work and what the reward will be. The contract is made for a week, and the accompanying data sheet is evaluated daily. The data sheet should begin with small increments that help students achieve success quickly. Gradually these small increments can be increased.

When the teacher and the student have agreed to the stipulations in the contract, both parties sign it. In signing this "official" contract, the student is alerted to responsibility for his behavior.

Monitoring the behavior. Data should continue to be collected while the reinforcement plan is being used and after it is discontinued to determine the degree of progress (or regression). Unlike the data collected during the baseline period to determine the frequency of the undesirable behavior, the data collected after signing the contract should determine the frequency of the desirable behavior. The desired behavior should be built through a series of small incremental steps rather than large leaps.

If the contracted task is not accomplished, the time frame may need to be adjusted. For some students, it is easier to accomplish a difficult task in the morning. For others, the afternoon may prove more effective. Although classroom contracts may be adjusted, excuses are not accepted. Punishment should not be imposed. The student and teacher should continue to work together to find the best means of increasing the desired behavior.

If, despite the implementation of the contract and reward system, the student's disruptive behavior is not diminishing, it may be that the student is reinforced by receiving attention from peers. To encourage help from the class, set up a class reward such as a popcorn party or a special time to interact with peers. When the student does succeed, the teacher should be sure to reinforce the accomplishment. Success stimulates commitment.

Sample narrative. In discussing a student's problem, the teacher is an active listener. The decision-making process should involve the student and lead to self-management. The teacher helps the student achieve the goal by helping him or her realize that actions involve consequences and that actions can be changed.

The dialogue with a problem student may run as follows (Stefanich & Bell, 1987, p. 63-64):

Day 1
"Ed, do you know why you're here?"
"No."
"I've been watching you for the last week. How many times do you think you have interrupted this class?"
"I don't know."
"Well, I've been keeping track of how many times you interrupted this class during the past week. These data show that you interrupted 76 times. Did you realize that?"
"No. Seventy-six times?"
"What we're going to have to do, Ed, is to come up with something that will reduce the number of times you interrupt the class! When you constantly interrupt, you are making it hard for other people to attend to their task. Let's develop a plan. I believe that you're trying to get your driver's license, right?"
"That's right."
"Let's see if we can make a plan to help you decrease your interrupting in class. We'll write a contract. For every class period that you don't interrupt the class, you receive a point. When you have 10 points altogether, I've made arrangements with a driver's education instructor to give you a half hour behind the wheel. How does that sound?"
"Sounds great!"
"I'll write that on this contract....Now you sign here....And I'll sign here."
Day Two
"Ed, you didn't make it. I'll tell you what. Let's try just the first 15 minutes of each class period for not interrupting the class. Do you think that would be better for you?"
"Yes, I'll try."
Day Three
"You made it. You have a total of 3 points from yesterday. All you need is 7 more points and you'll have your driving time. Can you do it?"
"I'll try."
Day Four

"You made it."
"When do I start driving?"
"I've arranged for a driving lesson at 4:00 p.m. Saturday. Will you stick with the contract?"
"Sure will."

Conference with the student in private and enlist the support of other professionals when appropriate. The primary goal is always to gain the cooperation of the student, to maximize supportive actions when acceptable behaviors emerge, and to minimize punitive actions against the student.

Beyond Student Contracts

A series of more restrictive steps may be needed. Time-out within the classroom and time outside of the classroom under direct supervision can be tried. It may be necessary to consider a class for behavior disordered, an alternative school, or a residential school. A student who remains insubordinate or whose conduct endangers the welfare of others may be suspended or expelled after due process. Evaluate the situation. If the student's disruptive behavior is not improving or is preventing other students from learning, document the behavior, and state your case through the referral process.

In effective schools, students are afforded due process like that offered by the judicial system in a democratic society. The process carries out a sequential series of successively more restrictive alternatives until behavior is under control. Sometimes in a democratic society it is necessary to incarcerate or restrict individuals who behave in ways that interfere with opportunities for others to live their daily lives in safety and security. Likewise, in classrooms, teachers need mechanisms for establishing order. At times they will need the power to remove a source of conflict that serves to interfere with the delivery of positive learning experiences for students who are attending school to learn. So, in extreme cases, students who have exhibited defiant, noncompliant, or disruptive behavior must be removed from the regular classroom and sent to an alternative classroom or residential school.

Management Profile

The tool (Appendix A) can be used by a classroom teacher for planning and/or self-reflection, by a collaborative team in assessing an overall management strategy, by an administrator as an assessment tool, or by a supportive teacher peer willing to conduct an external assessment.

The tool works best when two or more assessments are graphed on the same profile and compared. In a self-assessment the entries could be, "What I perceive as my current management practices" to "What I would consider to be the ideal management profile for me." Multiple perspectives can be obtained by including the input of an external observer and comparing his or her perceptions with yours. Areas where there are discrepancies can be discussed and sometimes targeted as goals for self-improvement. Awareness is often a critical first step in improving instructional practice and the management profile can be a valuable tool in the process.

Chapter 3
Models and Applications

Teaching science provides greater flexibility and greater challenges in instructional delivery than any other discipline. Yet for many teachers, especially elementary school teachers, science teaching is often considered a daunting task. This is due to a number of reasons, such as certain preconceptions about science and poor or insufficient preparation at the university level. Although it would be naive to believe that there is a "recipe" for teaching and learning science, there are a number of models that can help teachers with their daily work in the classroom, in terms of curriculum goals and outcomes, content, student characteristics, available materials, time frame, and so forth. Implicit in all of these models is scientists' belief that "the world is understandable and that there are discoverable patterns throughout nature" (Howe & Jones, 1993, p. 6).

Whether or not science is described or defined as "a search for truth"--a statement that can raise a number of epistemological issues--there is no doubt that science is the active pursuit of understanding the natural world. It is not just a collection of laws and a catalog of facts, but a human endeavor--a creation of the human mind--which results in knowledge (what we know about the world). However, inherent in this endeavor are the processes (the tools of the scientists) and the attitudes and values (dispositions about the impact and the worth of science). Most specifically, in talking about science, reference is made to three man areas: knowledge base (concepts, laws, principles, and theories) that enable us to understand and explain phenomena and make predictions; science processes (skills such as observing, classifying, hypothesizing, experimenting, etc.) that scientists use to gain a deeper understanding of natural phenomena; and the attitudes and values necessary in approaching and also using science to improve the human enterprise and the quality of life for everyone.

The teaching of science has undergone considerable change during the last century. Early in the 20th century, lecture-laboratory was the most common approach. This strategy focused on dissemination of knowledge, both facts and scientific principles, through lecture and sometimes demonstration. This was followed by laboratory exercises in which students carried out experiments that verified the concepts taught during the teacher-directed instruction (Jenkins, 1989). However, this approach to science teaching was criticized and challenged as the knowledge base of science expanded and the expectations of the workplace changed. American free enterprise became centered on capturing the unique and creative ideas of the individual to improve production, create new products, and adjust to a changing workplace. These attributes, it was thought, should also be reflected in schools, the workplace of children. It is important in the educational process to nurture creative thinking and enlist free expression from students.

Changes in the science curriculum over the years led to important reforms in teaching and learning. The influence of thinkers like Dewey, Piaget, and Bruner led to a shift in the role of the laboratory, where the demonstration and reinforcement of ideas gave way to students actively investigating by using the processes of science. They saw learning as a process, in sharp contrast to the previous behaviorist approach that had viewed learning merely as a product. Learning through activity was the central point of their theories (Bruner, 1963; Piaget, 1970).

Dewey built upon the ideas of Rousseau to propose an educational theory that viewed student activity and the problem method as the main avenues for effective learning. He rejected subject-matter curriculum, not because of the nature of the subject matter itself, but because he objected to presenting students with a logical summary of adult experiences. Instead, he favored having students reach their own conclusions by engaging in their own experiences (Dewey, 1910). Thinking, according to Dewey, is a capability people have acquired in the evolutionary process because of the challenges of the natural environment. And this is where Dewey made one of his most important contributions to the nature of human thought. He rejected the idea that thought derives either from contemplation alone or from sensation. Man, he contended, starts thinking when a change in the environment affects his comforts, when circumstances offer different choices to a desired goal, and generally, whenever a problem arises. Therefore, the problem method is important to the learning process (Dewey, 1910).

Following World War II, the ideology of science teaching changed to focus more on the actions of the students not as recipients of information, but as active inquirers in the learning process. Federal government initiatives to actively facilitate the improvement of science curriculum following Sputnik led to major educational reforms. In the 1960s, curriculum reforms placed students as "original discoverers" who were supposed to “find” a pre-existing truth. Many of these reforms are found in current curriculum materials. Students were asked to investigate various problems, observe, state and test hypotheses, collect and interpret data. In short, students behave as "junior scientists." Curriculum reform also developed due to the infusion of federal monies into education and the commitment of the higher education community to support curriculum development efforts. These projects were grounded in contemporary learning theory and sound science. Funding came through the National Science Foundation along with private support. Progressive education was well under way, and new instructional models were developed.

Piaget, a genetic epistemologist interested in the construction--genesis--of knowledge, contributed greatly to this reform. He rejected the copy theory of classical empiricism and argued that each student constructs his or her own reality through activity. Piaget (1971) equated intelligence with action upon the objects of the environment. He distinguished between physical action (that results in knowledge about the nature and the characteristics of the object) and logic or mathematical action (that results in knowledge about relationships between the characteristics of the object). For example, knowledge about the characteristics of a simple pendulum (such as length and mass) derives from exploring the nature of the pendulum. However, understanding that the period of a pendulum swing is independent of the mass and depends solely upon the length of the pendulum comes from the coordination of those characteristics and constructing relationships between them. The constructed relationship between period and length requires a conscious action upon the pendulum and an exploration of it. This notion of "exploration" caught the attention of science educators and is one reason why Piaget should be considered one of the great contributors in developing Guided Discovery as an instructional strategy. Piaget believed students should explore and act on their environment in order to construct knowledge.

Bruner, on the other hand, after observing children in actual classroom settings, outlined an ideology of instruction that provided a theoretical foundation for the exploratory model (Bruner, 1963). His ideas went well beyond the original progressive ideas of Dewey and revolutionized science curriculum development. Bruner thought intellectual activity the same "whether at the frontier of knowledge or in a third grade classroom" and, therefore, students learning physics should behave like physicists (Bruner, 1963, p. 14). The student as at the heart of exploratory teaching as the sole agent of learning who autonomously explored his or her environment, assuming that there was something "out there" to be discovered.

These new approaches demonstrated that there is no one best method. Good teachers vary instruction based on the educational goals and purposes of the instructional sequences they share with their students. When the dissemination of knowledge is the most important thing, a focused and direct instructional approach may be the best form of delivery. In another instance, where the primary goal is to encourage students to develop their own curiosity and build confidence in their capacity to reason, an exploratory approach might be the most appropriate. This chapter presents five different approaches to science teaching and ways to modify instruction so that all students can be participants in the learning process.

For example, in *Mastery Teaching* (Chapter 5) you’ll learn the seven steps drawn from a model popularized at the UCLA Laboratory School and credited to Madeline Hunter (1982). The approach was a mainstay in staff training and administrative training workshops during the 1980s and 1990s. The strategy is particularly effective in providing learning alternatives for students through skill enhancement activities and small-group instruction.

Direct Instruction (Chapter 6) is a convergent strategy in which student learning is directed toward behavioral outcomes determined in advance and communicated to the students. Basic facts, principles, and concepts of good science understanding and sound scientific reasoning are learned using scientific process skills. The steps included in models of Direct Instruction are excellent guides when the primary goal is to develop defined student competencies.

Guided Discovery (Chapter 7) combines exploration, convergent instruction, and divergent reasoning into a single strategy. It is particularly effective as a strategy when students lack in prior experiences. It consists of three main phases: exploration, conception, and application. First, students develop a familiarity with the concept through hands-on exploratory learning. During the conception phase, the role of the teacher is more direct, vocabulary is introduced, and the conceptual scheme is drawn out and/or presented to the students. During the third phase, called application, the teacher has an opportunity to check for understanding as students relate what they have learned to a real-life situation. Contemporary science educators have modified and extended the application of guided discovery in creating the five Es (Expose, Explore, Explain, Evaluate, Elaborate) or in some cases, the seven Es (Expose, Engage, Explore, Explain, Expand, Evaluate, Elaborate). However, the general concept remains the same from general awareness to teacher-directed learning to concept application.

Inquiry Teaching (Chapter 8) is an approach used to determine if students can demonstrate an understanding of a concept by challenging them with an unfamiliar task or discrepant event. The teacher serves as a facilitator of learning rather than as a source of knowledge. Teaching through inquiry helps students apply conceptual frameworks for problem solving and expands their valuable abilities to use higher order reasoning. It also helps them develop process skills.

Exploratory Learning (Chapter 9) allows teachers to facilitate student learning, and, as in inquiry teaching, the teacher does not act as a primary source of knowledge or dispenser of information. This strategy helps students develop confidence in their ability to learn and reason in a supportive and nonthreatening environment. The approach provides for a high level of interaction among students and is an ideal instructional model for cooperative learning strategies. Because the terms "inquiry" and "exploration" are sometimes used interchangeably, the different connotations as perceived by the authors will become evident later in this chapter.

Mastery Teaching

The Mastery Teaching model, developed from the research of Madeline Hunter and Associates, is based on observations of effective teachers' teaching and provides a variety of techniques to make teachers more effective. It starts with the assumption that the teacher, as an instructional leader in the classroom, has a profound influence on student learning. Teaching is defined as "a constant stream of professional decisions made before, during and after interaction with the student: decisions which, when implemented, increase the probability of learning" (Hunter, 1982). According to Hunter, the first decision of teaching is based upon the content, the "what" of teaching; the second decision is directed to the student behavior that makes learning possible, the student's "how" of learning; and the third decision is directed to the teacher's own teaching behavior; "what" the teacher does to increase learning. The Mastery Teaching sequence in this publication is an adaptation of the strategy suggested in the Hunter Model to science instruction. The authors have integrated into this the research on best practice in science teaching as it relates to inclusive instruction. The Mastery Teaching seven-step model is outlined in Figure 7.

Note that many of the arrows in the Mastery Teaching model (see Figure 7) go in both directions, indicating that the process is inclusive rather than sequential. One-trial learning is not good teaching. Many students need repeated exposure to the concepts in a variety of contexts before a schema develops. Repeated experiences are needed before the learner makes the transition from rote knowledge to conceptual understanding. Students need an assortment of skill enhancement activities, and good teachers provide these in a variety of formats using large-group instruction, cooperative learning groups, and opportunities for independent practice. These must all be provided in a context of continuing feedback, acknowledgment, and support of the student's work.

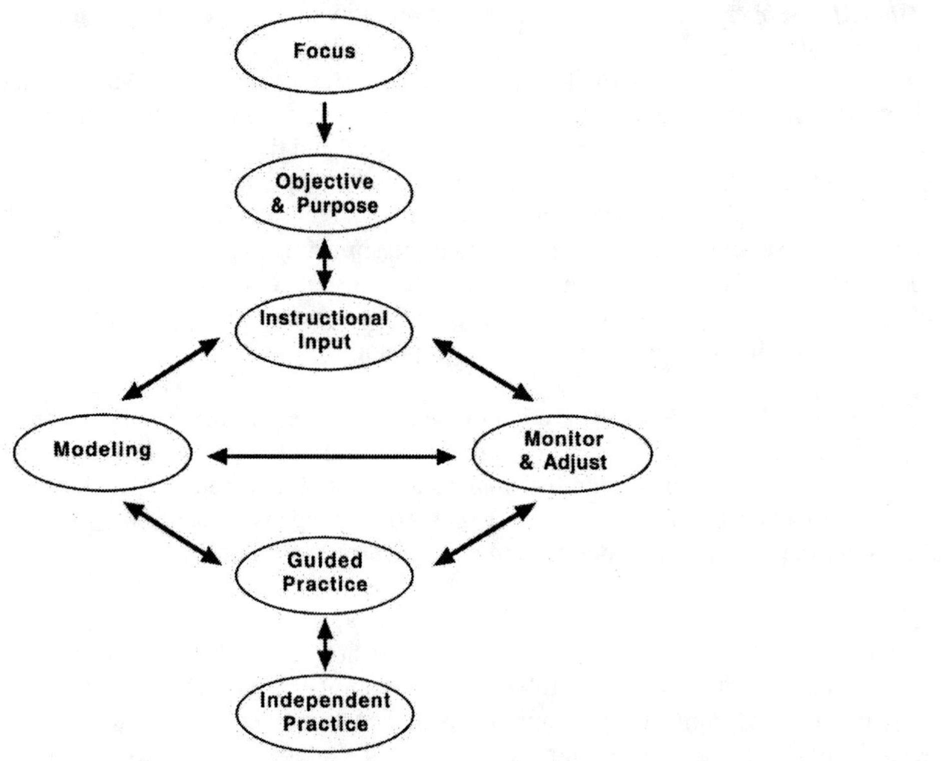

Figure 7. Mastery Teaching.

Focus or Anticipatory Set

The first step is to create within the students a motivation to learn. It is important to realize that motivation is learned and is not a generic attribute of children or students, particularly after the primary grades.

The teacher will provide students with an adequate background so they can learn what is to be taught. Keep in mind a statement of Thomas Edison: "Discovery favors the well-prepared mind." When using the Mastery Teaching strategy in science, a good beginning point may often be to provide students with an opportunity to explore with hands-on materials and to share their ideas on the topic. Computer programs such as Inspiration can be used to construct a “concept web.” Content reading strategies such as KWWZ can be used as another means to assess prior knowledge of students and establish a focus for instruction. This can be very valuable to the teacher as a form of diagnostic evaluation and pre-assessment. Prior knowledge can be examined informally and misconceptions recorded to be addressed later in the instructional sequence.

Another important element is the feeling or tone of the instructional setting. Students are more inclined to put forth effort when they find a pleasant learning situation and anticipate that they will be successful. While unpleasant tones can also stimulate student learning, they often have undesirable side effects.

During this first phase of Mastery Teaching, the teacher needs to develop a moderate level of concern. When there is no concern, learning does not take place, and when there is too much concern, there may be too much anxiety for effective learning. Excessive intimidation through testing, concept density, or teacher posturing can cause students to avoid the context and/or the teacher in the future. The teacher must keep in mind the experiences students have had in the context of learning--the more success they have experienced in the past, the more likely they are to remain persistent and feel greater optimism toward learning.

Objective and Purpose

The second step in Mastery Teaching draws heavily from Bloom's research and his pioneering work on what teachers can do to help students learn. Bloom (1976) indicated that if you clearly communicate to students what you want them to learn and provide the necessary time and appropriate learning conditions, 80% or more of the students can reach the same high level of achievement attained by only the top 20% under more traditional forms of instruction.

In a report on incorporating Mastery Teaching strategies in school systems across the United States, Guskey, Passaro, and Wheeler (1995) note that students with disabilities often experience greater achievement in mastery learning classes than a general student population in traditionally taught classrooms. The authors state that Mastery Teaching instructional strategies provide a useful and purposeful technique for accomplishing an inclusive environment. Hunter (1982) states that students will usually extend more effort if they know what they will learn today and why it is important to them.

An effective and easy way to prepare objectives is to take into account the following: A (audience), B (behavior), C (conditions), D (degree), and F (format). Most important, the teacher should know exactly what learning outcomes he or she is teaching so the teacher can ascertain with evidence that the learning outcomes have been achieved and the teacher can go on, or that the outcomes have not been achieved and additional experiences are necessary for the students.

Instructional Input

The role of the teacher as the instructional leader in the classroom is important. Professional educators are responsible for determining the best way for students to acquire the information, be it through skills, concepts, or generalizations. It is quite apparent that the efficiency of the learning process is affected by the decisions teachers make. It is important that the teacher present the information in the simplest, clearest, and most understandable form. Whenever possible, the teacher should cite examples that are within the realm of student experience to help learning and retention.

However, it is also important that teachers take into account students' misconceptions when providing instructional input. Studies conducted over the last three decades have provided strong evidence that students enter the classroom with a variety of ideas about the world, which, unfortunately, interfere with formal instruction (Driver, Asoko, Leach, Mortimer, & Scott, 1994). Contrary to the behaviorist view of the mind as an "empty bottle" waiting to be filled by the teacher, students appear to be continually trying to make sense of the world by building models or schemata. Resnick (1983) has made explicit the point that students construct understanding and they don't mirror all they are told or read.

Although misconceptions and prior ideas in general are addressed through conceptual change teaching models, these misconceptions and prior ideas can also be considered in Mastery Teaching. Therefore, teachers should help students experience "dissatisfaction" with their existing conceptions (Posner, Strike, Hewson, & Gertzog, 1982) and generally link instructional input with these ideas during this phase of the instruction. Instructional input at this point serves an important role in the teaching process.

However, when expository methods are used, the presentation should be brief and to the point. The story of the minister who wished to improve her homilies illustrates the essence of the instructional input segment of Mastery Teaching. The minister asked one of her parishioners: "Do you have any suggestions on how to improve my homilies?" The parishioner said, "I have three: 1) Have a good beginning, something that grabs the attention of the congregation, 2) have a good closing, something that they can reflect on, and 3) more important than the other two, have them relatively close together."

Modeling

In teacher modeling, the next step in Mastery Teaching, the teacher demonstrates the concept or skill or shows a product that demonstrates how the concept or skill can be used to understand a situation or solve a problem. The teacher needs to make sure the model and examples are unambiguous and demonstrate the principle or process being taught. Whenever possible, the modeling should include tangible materials so the students can directly observe the process or product.

Guided Practice

Students need opportunities to have repeated and varied experiences to apply the concept being learned. The difference between having knowledge and being able to use it to solve problems is the quantum leap in learning. Guided practice involves having students try something, having a chance to share ideas with others, gaining feedback, and using the information to revise or clarify their initial perceptions.

One of the best ways to undergo guided practice is through an assortment of hands-on skill enhancement activities. In science, this may be games, computer simulations, experiments, critiques of trade books, etc., while working in cooperative learning groups.

Simply learning information is not enough: the information must be understood well enough to use it to build complex concepts and generalizations. During this aspect of Mastery Teaching, it is important for students to have opportunities to apply their thinking to new problems or situations. Finally, the students should have some opportunities for synthesis in which they invent or create something new to the creator.

Independent Practice

Students need opportunities to investigate their own cognitive constructs. Simply doing an experiment again does not make the knowledge perfect. Practice without knowledge of results is a waste of time and may reinforce misconceptions. Students need opportunities to test their ideas and obtain feedback to check materials. This does not always require teacher involvement. If criteria are clearly established, students can evaluate their own performance or use materials to check the correctness of their thinking.

Hunter (1982) offered four critical questions on independent practice: a) How much material should be practiced at one time? b) How long should the practice period be? c) How often should students practice? and d) How will students know how well they have done?

The first step is to define a short meaningful "chunk of information" and introduce it to the students. Then give them several opportunities to go over it again in slightly different ways. Spend a short intensive period on each activity, and check back with the students so they know what is to be learned and remembered. Once the information is learned, students need additional distributed practice to reinforce the learning and build long-term memory. Finally, students need affirmation that their reasoning is correct and why it is correct. It is best if they can evaluate their own performance or use materials to check correctness.

Most important, students do not learn at the same rate. For some students, very little stimulation is necessary before they acquire the essential concepts of the unit. They should have opportunities to extend and enrich their learning. For others, additional practice is needed to help them acquire the most basic information contained in your educational objectives.

Monitor and Adjust

The effective teacher in Mastery Teaching understands that it is commonplace for students to come up with misconceptions. The teacher needs to prompt the students to redirect thinking in a way that is comfortable and safe for the student. This can be done by supplying a question or statement such as, "Your thinking is right, if...," or "I'm not sure what you are thinking. Let's go on to see if it clears up for you" (Hunter, 1982, pp. 87-89).

It is important to relate what is being learned to a student's past experience. The teacher can bring forth something the student already knows and connect it to the situation, thus bringing in the new information. Transfer and association are two powerful tools. Using examples from the students' own experiences and providing the association of what they already know to the new situation is important. Strategies might include having students generate examples, citing specific examples, or citing examples that are more complex.

Summary

In Mastery Teaching, the instructional process is not linear. After the focus and the objectives or purpose of the lesson sequence are identified and clarified, students undergo a very interactive process of receiving information through instructional input, reviewing concepts through modeling, and having opportunities for guided and independent practice. Throughout the process there is constant monitoring and feedback with ongoing adjustments by the teacher. This publication presents an instructional sequence titled Investigating Bones which employs the Mastery Teaching instructional process. The sequence was designed based on the interpretation of Mastery Teaching from participating in seminars about the model and from applying the model to the theoretical base of effective instruction in science.

Direct Instruction

Background

Direct instruction is distinguished by having each educational activity specified. This approach to instruction provides direct learning opportunities to help students attain the identified outcomes. Using a convergent instructional delivery, both the teachers and students direct the learning to the noted expectations (Bartz, 1991) (see Figure 8). Direct Instruction is a businesslike approach to education, with careful attention to time management and task analysis (Englemann, Becker, & Carnine, 1993).

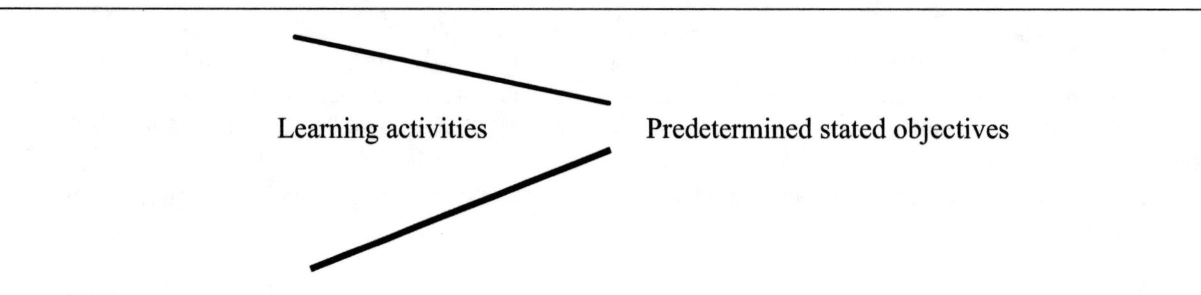

Figure 8. Direct Instruction.

The Direct Instruction approach to education is currently practiced in most countries of the world. The approach was suggested as an outcome of the Eight-Year Study of the late 1930s. R.W. Tyler is generally credited with conceptualizing and tailoring the model as a defined approach to instruction (Smith & Tyler, 1942). Tyler's approach follows these steps:

1. Establish broad goals or objectives.
2. Classify the goals and objectives.
3. Define objectives in behavioral terms.
4. Find situations in which achievement of objectives can be shown.
5. Develop or select measurement techniques.
6. Collect performance data.
7. Compare performance data with behaviorally stated outcomes.

The approach was specifically applied to science instruction when Robert Gagne utilized it in designing the instructional framework for *Science: A Process Approach*, an elementary science program developed under the direction of the American Association for the Advancement of Science (AAAS). Gagne's sequential and hierarchical model stresses the importance of the hierarchy of learning (Gagne, 1974). According to this model, we should start with simple learning tasks and proceed sequentially to tasks that are more complex. Therefore, experiences developed using the tools of the scientist should lead to basic concepts, and these should precede the problem situation. Students should be helped to develop a coherent conceptual framework.

In discussing the knowledge structure in the everyday and scientific domains, Reif and Larkin (1991) make the point for the "explicit teaching of scientific meta-knowledge." They support the approach of Direct Instruction. They maintain that everyday knowledge consists of interrelated concepts forming a large network of associated knowledge elements. New knowledge is acquired through experiences and stored with information reflecting its acquisition context, but without any global integration. Coming to science from everyday life, many students do not fully organize their newly acquired scientific knowledge so that it is coherent and logical. Instead, students often transfer into the scientific domain informal concept-specification methods and predominantly associative knowledge organizations that are efficient in everyday life, but inadequate in science. The resulting knowledge may be only locally coherent (i.e., inferences may only be possible among closely associated knowledge elements and contradictions may occur). For this reason students should be helped to organize their knowledge so that the logical relationships between knowledge elements become highly explicit. Coherence and logical organization (a characteristic of scientific knowledge) facilitate remembering, avoiding inconsistencies and contradictions.

Use in the Regular Classroom

Direct Instruction is a strategy intended to improve learning by getting students to focus on thinking for understanding rather than just thinking for knowledge. According to Gagne, it is important for students to think like scientists at an early age, thereby starting with the processes or "tools" of science. The natural progression of this way of thinking in secondary and postsecondary education is the integration of process skills with the development of conceptual frameworks. Gagne and Briggs (1979) have identified nine events of instruction. Not all of the events invariably occur, and the order may vary depending upon the objective(s). The instructional events and teacher behaviors are as follows:

1. Gain the learner's attention--introduce stimulus change.
2. Inform the learner of the objective--provide a description and example of subordinate concepts and rules.
3. Stimulate prerequisite learning--stimulate recall of subordinate concepts and rules.
4. Present stimulus material--present examples of concept or rule.
5. Provide learning guidance--provide verbal cues to proper combining sequence.
6. Elicit the performance--ask learner to apply rule or concept to new examples.
7. Provide feedback about performance correctness--confirm correctness of rule or concept application.
8. Assess performance--learner demonstrates application of concept.
9. Enhance retention and transfer--provide spaced reviews including various examples.

Following a meta-analysis of research on instructional practice, Rosenshine (1983, 1986) provided suggestions for further elaboration on effective educational practice using Direct Instruction. He termed the approach "explicit teaching" and identified six instructional functions:

1. Provide daily review--check previous day's work and reteaching if necessary
2. Present new material--provide examples, demonstrations, and/or models while monitoring students' understanding.
3. Conduct guided practice--question with student participation.
4. Provide feedback and correctives--explain, review, reinforce student responses.
5. Conduct independent practice until student responses are firm and automatic.
6. Provide weekly and monthly reviews--regular practice with previously learned material.

Direct Instruction and Students with Disabilities

When one considers Direct Instruction as a strategy for the delivery of science instruction to students with disabilities, it appears to be well grounded as a foundation of educational practice in special education (Englemann, Becker, & Carnine, 1993). For instance, the elements of Individualized Educational Plans (IEPs) are required to demonstrate compliance with mandates for special education services. The formatting of the IEP requires statements of objectives, a plan for the student to accomplish the learning outcomes, and an assessment process to determine if the outcomes are being attained. However, the greatest limitation of Direct Instruction as an appropriate approach to delivering instruction to students with disabilities is that the thinking of the student is subservient to the thinking of the teacher.

The teacher plays an important role in the selection of the instructional sequence. It should be selected so that it produces the right amount of disequilibration and challenge. Although student interests are important, it is the teacher's responsibility to ensure that students receive exposure to the concepts contained in the science standards and develop the process skills necessary to carry out their role as independent inquirers.

Summary

Although the Direct Instruction approach is useful to its many adherents, critics assert that it can result in tunnel vision and low expectations and can limit students' free intellectual development. The convergent nature of the strategy often leads to a linear, inflexible approach to instruction and neglects important alternatives that emerge as a result of experiential learning. There is a tendency to overlook outcomes other than those covered by the activity and to neglect transactions and interactions that occur within the program of study. Once the objectives are established, they become the driving force of the curriculum and the value of the objectives themselves becomes overlooked. Alternative elements in planning programs are often not considered, and standards for evaluation are often at the knowledge or comprehension levels rather than at higher levels such as analysis, synthesis, or application (Simmons, 1991).

On the other hand, adherents to Direct Instruction ascribe to its simplicity (Englemann, et al., 1993). It is easily understood, easy to follow, and provides clear indications of what educators expect of students. In so doing, it allows public constituencies to have a decision in the educational arena about what their children are taught. It provides an opportunity to hold teachers accountable for student learning. There is an often-stated quote relating to education, "If you don't know where you are going, any road will get you there." Direct instructional approaches can help educators reflect on their intentions and clarify formerly ambiguous generalities about educational outcomes--in short, to know where they are going. It can bring educators to focus on providing for the students' academic needs rather than shrouding education within the cultural mores and values of the teacher. It lends itself well to school and teacher accountability in guiding and directing student learning.

An instructional sequence called Suffocating Candle, using the Direct Instruction approach, is presented in Chapter 6. The sequence draws from a learning module contained in *Science: A Process Approach.* Once the methodology and the structure are understood, essentially any concept or idea can be organized using Direct Instruction as a strategy, especially science facts, simple concepts, or basic scientific procedures and processes (Carin, 1997; Flick, 1995).

Guided Discovery

Background and Basic Characteristics

Guided Discovery is an instructional strategy that builds upon the foundations of Piagetian constructivism, namely upon the idea that the source of knowledge and understanding is the child's actions on objects of the environment (Piaget, 1970, 1973). This strategy, apparently, generally places more responsibilities on student input than Mastery Teaching and Direct Instruction.

Although there has been a shift in metaphors over the last two decades (Driver et al., 1994) since the notion of discovery was replaced by that of construction the idea that discovery learning involves the construction of patterns and regularities and results in meaningful experiences for the students had been remarked upon by Bruner (1961) in his seminal article "The Act of Discovery."

> Emphasis upon discovery in learning has precisely the effect upon the learner of leading him to be a constructionist, to organize what he is encountering in a manner not only designed to discover regularity and relatedness, but also to avoid the kind of information drift that fails to keep up account of uses to which information might have to be put. (p. 27)

Certainly there is a difference between the notions of discovery and construction, with serious, epistemological implications. And certainly the notion of construction is more appropriate in the context of scientific research than the notion of discovery. It would even appear more appropriate in the context of school science learning. For example, students construct the concept of moment of force, that is, a relationship between force and distance in their attempt to understand through hands-on activities the behavior of certain objects. They also do this for the concept of specific heat capacity and many other concepts, laws, and principles.

However, it is equally true that certain concepts are difficult, if not impossible, to be constructed by students, regardless of the amount of guidance and help from the teacher. These concepts have to be introduced in some way. In such a case, students are discovering something that has been previously constructed by others (e.g., the DNA model, Bohr's atomic model). Yet the point is not to be caught up between arguments about terminology--although this could be extremely important, given that language does create reality--but to encourage students to explore materials and to guide them to develop the concepts and principles involved in the activities. The Guided Discovery model can indeed help students develop concepts through active exploration.

The main characteristics of the Guided Discovery model are (Bentley, Ebert & Ebert, 2000; Howe & Jones, 1993; Wolfinger, 2000) are as follows:

- Students actively participate in hands-on activities.
- An objective is to be attained.
- The teacher guides students (in the form of initial material selection, the type of data that students collect, and the type of questions that they will be asked).
- The lesson starts with a challenge that provides purpose to the students.
- The lesson continues with guidance from the teacher and a discussion of the results found by students during their investigation.
- The lesson sequence ends with an activity in which students apply the concept through exposure to an unfamiliar task.

In its most basic form, Guided Discovery begins with students' involvement in a challenging hands-on activity. This is followed by firsthand observation and data collection. Then comes the teacher's guidance in order for students to draw certain conclusions. It is apparent that Guided Discovery is an inductive process, but it is also done deductively. This happens if students begin with a concept or law and then collect data in order to verify it, or simply apply the concept or law to a new situation. In fact the above two processes -- the inductive and deductive discovery -- have been incorporated into the Learning Cycle model, which is the primary representative of Guided Discovery.

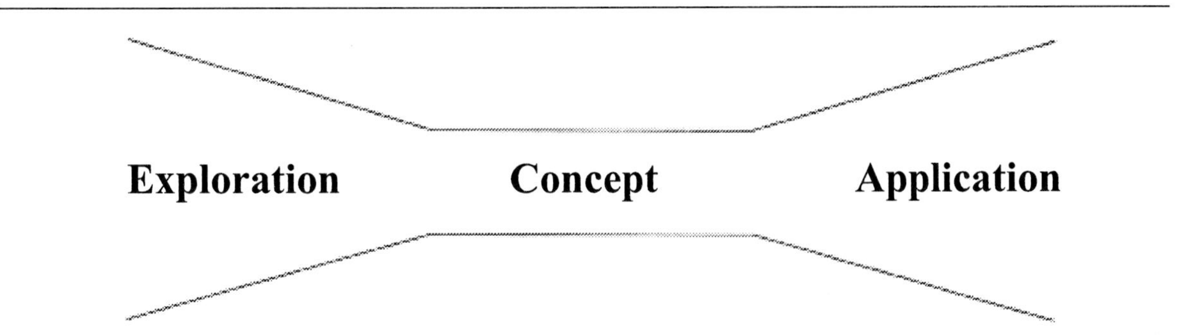

Figure 9. Guided Discovery.

Formalizing Guided Discovery as a teaching strategy came from the work of Robert Karplus and the Science Curriculum Improvement Study Program (SCIS). Karplus studied under Piaget and implemented his epistemology as the director of SCIS. The three-phase strategy of Guided Discovery includes exploration, concept introduction, and application.

During exploration, the students explore new materials and new ideas with minimal guidance or expectation of specific accomplishments. This builds on the idea that play is the work of children, and meaningful play provides essential building blocks for concept development.

In concept introduction, the teacher introduces a concept or principle that leads the students to apply a logical pattern of reasoning to their prior experiences. This second step should always follow exploration and relate to the exploration activities. The role of the teacher is to help students engage in self-regulation to develop concepts relating to their metaphysical world.

The application phase extends the range of application of the new concept. The teacher's role is to provide additional activities that expand and/or alter students' concepts to account for new evidence, and to engage students in observations that might challenge the original conception.

The teacher's role must change in each phase of the Guided Discovery instructional strategy. In the first stage(s), when the teacher is a supportive adult, the strategies include the following:

- Encourage and accept student autonomy, initiation, and leadership.
- Ask thoughtful open-ended questions.
- Allow wait time (rather than answering questions).
- Encourage students to connect ideas and phenomena to their prior experiences.

During the concept phase, the teacher more directly guides student learning to the concept. Strategies might include the following:

- Ask students to explain the concept in their own words.
- Encourage operational definitions in which students define a concept or principle based on real-life observations or occurrences.
- Allow wait time after asking questions.
- Anticipate and note students' alternative explanations, and address any conceptions that do not represent those currently held by scientists.
- Have students explain the concept in their own words to a peer or to the class.

During the application phase, the teacher is again a facilitator and a guide. Strategies might include the following:

- Encourage students to connect ideas to phenomena in their daily lives.
- Ask students to predict outcomes and reflect on why things might be happening differently than expected.
- Ask students to reflect on outcomes and predict whether the concept can be applied to all related events.
- Encourage students to elaborate on their responses.

The three-phase strategy in Guided Discovery provides an opportunity to develop divergent thinking in the exploration phase, convergent thinking building on an understanding of the metaphysical world in the concept phase, and divergent discovery during the application phase.

Learning Cycle

In recent years, the principles of Guided Discovery have been used in many of the curriculum materials developed for students from preschool to postsecondary education. In many science programs the term "Learning Cycle" has become synonymous with Guided Discovery. Marek, Eubanks, and Gallaher (1990) have summarized the assumptions of the Learning Cycle:

> **Prior knowledge**: Students begin with the knowledge, skills, and understanding that they bring to the classroom. Students already have what they consider to be reasonable explanations for how the world works based on their limited experiences.
>
> **Common experiences:** The purpose of the curriculum is to provide students with a common set of experiences that invite them to examine their current understanding of concepts.
>
> **Specific information:** Students are provided with specific information about the concept to introduce terms and to examine how those terms relate to their previous experiences.
>
> **Additional experience:** Additional experiences challenge students to apply their ideas and the information they receive to confirm, refute, or expand what they have been thinking.
>
> **Constructing an understanding**: For students to understand a concept, they must be actively involved in their learning. Instructional processes that involve students in a questioning environment and coerce them to ponder, discuss, argue, and come to conclusions may facilitate conceptual understanding.

Roger Bybee, as director of the Biological Sciences Curriculum Study Project (BSCS), has extended the framework of the Learning Cycle into the following five phases (as cited in Biological Sciences Curriculum Study, 1990):

> **Engagement:** Engagement activities mentally engage the student with an event or a question. These activities help students make connections with what they already know and can do.
>
> **Exploration:** During exploration activities, the students work with each other and explore ideas together. They acquire a common base of experience, usually through hands-on activities. Under the teacher's guidance, students clarify their understanding of major concepts and skills.
>
> **Explanation:** During these activities, the students explain their understandings of the concepts and processes they are learning. The teacher or another student clarifies student understanding and introduces and defines new concepts and skills.
>
> **Elaboration:** Students apply what they have learned to new situations and build on their understanding of concepts. They use these new experiences to extend their knowledge and skills.
>
> **Evaluation:** In these activities, students assess their own knowledge, skills, and abilities. Evaluation activities also focus on outcomes that a teacher can use to evaluate a student's progress.

Summary

The process of Guided Discovery changes the traditional predisposition of learning science. Instead of assuming the first step to learning science is to master its special vocabulary, teachers guide students to build their own cognitive structures. Conway (1990, as cited in Dodd & Himmelstein, 1996) has stated that rote learning and repeated practice are not likely to result in understanding or useful knowledge that will extend beyond the last examination. In teaching through Guided Discovery, the teacher's responsibility is to analyze and synthesize input from students and connect it with their thinking processes. Then the teacher helps students with self-organization and their reorganization of knowledge within their own schemata. In this way, learning is built on experiences of the students.

As an example of Guided Discovery, an instructional sequence based on the Science Curriculum Improvement Study Module, Energy Sources, is presented in Chapter 7. Once a teacher understands the methodology and the structure of Guided Discovery, essentially any concept or idea can be organized using the model.

Inquiry Teaching

Background and Basic Characteristics

The origins of Inquiry Teaching can be traced back to ancient Greece and the teaching of Socrates, who, through proper questioning, led students to acquiring knowledge and understanding. However, the contemporary meaning of Inquiry Teaching is that of investigation. John Dewey and Jerome Bruner are generally credited with bringing the concept of "problem solving through inquiry" into the arena of contemporary pedagogical practice.

In fact, it was Dewey's idea about the problem method that made the major contribution to the development of Inquiry Teaching. Dewey (1910), in his book *How We Think*, argued that consciousness of an obstacle is the source of reflective thinking. Therefore, in the context of school learning, the starting point of the teaching and learning process should be a problem, that is, a situation that causes confusion, perturbation, or perplexity.

Inquiry Teaching involves drawing upon the intellectual abilities of learners to solve their own problems. In this way, the effective teacher can gain insights into how information is processed and can bring to light both good reasoning and misconceptions that may have developed (Howe & Jones, 1993). Unlike Guided Discovery, Inquiry Teaching is much less structured in regard to time and method used by the students, and the teacher's role is mostly limited to providing the starting point and the materials. There is no direct involvement (as in Guided Discovery, for example); instead, the teacher provides minimal guidance and participates in the discussion at the end of the investigating process.

Inquiry can be initiated by students themselves when they are confronted with a problem or a challenging question. They can be helped, of course, by the teacher in selecting their materials, but they can also plan, conduct, and evaluate their own efforts. When inquiry is initiated by the teacher, he or she can decide on the topic to be investigated (e.g., shadows, rolling objects) or the concept (e.g., forces, heat). The teacher then present students with a problem situation, that is, a discrepant event (e.g., the existence of an ice cube in the middle of a clear liquid) or a challenging question or task (e.g., how can we make an egg float in the water, how can we build a high tower using paper so that it does not topple).

In discussing the notion of a problem situation, it should be pointed out that as the initiator of the learning process the problem situation must be carefully selected to produce the right amount of disequilibration and challenge. This is extremely important. It would be naive of teachers to expect students to respond to problems that require them to apply principles beyond their experiences or developmental capacities. The teacher should select and present discrepant events in such a way that students become aware of the obstacle and the mystery inherent in the problem situation.

Suchman and his associates' research in the 1950s (as cited in Pilz & Sund, 1974) served as an impetus to change the ways in which teachers and students interact. This research has provided a strategy whereby a traditional classroom teacher could allow students to engage in inquiry learning. The model was developed based on the following three ideas of Hutchings (1970):

- The teacher must assume the role as director of learning rather than as a dispenser of knowledge.
- Students must develop questioning skills so they can effectively gain information, which can be accommodated to formulate hypotheses.
- Pupil-pupil rather than pupil-teacher interaction must be stressed.

Suchman (as cited in Piltz & Sund, 1974) presented a communication diagram using vertical channels to portray teacher-dominated learning and a horizontal channel to portray student-dominated inquiry learning. A modification of the diagram is presented in Figure 4. The steps in Inquiry Teaching are as follows:

1. To prepare the students with sufficient background knowledge to provide them with the skills to solve the problem or discrepant event
2. To present the discrepant event
3. To allow the students to ask questions to obtain additional information (However, the teacher must respond only with "yes" or "no" and sometimes "maybe.")
4. To encourage students to present theories or explanations of the event (The teacher should not indicate whether the theory is correct or in line with the teacher's own thinking.)
5. To continue to nurture problem-solving skills by being an accessible, non-judgmental listener

The main characteristics of Inquiry Teaching are as follows (Bentley, Ebert & Ebert, 2000; Friedl & Koontz, 2001; Mack, 2000; Orlich, Harder, Callahan & Gibson, 2001; Wolfinger, 2000):

- More learner autonomy
- Emphasis on process (rather than specific content)
- More flexibility in terms of time
- A problem situation or a challenging question or task as a starting point
- A supportive and facilitating role on the part of the teacher
- A "correct" idea is never given as an answer to a question (since this would defeat the very purpose of inquiry)

Given that students can make their own choice regarding the method they will use in their investigation as well as the fact that the emphasis is on science processes (e.g., observing, classifying, interpreting, measuring, predicting, inferring) rather than on specific content (e.g., Newton's second law, the concept of electric resistance), Inquiry Teaching can best be used for helping students develop background knowledge and inquiry skills. For this reason, inquiry is "a no-fail science teaching strategy" (Wolfinger, 2000, p. 235).

Figure 10 shows traditional teaching presented along the vertical axis in which students are recipients of information and teachers are disseminators. Students demonstrate their knowledge by responding to teacher questions. The thinking and transitions to concepts and applications represent the thinking of the teacher, not the cognitive constructs of the students. Using the horizontal axis of facts, concepts, and applications through student processing demonstrates Inquiry Teaching in which students: a) develop a response to a problem or discrepant event, b) accumulate their own facts, c) form their own concepts, and d) apply their knowledge through their own processing.

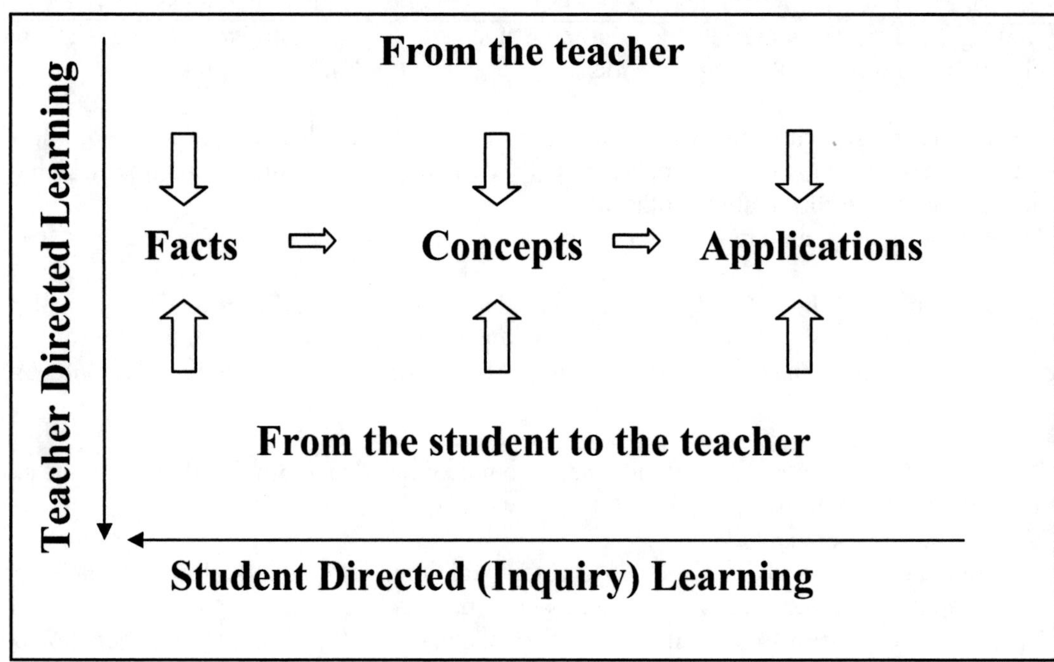

Figure 10. Inquiry Teaching.

Advantages of Inquiry Teaching

Inquiry is fundamental to scientific investigation. The 1996 National Science Education Standards target the ability to understand and perform scientific inquiry as one of the four critical components of science instruction. Inquiry aids students in constructing scientific concepts, metacognition, life-long learning strategies, and in developing an actively curious mind-set associated with seeking science knowledge (Haury, 1993; Martin, Sexton, Wagner, & Gerlovich, 1997).

In good Inquiry Teaching, the learners come to believe that outcomes are subject to their own skill and ingenuity to conceptualize. Admittedly, it is easier and faster to give answers (Otto, 1991). But if the aim of education is to form one's intelligence rather than to stock one's memory and to produce intellectual exploration rather than mere recall, then students must be presented with a learning environment that stimulates the use of inquiry processes in generating solutions to real-life problems (Zorfass et al., 1991). By looking at the unique ways in which students reason, their uniqueness can be fostered. All students need opportunities to express themselves, not within a prescribed role, not as an expert, not in accordance with rules and conventions, but as persons with unique skills and talents (Hopfenburg, Levin, Meister, & Rogers as cited in Zorfass et al., 1991). Teachers must concentrate on the processes of reasoning rather than the product.

> The justification of Inquiry Teaching is reflected in Piaget's (1971) own words: In the majority of cases, an intolerable overloading of the educational program may in the end do harm to both the physical and intellectual health of students, and retard their thinking proportionately to the extent we wish to perfect it (p. 96). . . .When the school requires that the student's effort comes from the student himself rather than being imposed, and that intelligence should undertake authentic work instead of accepting predigested knowledge from outside, it is therefore simply asking that all of the laws of intelligence be respected. (p. 159)

Summary

In Inquiry Teaching, the teacher's role is to focus on the process rather than the product (Martin, 1997), to focus on the students' reasoning skills rather than on accurate direct answers. Always keep in mind that the primary goal of Inquiry Teaching is to develop higher order thinking skills in the learner, not to disseminate information (Victor & Kellough, 1997; Zorfass et al., 1991). Reflect on the statement, "If a teacher criticizes a child for inventing the wheel, the teacher must be more interested in wheels than invention."

A limitation of Inquiry Teaching is an assumption that all students, when challenged with problem situations, will persist in the learning task until they feel a sense of understanding or accomplishment. Many students elect not to persist when they perceive discontent or frustration; others need teacher affirmation to feel successful. A further complication is that the processing skills required in inquiry are not commonplace in the classroom and take considerable time to develop. The application requires a substantial long-term commitment from the teachers who utilize it. We believe the rewards are considerable but the efforts cannot be lighthearted from either students or teachers. An instructional sequence investigating density through a series of discrepant events is presented in Chapter 8. Context-related inquiry problems are also contained in the instructional sequences shared in Mastery Teaching and Exploratory Learning.

Exploratory Learning

Exploratory Learning, though similar to Inquiry Teaching, is a totally divergent instructional strategy. It represents phase one of the Learning Cycle and appears to be a good model for both very young children and more mature learners. On the one hand, it helps young children develop autonomy by pursuing their own interests and problems; on the other hand, it can help older students (and, of course, students of all ages) develop inquiry skills and certain attitudes toward scientific research. In Exploratory Learning, after the topic is introduced, students determine the substance and direction of learning by their actions (see Figure 11).

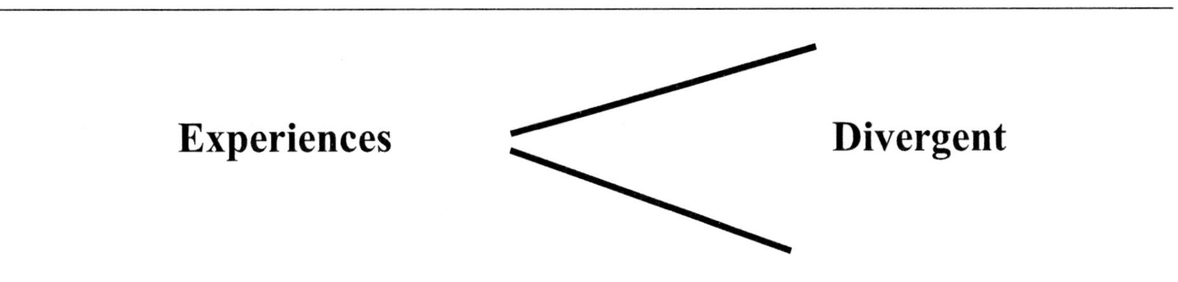

Figure 11. Exploratory Learning.

Because the terms "discovery", "inquiry", and "exploration" are used interchangeably, it is a good idea to define Exploratory Learning as "open inquiry" in the sense that it is totally unstructured in terms of time, specific outcomes, teachers' interaction, method and even materials. Whereas in Inquiry Teaching, students are confronted with a challenge that builds on their existing conceptual frameworks to explain a phenomenon, in Exploratory Learning the activities students engage in are assumed to have intrinsic merit.

In Inquiry there is a focus upon a certain concept or principle, which is presented through a discrepant event or a challenging situation. In Exploratory Learning there is no such focus. An approach suggested by Kamii and DeVries (1993) in which children play with various materials and are asked to do what they can think of with these materials, is representative of the exploratory model.

In designing curriculum, exploratory teachers organize learning around conceptual clusters of experiments, investigations, and discrepant situations. The experiences are presented holistically rather than in separate isolated parts. An awareness of students' ideas and opinions provides teachers with a window into their reasoning. The teacher's role is to transform ideas into action.

Topics can come from a distinct curriculum framework; the guide can be any curriculum material, even a textbook. The teacher's challenge is to accumulate and utilize resources, from activity manuals to trade books, to enable students to explore the topic freely. The teacher designs student opportunities to experience the lesson concepts through direct encounters with materials or information. The teacher must enter the classroom with one or two big ideas, not "stepping stones" of skills or objectives. The teacher is there to offer intellectual opportunities as "invitations" to maximize the possibility that students themselves will create new conceptual learning.

In a good Exploratory Learning classroom, the students are instilled with an understanding that the world is a complex place in which multiple perspectives exist, and that their thinking processes are unique, often elusive, even messy endeavors that the learner may not even understand. Formal evaluation is not encouraged, and grades should be biased on the behaviors the teachers want the students to exhibit, not on the content of the lessons. For example, if commitment to investigation, cooperation with peers, sustained involvement, and respect for materials and management protocols in the classroom are your expectations as a teacher, these should be the basis for grades. In Exploratory Learning, the most cognitively limited students should be able to obtain an "A" grade. Proponents of Exploratory Learning believe that as soon as formal evaluation measures are established, they communicate to students that there is certain information that is important, and certain ways of thinking are better than others. These conventions prevent children from developing self-confidence in their ability to reason and limit the development of the meta-cognitive skills of self-regulation, capacity to sustain judgment, persistence, and confidence in one's ability to reason.

Assessment in Exploratory Learning is through observing student/student interactions, participating in student/teacher interactions, and watching students work with ideas and materials. Although it is natural, it is not easy. Teachers are often perceived as sources of knowledge, and all of the conventions of schooling have conditioned children and adults to carry these expectations. Teachers are generally not good listeners, and it is always easier to teach and test a prescribed curriculum than to mediate and assess learning. Under the traditional test-teach-test model, the process of learning essentially shuts down while assessment occurs. It also brings closure to each learning sequence until the next teacher again opens the "box" to stuff in more information relating to a particular schema.

Summary

Critics might voice concerns that Exploratory Learning does not value all that science and technology have contributed to the world. The intent of Exploratory Learning is quite the opposite. It is to develop in children a confidence and understanding of the world of science without adult-imposed reasoning constraints. In fact, adults might possess many misconceptions and have serious limitations in their own capacity to reason beyond the limits of what they think they know.

An instructional sequence, Puzzling Powders, utilizing the Exploratory Learning strategy is presented in Chapter 9. The sequence was built from the original *Mystery Powders Guide* from the Elementary

Science Study. A second sequence on Electricity is constructed by the author, drawing from a variety of resources. The Elementary Science Curriculum, developed under the direction of Robert Morrison, is probably the best example of a science curriculum based on the tenets of Exploratory Learning. Once you understand the ideology of exploratory teaching and the foundations of constructivism, essentially any concept or idea can be organized using Exploratory Learning as a strategy.

Summary and Conclusion

Undoubtedly, there is no magic key to teaching and learning science. The variety of factors involved makes it impossible to apply a general model of instruction. However, there are a number of features, or rather conditions, that an instructional model for science should satisfy. Although not the magic recipe, the following conditions could help toward optimizing science instruction.

1. Presenting science as a field of inquiry in which students are given the opportunity to consider alternative models and ideas. There are no axiomatic statements and absolute truths, no actual imposition of subject matter but, instead, workable models and beliefs that will most likely be abandoned at a later stage.

2. Starting from a problem situation to create confusion, perplexity, disequilibration.

3. Providing students with opportunities for creative work through activities requiring divergent thinking, such as hypothesis formation, model construction, concept mapping, and thought experiments.

4. Allowing students to exchange ideas and confront each other's point of view without the teacher imposing the "correct answer."

5. Utilizing multiple intelligence theory in the planning and design of instruction.

6. Modifying instruction in ways that all students, if they exhibit full effort, can have successful and meaningful experiences in science.

With the recent emphasis on constructivism, terms such as "active participation, disequilibration, problem solving, sharing of ideas, and restructuring" have become so commonplace -- in fact they have become almost synonymous with science education itself -- that it would be impossible to think or do without them. Mastery Teaching, Guided Discovery, Inquiry Teaching, and Exploratory Learning build on constructivism. They all foster exploration and provide challenges to students. In these models the teacher has an indirect role as a facilitator and guide, not as a source of information. The classroom becomes a place of curiosity, exploration, and inquiry. The major activity of the teacher is to provide students with hands-on materials that will allow them to explore natural phenomena. Students, in such a classroom, develop their own understandings and are free to utilize a vocabulary that is familiar to them.

However, despite criticisms against expository teaching, its merit in inclusive classrooms should not be dismissed. In addition to providing clarity for the general student, it may have special merits for students with disabilities. In fact, for visually impaired students, direct verbal instruction appears to be a potential tool in the hands of science teachers. Students with motor and/or visual impairment can be helped to understand concepts that would be very difficult to understand otherwise. In general, tactile (hands-on) experiences in combination with verbal instruction appear to be a good teaching strategy for students with sensory impairment. This is [two words] for students with all types of learning disabilities. When given opportunities to encounter learning experiences that involve many modalities, direct sensory experiences, freedom to move large muscles, and chances to show what they have learned may cause disabilities to "disappear."

Science teaching is the art of helping students learn and value their learning through their own discoveries. The models presented here are all interactive in that they promote student inquiry in a hands-on, minds-on way. The outcomes are student mental constructions based on experiences in the classroom, built upon through exposure to resources that can extend student thinking. Students value learning when they perceive success; persistence and attentiveness are the rewards afforded to their teachers.

Teacher actions and attitudes are still the most critical factors in teaching. Successful teachers model inclusiveness and celebrate diversity, vary instructional strategies based on their primary educational outcomes, are flexible in classroom management, and focus on developing student abilities, not just the acquisition of information. Teachers can design instruction for all students to have successful learning experiences. Expectations must be high but varied; learning must be valued even when the accomplishments of some are not equal to those of their peers. Science has the most impact when it is valued and when it relates to the individual. A good classroom environment is one in which student-to-student interaction is encouraged, cooperation is valued, and students' freedom to chase their own ideas is abundant. The teacher should provide an environment that honors students as emerging thinkers, supports risk-takers, and nurtures those who challenge their current understandings. Student willingness to follow trails of interest, to make connections, to reformulate ideas, and to reach unique conclusions should be sustained. The end of an instructional sequence should be determined by waning student interest rather than a defined curriculum.

Science is something that all students can do and understand, regardless of their gender, ability, or any other characteristics. What is needed, however, is confidence in teachers' ability that they can in fact help students do and understand science, and the belief that all students can succeed in doing so. The models presented here can help, in many ways, teachers move towards the former. But the latter idea certainly lies within each teacher's power. If teachers believe in student success, they will most likely develop more confidence in their ability to teach science in an effective way. Just as critical is the teacher's belief that all students can, in one way or another, do and understand science.

Chapter 4
Major Categories of Disabilities

Any practicing professional educator needs a sound understanding of the students served. Yet it is almost impossible for regular educators to keep up with the increasing number of students in their classrooms who have a disability label and to maintain familiarity with appropriate interventions for each of the disabilities. At one extreme, McGuinness (1989) described one third of all elementary school boys as an abnormal population because they are fidgety, inattentive, and inalienable to adult control. On the other hand, some believe inattention and moderately deviant behaviors on occasion are a normal part of being a child or young adult. As medical and behavioral models become more refined, along with increasing accountability requirements that all students have successful learning experiences, more pressure and more responsibilities are being placed on the classroom teacher.

Legal changes have also mandated regular education for many students with disabilities. IDEA 2004 continues the prior IDEA protections in nondiscriminatory evaluation, individualized education, and least restrictive environment placement. The definitions in this chapter are presented to familiarize science teachers with some of the major categories of disabilities commonly found in educational environments and to help them think more about teaching individual students rather than focusing on the academic content in the instruction.

Under IDEA the local education agency is responsible for determining first, whether the student has a disability, and second, the student's educational needs. However, few examiners and few special education personnel understand science well enough to determine educational needs within science classrooms or appropriate interventions during science lessons. Only through active participation from teachers of science will the educational science needs of students with disabilities be addressed.

To accomplish this goal, collaboration is essential. Without the leadership of the regular classroom science teacher, student needs will not be adequately served. In too many instances, especially where the student has a severe/profound physical or mental impairment, classroom aides, who often have neither the expertise nor the experience, are primary decision makers regarding accommodations. This is a serious issue that must be addressed if equity is to exist in our schools.

Equity Issues in Education

Although Americans are committed to fairness and adhere to democratic principles, strong evidence shows that some groups are more likely to garnish privileges and opportunities than others. A difference exists between public support for the principles of equality and the public's willingness to support policies for implementation. Many hold views of rugged individualism—the idea that anyone, no matter how limiting one's circumstances or how great the barriers, can bootstrap his or her way to success. Consequently, when members of groups who have traditionally been disfranchised with the majority culture do not appear to take opportunities, it is perceived as "their fault"; they did not try hard enough, or they did not demonstrate the persistence it takes to be successful.

Mantsios (2000) iterates that our society maintains an illusion that social class distinctions do not exist; hence, this common consensus makes issues of social class appear irrelevant, and renders class as an illusive, seemingly unimportant, constituent in American life. The middle and upper classes tend to see those in lower classes in negative and distorted ways, ignoring their actual plight, rather conceptualizing them as an inconvenience and irritation.

In western society, individuals identified as able-bodied, white, young, and male are most often viewed as possessing the traits that are perceived as normal (Vernon, 1999). Thus minorities, persons with disabilities, and/or females fall outside of the parameters of what is considered to be normal.

The majority of teachers are Caucasian and they tend to perceive white students as more capable – a well-intentioned but unexamined perspective that places students who are not middle class and white at a disadvantage (Hale, 2001). Heshusius (2004), in writing on consciousness and fear of disabilities, states that "it is natural for us as humans to maintain the images that create a safe, stable, and socially desirable notion of 'self' for ourselves, fearing those selves that threaten those images" (p.286). Kozol (2005) affirms research reported in his earlier publications, that racism and social class marginalize minority students, particularly those in urban schools.

Equity issues are important considerations. The extent to which females, minorities, and persons with disabilities feel a sense of equity importance and appreciation has a significant bearing on the climate and culture within the school community and in the way the culture is perceived by outside constituents. Further elaboration concerning these groups follows.

Gender. Although significant advances have occurred for women during the past decade, women tend to have many anxieties related to attitudes toward science. Women are underrepresented in the upper echelons of the scientific community. Zinn (2003) believes that deeply ingrained beliefs about the unequal status of women as being "how things simply are" so that the inequalities and oppression are endured and largely ignored. Social forces and personal beliefs play a significant role in perpetuating these gender differences in educational and vocational patterns. Garland-Thompson (1997) suggests that many parallels are associated with females and persons with disabilities. Both are excluded from participation in many aspects of daily life, are defined in opposition to the norm, and are perceived as deviant and inferior.

American Indians/Alaskan Natives. Although American Indians and Alaskan Natives account for only 1% of the population, they represent 50% of the diversity in the United States. The school dropout rate is higher for them than for any other group even though American Indians and Alaskan Natives score relatively high on achievement measures. If we are to become more successful with this constituency, we must consider the society, culture, community, and family that help form each individual's constellation of characteristics.

Black Americans. The classification used by the Federal Government representing countries of origin includes African Americans and Caribbeans together. In addition to the cultural challenges, disproportionate numbers of Black students are from poor families and receive their education in disadvantaged schools. The schools often have limited resources and low expectations.

Hispanics. The term "Hispanic" includes people from across the Americas, ranging from Mexican Americans who have lived in the United States for generations, to refugees who speak no English and have little experience with formal schooling. Hispanics are the fasting growing group in the United States. Socioeconomic status, geographic location, gender, immigrant status, and proficiency in English language all interact and have an impact on students' performance.

Asian Americans. This constituency includes many substantially different subgroups, including Filipino, Chinese, Korean, Japanese, Southeast Asian, Pacific Islander, and other Asian countries of origin. They comprise about 3% of the overall U.S. labor force. Frequently, this constituency is described as a "model minority" for their academic performance in general. However, they face many cultural and educational challenges, and educators must respond to the uniqueness of the individual even though there may be strong indications of success in their community at large.

English Language Learners. Classrooms are experiencing greater numbers of students with limited language proficiency. Basic strategies such as simplifying oral and written language, grouping students so they can discuss with one another, working with other professionals to translate materials into a student's native language, and teaching teachers to work in collaborative relationships are formidable challenges in the reform of teacher education.

Urban students. Many urban schools are in crisis and perceived by the public as unsafe, unsound, and locked in permanent decline. Yet science is a natural discipline that could more effectively connect students with the world in which they live. Seeking partnerships with parent groups, business, and industry might help urban students develop more positive educational dispositions toward science.

Rural students. Almost 30% of the nation's public schools are rural, with one in six students attending a rural school. Students attending small schools may not have the curriculum support and variety of curricular choices made available to students in large school districts. This is especially critical in providing sound, challenging, equitable opportunities in science.

Persons with disabilities. Students with disabilities are often divided into two large categories that can overlap. One group consists of those with physical impairments, and the other includes those who manifest cognitive, social-personal, or intellectual disabilities that affect their ability to perform up to a school's expectations. Society often tends to devalue persons with disabilities, leading such individuals to devalue themselves. The results of low expectations are often cumulative, forcing many students with disabilities to pursue careers far below their talents and abilities. Gallagher (2001) iterates that disabilities exist only because of the way we define a group, and associate meaning. It is not the differences that are real but our constructed definitions (p. 643).

Equity issues concerning all of these groups are among the most challenging to our society. They simultaneously demand acknowledgment and response, but also foster resistance. Banton and Singh (2004) state, "No human being is reducible to one singular identity; we are indeed all -gendered, raced, classed- and nobody can escape the social construction of disability" (p.113). Mantsios (2000) believes we have become the most stratified society among advanced industrial nations. Class distinctions exist in every aspect of our lives, especially influencing the quality of schooling one receives, health care and safety. Although a growing body of literature is emerging, the knowledge base about issues of diversity and equity is very limited.

Petersen (2006) investigated the intersectionality of gender, race, disability, and class in American schools. She presents a powerful case that by having several stigmatizing identities often exacerbate oppression. Vernon (1999) states, "one plus one does not equal two oppressions" (p.385), they can be experienced simultaneously or singularly depending upon the context. Peterson (2006) argues that individuals' lives cannot be understood through only one aspect of identity, albeit gender, race, disability, or class. An understanding of one's experience can be known only through a thorough inquiry into the multiple dimensions of one's identity.

Learning alternative assessment strategies is also essential for educational equity. The development, administration, and scoring of assessment tools are areas ripe for bias. There is strong evidence that individual assessments are being grossly misused to classify and track students, to diagnose what is wrong with their knowledge, and in general, to grant legitimacy to practices that constrain their opportunities to learn. Blomgren (1992), in her investigation of testing, found special education students who are repeatedly tested often have increased anxiety about school, lower levels of self-confidence, and tend to blame themselves for poor performance. Teachers' preparation programs must examine alternatives such as authentic assessment, performance assessment, and open-ended forms of assessment that allow students to communicate what they know and understand. Many students are unable to demonstrate their true level of understanding under traditional testing conditions. Using the same measure for all students without adjusting for testing conditions or the reporting mechanisms could result in discouraging scores, rather than a valid assessment of what students have learned.

With the implementation of assessment policies tied to the enactment of No Child Left Behind (NCLB), classroom teachers are often frustrated by the burden of inappropriate testing conditions, particularly for students with mild to moderate disabilities. Meek (2006) provides a touching summation of the impact of common testing for all but 1-3% of the students, those with the most severe disabilities. She notes that although these students do not warrant exclusion from exposure to mainstream curriculum and high expectations, there is a need to sample and examine their progress in more humane and valid ways. Meek (2006) notes, "NCLB exams are simply too densely written, too long in duration, and too difficult in terms of readability and required level of conceptual understanding to warrant their indiscriminate administration, even with such common accommodations as extra time and extra breaks" (p. 295).

Wasta (2006) is concerned about the impact of NCLB implementation on both schools and the teaching profession. He notes that many dedicated teachers who work with special needs students are likely to leave the field after confronting a morale breaking fact that the tasks they face are impossible. He also notes that there is already a backlash of shuffling education students between schools in efforts to recover from citations reflecting lack of Adequate Yearly Progress (AYP).

The intentions of NCLB are laudable and hold promise for better education for millions of students that were poorly served. However, without modifications in the current language the actions are likely to damage the educational process through driving out dedicated teachers and through inadvertent cruelty to students when the assessment process does not give due consideration to the emotional impact of the process or the validity of the measures. The challenges are multifaceted, and rather than believing that all students will be performing at proficient levels by political dictate, examining other less optimistic possibilities might better serve our long-term educational needs.

In addition, technology literacy for future educators is essential to help understand technology-related assistance in making information more accessible for all. The 1988 Technology-Related Assistance Act and its 1993 amendments provide federal funding to help states establish programs to provide for technology-related assistance. For more information visit web sites for RESNA, DO-IT (Disabilities Opportunities, Interworking and Technology), EASI (Equal Access to Software and Information), and Closing the Gap. We must draw from professionals who have discovered successful methods for teaching all of their students. We must develop teams of educators who work together to create caring and innovative classrooms.

The following definitions of various disability categories are only a starting point. It is hoped that these ideas will help all science teachers think about the students in their classrooms and these students' unique educational needs.

Connecting Science Learning with Culture

Instructional Congruence

An increasing awareness shows that traditional science instruction favors male children without disabilities. The majority of persons involved in science related professions who receive their education in American schools come from middle level or high socio-economic backgrounds and from English-speaking homes (Gibbons, 2003). Research on student achievement shows mixed results on efforts to close the gaps on gender differences, socio-economic backgrounds, ethnicities and cultures, and students with disabilities (Loucks-Horsely, Hewson, Love, & Stiles, 1998). However, it has been consistently shown that when teachers assume responsibility to engage all students, the gap narrows and classroom achievement improves (Haycock, 2002). In a three-year study involving Latino students, Lee and Fradd (2001) reported that pre-unit and post-unit scores doubled when teachers employed the principles forwarded in the instructional congruence approach to teaching.

To understand how someone with a disability might feel in a science classroom, many of us can relate to the analogy of instructional manuals that come along with new appliances, electronics, or children's toys to be assembled. The instructions probably make perfect sense to the author but to the new user they often create a myriad of frustration that requires the assistance of someone familiar with the item and/or the operation. Why should one expect anything different from students who are being introduced to a new concept or principle?

Instructional congruence can help teachers and students make connections between learning and an individual's experience. Instructional congruence occurs when teachers mediate the nature of academic content and inquiry with consideration for language, cultural diversity, and disability (Lee and Fradd, 2001). The basic premise of instructional congruence is centered on teacher behaviors and choices. The essence of the concept is to teach through the minds of the learners rather than expecting to learners to adapt to the thinking processes forwarded by the teacher.

There are a number of ways that teachers can enhance instructional congruence for their students to enhance the learning of science concepts. The instructional congruence model is well suited for establishing personal relevance through the study of real world problems such as the study of infectious disease (Johnson, 2005).

One of the most basic ways of teaching is to -on investigations where students can work cooperatively and collaboratively with peers. Another is to allow and encourage conversation with other students, their parents, and other professionals. A third is to provide assistance with the vocabulary and pre-requisite knowledge or skills. Finally, teachers and students can look at connections through literature and everyday life experiences relating to the concept being studied (Lee, 2004).

Addressing the Needs of Students from Other Cultures

In recent years additional collaborative research supports the basic effect of school studies done in the late 1970s and early 1980s. In related publications Eggen (2002), Taylor, et al (2000), Watts (2003), and Zeichner (1996) note characteristics of teachers who are able to produce relatively high levels of student achievement in culturally diverse settings. These are:

- Teachers have a clear sense of their own ethnic and cultural identities.
- Teachers are personally committed to achieving equity for all students and believe that they are capable of making a difference in their students' learning.
- Teachers develop a personal bond with their students in a democratic and cooperative learning atmosphere.
- The curriculum is inclusive of the contributions and perspectives of the different ethno-cultural groups that make up the society.
- Teachers provide scaffolding that links the academically challenging and inclusive curriculum to the cultural resources that students bring to school.
- Parents and community members are encouraged to become involved in students' education and are given a significant voice in making important school decisions in relation to program, i.e., sources and staffing.

It is the teacher who must assume responsibility to integrate the nature of science with the culture and language of the students. McCarty & Watahomigie (1999) emphasize the need to impart to students a strong sense of cultural identity. This requires involvement with the community in informal settings. It also involves conversation with students about things other than science such as home, family, festival celebrations, and things done outside of the school day. Reading about characteristics of the cultures or the manifestations associated with a disability of your students can be very valuable. Lessons in which the teachers can include a component from other cultures drawing from literature or tools can provide critical associations for the learners. Appropriate picture books are valuable additions for students at any age (Wood & Tinajero, 2002).

Conversation and discourse, writing, and artistic expression can help improve student comprehension. Equally important, these types of experiences often yield a deeper understanding of the science concept that results from increased communication, interaction, and reflection. Having opportunities to talk about science may be as important as having students study science concepts. Very often it is through interaction that we all make the intuitive leaps and connections that are so important for persistence in future lessons.

Almost any practicing scientist will talk about persistence as an essential skill for science learning. Working through a period of frustration and discombobulation is common even among the most able learners. Learning about how the world works is not easy. Science concepts and their connections must be internalized, not memorized or learned literally. The habit of mulling and reorganizing thoughts that don't seem to fit together is the essence of thinking like a scientist. Teachers need to remain diligent in enlisting student persistence in the learning process.

Several educational practices yield higher levels of engagement in schools which have large numbers of students from other cultures. These are:

<u>Enhancing Instructional Congruence in Science</u>

- Hands-on investigations
- Allow and encourage conversation with other students
- Provide assistance with vocabulary
- Provide assistance with pre-requisite skills
- Look at connections through literature
- Look at connections to everyday life experiences relating to the concept

<u>What Teachers Can Do to Help Students from Other Cultures</u>

- Take time to listen
- Do not compromise values and expectations
- Teach well – be activity-centered when possible
- Use community member support for discipline and management
- Bring in responsible elders
- When appropriate, modify strategies and outcomes
- Provide scaffolding
- Provide assistance with literacy

Gender

The last two decades have reflected substantive changes in the percentage of women pursuing degrees in science and engineering. A National Science Foundation Report notes that in 2001 women received over half of the bachelor's degrees and 37% of doctoral degrees in science and engineering. However, problems associated with women in science persist that require a continuing focus and attention from teachers and professors. Math and science are "critical filters" (Beane, 1985). If students don't take advanced classes in these subjects during high school, they are screened out of many college majors and jobs that pay well.

Women indicate declining interests in entering STEM (Science, Technology, Engineering, & Math) fields beginning in the 7th grade (VanLeuvan, 2004), and they are more likely to drop out of science majors after entering a college or university (Vidal-Arwin, 2002). The participation of women in the physical sciences, mathematics, and engineering "still lags significantly behind that of white men and Asians" (NSF, 1999, p. 39). Relative to the percentages of women with degrees in STEM, there are significant under-representations in the upper echelons of the scientific community and in high level faculty positions. With regard to the workforce, the disparities in participation between groups of men and women remain striking, as noted in NSF figures (NSF, 1999, p. 3). From the standpoint of gender gaps:

- Women are 51.1% of the population, but only 22.4 % of the science and engineering workforce.
- Men are 48.9% of the population, and 77.6% of the science and engineering workforce.

Women scientists report more sexual harassment and gender discrimination in the workplace (Settles & Cortina, 2006). In the university environment, women scientists are more likely to note a hostile and chilly atmosphere for women on campus, an unconscious bias towards women concerning promotion, and the inability of universities to deal with balancing families and work (Reitz, 2005).

No evidence concludes that girls are born less inclined to mathematics or mechanics than boys, but there is strong evidence that society believes this to be the case and encourages a division between boys and girls. Classroom attitudes of teachers, books written for children, and subtle but constant parental and societal pressures persuade children that boys are better at science, engineering, and mathematics than are girls and that girls are better with words than are boys (Vetter, 1996, p. 30). Vidal-Arwin (2002) reported that some teachers have negative biases towards women's abilities in science. Surveyed students indicated that women's contributions were rarely discussed in science classes. Comments from female students indicated some disliked the mathematics and the hard work required (VanLeuvan, 2004). Numerous studies have focused on the unresponsive, downright "hostile climate" for girls and women in math and science classrooms, from the precollege level through graduate school and into the workplace (Sadker & Sadker, 1993). Girls with disabilities face double discrimination. They are hit with the bias that girls can't do math and science and that people with disabilities can't do math and science. This is compounded by a perception that somehow their disability makes them weak, needy, incompetent, or dependent, which often translates into protecting them from challenging work and learning (Wahl, 2001).

In a survey of girls in grades 7-12, VanLeuvan (2004) found that they liked discovery and using mathematics, and they had positive views regarding STEM careers. Regarding practices that make a difference, women noted a positive non-sexist climate and effective leadership (Settles & Cortina, 2006). In another study, students noted the presence of female faculty, mentorships, research opportunities, and cooperative rather than competitive learning environments, demonstrated an appreciation for women's participation in science and an emphasis on programs to build pre-college mathematical skills (Vidal-Arwin, 2002). In a survey of women science majors, over 90% of the women had a guide of one type or another and stated that guides during college were more influential than guides prior to college (Downing & Crosby, 2005).

Girls have strengths based on their talents and form a science perspective somewhat different from their male counterparts. Wahl (2001) offered teachers these suggestions for encouraging female participation in science:

1. *Assume interest.* Even if girls don't ask, it doesn't mean they're not interested. In research conducted about girls' participation in science and math, girls would not necessarily seek out the experience, but once presented with it, they engaged with enthusiasm and persistence (Frederick & Nicholson, 1986).
2. *Assume talent.* With the suggestion that there are many kinds of intelligence, it is clear that people excel in different ways (Sternberg, 1990; Gardner, 1993). Discard preconceived notions about who can do math and science. Give credit for approaching problems from various perspectives and for generating alternative strategies.
3. *Assume participation.* The rhetoric of the reform and standards movements talks about "all students." The phrase remains rhetorical unless every student is engaged. Don't protect girls because you're worried it might be too hard for them or rush to rescue them from making mistakes or taking risks. Create an environment that makes it comfortable for everyone to take part (Wahl, 2001).
4. A*ssume "all students" includes everyone, but that "all students" are not the same.* Each child needs something different to learn and achieve, and as educators we need to figure out what that is.
5. *Make learning accessible.* Accessibility applies to the social as well as the physical organization. Make it easy for girls to get in and use space, and provide materials and tools in accessible formats and designs. Talk with each student about what she needs and prefers in the way of support and accommodation. Give the message through the environment and the atmosphere you create that girls are welcomed and expected to perform well.
6. *Educate yourself.* Learn all you can about human development and contextualize your understanding of the influences of society on human development.

The following strategies are ways to put these principles into practice.

Strategy 1. Encourage girls to question, explore, and challenge. Inquiry is fundamental to good science and good science education. It is a means of motivating and engaging girls and necessary to achieving high quality outcomes in math and science. It lays the groundwork for serious and deep investigation. Encourage girls to ask questions, identify questions worth pursuing, and persist in the investigation; to take intellectual risks; to make mistakes and try again in the quest for understanding; to get messy; to persist even in the face of demands from others for attention and service. Support girls to resist traditional socialization that values being neat, getting the right answer, and being compliant and unquestioning. Help girls – and boys – to challenge constraining stereotypes about who can do math and science and who can be a scientist.

Strategy 2. Keep girls in the science track – and change the tracks. Make sure girls are enrolled in the most advanced sequence of math and science courses possible and have the support to succeed. Consider eliminating tracking and segregation from math and science education. Clearly, these suggestions require much more than what a single teacher can accomplish alone, but it is essential that educators, individually and collectively, speak out and become a force for change in schools, districts, and states.

Strategy 3. Rethink teaching and classroom organization. Different people learn in different ways, and many people learn best when taught using more than one approach. You want girls to use all the senses they have available to them in exploring science – touch, sound, sight, smell – and to invent new ways to explore.

Similarly, make it clear that there are multiple ways of solving problems. Traditional approaches to math and science have sometimes implied that there is only one correct approach to an answer.

Reformed math/science education emphasizes children developing and explaining their own strategies, proposing their own research designs, and inventing their own problem-solving algorithms.

Don't make time an issue when it is not central to the math or science concept. It is true that some students may need extra time. It is just as likely that other students need extra time as well, yet most classrooms, especially math classrooms, credit the quickest and the first. It is not a matter of slowing a whole group down but of structuring the learning process so that each student can proceed at his or her "right" pace.

Develop cooperative relationships for teaching and planning among specialists and teachers. A promising approach is collaborative teaching, bringing together the expertise of special education teachers with that of science and math educators. Use cooperative learning and peer tutoring as ways to tap students' talents to share what they know with each other (U.S. Department of Education, 1997, p. III-68).

Strategy 5. Create networks and connections. Decreasing girls' isolation, showing them that there are others like them who have been successful in math and science, and providing them with networks for support can go a long way toward helping girls with disabilities persist in science. Connect girls to mentors, role models, and each other around the experience of math and science. Expose them to careers and real life applications of math and science through field trips, partnerships with industry, internships, and opportunities to engage in serious research and exploration.

American Indian Students

The education profession is dominated largely by white teachers with a higher predominance of females in the education of young children. Starnes (2006) iterates clearly that what teachers don't know significantly impacts their effectiveness as educators. She notes that we don't recognize or respond to the chasm that exists between customary methods and curriculum with the way children from other cultures learn. Fleming (2006) notes that because American Indians are not referenced in the curriculum they become among the least understood ethnic groups in the United States. He refers to common stereotypes:

> Stereotyping is a poor substitute for getting to know individuals at a more intimate, meaningful level. By relying on stereotypes to describe Native Americans, whites come to believe that Indians are drunks, get free money from the government, and are made wealthy from casino revenue. Or they may believe that Indians are at one with nature, deeply religious, and wise in the ways of spirituality. Stereotypes, some believe, have a basis in reality. They can be a product of oversimplification, exaggeration, or generalization. Their harm is that they define an individual by attributes ascribed to the group as a whole.

In addition the little we know about the history, culture, and communities of Native Americans comes from white educators. A special challenge exists because each culture and each community is unique. The hardships associated with efforts at extinction, slavery, forced migration, forced religious conversion, and disease are all imbedded in historical roots. These are complicated with contemporary social challenges involving poverty, unemployment, teen pregnancy, substance abuse, higher than average dropout rates, and higher than average suicide levels.

American culture is strongly impacted by the presence and influence of American Indians, however awareness and sensitivity to their unique needs are largely ignored in the curriculum. Gibson (2006) states, research indicates that American Indian students still attend schools where they do not see themselves reflected in the school's guiding principles, in the curriculum, or even in their own classrooms. The nation can take an example from the efforts of the State of Montana regarding curriculum innovation to improve educational quality for American Indian students. Historically one can look to the 1972 Montana Constitutional Convention which produced what many consider to be one of the most progressive state constitutions in the nation. Article X, Section 1(2) of this new constitution says that the state "recognizes the distinct and unique cultural heritage of the American Indians and is committed in its educational goals to the preservation of their cultural heritage" (Juneau & Broaddus, 2006).

There was limited activity regarding the article until 1999 when a state representative, Carol Juneau (Mandan/Hidatsa), shepherded a bill through the legislature that became known as Indian Education for All (IEFA). The bill established three primary objectives with regard to Indian education in the state:

- Every Montanan, whether Indian or non-Indian, is to be encouraged to learn about the distinct and unique heritage of American Indians in a culturally responsive manner.
- All school personnel should have an understanding and awareness of Indian tribes to help them relate effectively to Indian students and parents.
- The education system should work cooperatively with Montana tribes when providing instruction and implementing any educational goals.

This was followed by a 2004 Montana State Supreme Court decision that the state's funding of schools was indeed unconstitutional because it was not based on any definition of "quality" as the constitution requires. It ordered the legislature to define "quality" based on educationally relevant factors and then to fund that definition. This action was initiated in 2002 when educators from across the state formed the Montana Quality Education Coalition (MQEC) and sued the state, claiming that the funding scheme for the education system was unconstitutional (*Columbia Falls v. State)*. MQEC won. Article X, Section 1(2), the Indian education provision, proved to be the strongest part of the lawsuit. The district court found that the state had shown no evidence of its commitment to implement IEFA, and, in fact, the court found the state "defenseless." This was quite a coup for the education community, and there was a surge of hope that, at last, Montana would be able to live up to its promise (Juneau & Broaddus, 2006).

The Montana legislation requires that <u>all</u> Montana students learn about the "distinct and unique" heritage of each of the state's 12 tribes. The curriculum must include seven broad topics known as essential understandings. These are (Starnes, 2006):

1. There is great diversity among the 12 tribal Nations of Montana in their languages, cultures, histories, and governments. Each Nation has a distinct and unique cultural heritage that contributes to modern Montana.
2. There is great diversity among individual American Indians as identity is developed, defined, and redefined by entities, organizations, and people. A continuum of Indian identity, unique to each individual, ranges from assimilated to traditional. There is no generic American Indian.
3. The ideologies of Native traditional beliefs and spirituality persist into modern-day life as tribal cultures, traditions, and languages are still practiced by many American Indian people and are incorporated into how tribes govern and manage their affairs. Additionally, each tribe has its own oral histories, which are as valid as written histories. These histories predate the "discovery" of North America.
4. Reservations are lands that have been reserved by the tribes for their own use through treaties, statutes, and executive orders and were not "given" to them. The principle that land should be acquired from the Indians only through their consent with treaties involved three assumptions.
    - Both parties to treaties were sovereign powers.
    - Indian tribes had some form of transferable title to the land.
    - Acquisition of Indian lands was solely a government matter not to be left to individual colonists.
5. Federal Indian policies, put into place throughout American history, have affected Indian people and still shape who they are today. Much of Indian history can be related through several major

federal policy periods: Colonization Period, Treaty Period, Allotment Period, Boarding School Period, Tribal Reorganization Period, Termination Period, Self-determination Period.

6. History is a story most often related through the subjective experience of the teller. With the inclusion of more and varied voices, histories are being rediscovered and revised. History told from an Indian perspective frequently conflicts with the stories mainstream historians tell.
7. Under the American legal system, Indian tribes have sovereign powers, separate and independent from the federal and state governments. However, the extent and breadth of tribal sovereignty is not the same for each tribe.

A spirit of optimism regarding the enactment of IFEA is shared by Wendy Hopkins (2006), a member of the Little Shell Chippewa Tribe:

> Indian people have had to live in a white world; some have learned how to adapt. But when Indian kids meet non-Indian people, they know non-Indian people have ideas about what it means to be Indian and that a lot of those ideas are not very good. With IEFA, Indian kids will have more confidence that the people they meet know about them, that they are good people, and that they can be like everyone else. They will set aside the belief that being from the reservation means they are somehow less. As a teacher, I always remind myself that kids do not care how much you know until they know how much you care. If Indian students feel that their teachers care about them and believe in them, they will do well.

There are teaching practices that are significantly more effective for all students, and they are highly congruent with best practice in science education. Classroom teachers that employ hands-on, experiential learning in an informal, flexible learning environment achieve better student learning outcomes (Gilliland, 1999; Simpson, 2002). Collaborative processes where students are given opportunities to work together yield both higher learning outcomes and more positive attitudes (Hilberg & Tharp, 2002). Rhodes (1994) notes that informal classrooms where teachers act as facilitators are beneficial to native students. Cajete (1999) suggests that teachers present the whole concept before focusing on segments and details when working with students from other cultures. Pewewardy & Hammer (2003), note the value of reflective processing where students are given opportunities to build new knowledge out of prior learning.

Many students from other cultures are visual learners. In a study of cognitive styles Riding and Rayner (1998) reported that for visual learners' performance almost doubles with information that includes text and illustration as opposed to text alone. Whenever possible, bring in visual aids or models.

Specifically reflecting on her work with Native American youth, Starnes (2006) offers a number of suggestions for teachers. First and foremost is the need to seek out a mentor who will help guide decisions through the cultural and historical circumstances unique to the cultural context where you are teaching. Teachers need to attend appropriate cultural, social, and sporting events so the community senses there is intent to be connected. When possible bring in responsible elders as speakers to students and in other roles where they can enhance school-community relationships and communication. Non-native teachers need to become educated abut history from the perspective of the community and examine difficult realities where one looks at injustices committed against people by other people or by government policies and practices, both historical and contemporary. An example of successful implementation of this practice is reflected in the words of Ngai and Allen (2006). They state:

> At Lewis & Clark, teachers and students learn from five elders and eight tribal members who come to our classrooms regularly to share stories based on an indigenous world view, to teach us what they learned from their ancestors, to speak with us in their Native language, to bring us humor and wisdom, and to open their hearts for new relationships that heal old wounds and bridge current gaps between Indians and whites.

> Through the voices and faces of the local Indian people, Indian children of different tribes have been able to connect personally with their learning, and non-Indian children have discovered a new cultural realm in which "my" perspective is only one of many, and "the others" are fascinating and enriching. Listening to Salish neighbors talk about how much they value their unique cultural practices, children have found "culture" a dynamic subject, and ethnic minorities have found it safe to explore and express their own search for cultural identities.

It is also necessary for teachers to create materials and activities specific to their curriculum because there is a general unlikelihood that commercial materials exist. Lastly teachers must be patient and expect different cultural issues to emerge again and again. One must understand that it takes time to change generations of cultural interactions and mistrust.

There is a danger in considering any cultural group as homogeneous. One must consider the rich diversity and uniqueness within and between tribal nations as much as one must consider the diversity and uniqueness of those reflected in European heritage. When one looks at curriculum materials, European cultures are differentiated by leadership, geography, time, and chronology. American Indian nations are no less unique and independent. They are now and have always been sovereign nations with individual languages, economies, and cultural norms as varied as those of Europe. Just as the French, German, and Danish peoples, though all European, labor under misconceptions, stereotypes, and gaps in their knowledge and understanding of one another, so, too, do many tribal people in Montana. It is not uncommon to find that Indian people are as divided by generations-old conflicts and as separated by cultural divides as are their non-Indian counterparts (Starnes, 2006).

Our responsibilities as educators are eloquently stated in an article by Wendy Zagray Warren (2006): "No one is asking me to rewrite my entire curriculum. Instead, I need to slowly develop a new habit of mind so that the Essential Understandings become an automatic part of my planning. Not only is that my responsibility, it is also my pleasure and my honor."

Starnes (2006) provides several insights about responsibilities of community members and educational leaders to help classroom teachers. She suggests that there be required days of professional development where teachers are informed about issues, the impact of legislation, and local history. She also suggests tours and attendance at cultural events. There should be an ongoing and personal mentoring program thoughtfully developed, written down in detail, and implemented. She stresses there must be a culture of safety toward risk-taking, protection from controversy, and emphasis on the positive rather than what went wrong.

English Language Learners

For students who do not experience the English language as young children, one can expect delays in their conceptual understanding of science. These delays exist even in students who appear to have good social verbal skills and effective communication with everyday vocabulary. Science can be particularly difficult because it is a broad field with an ever-increasing limitless input of new information into the discipline(s). Therefore it is essentially impossible to adequately define core knowledge. A second factor is that much of science learning is conceptual, requiring that teachers draw on past experiences and apply the empirical evidence from those experiences to learn new concepts. When the language connections are not refined, students are not able to effectively draw from this knowledge.

In an ethnographic study of a group of largely Hispanic students from Mexico, Curtin (2006) reported that the students liked school in the United States. They felt materially comfortable and safe, even though they attended and urban school in a low-socioeconomic section of a large city. However, even though they felt fluent in English, they noted they struggled with the content and vocabulary in science. Without direct communication and teacher engagement with the learner(s), the learning gaps that are likely to occur makes science an insurmountable hurdle. The following suggestions are offered to guide instruction with English Language Learners.

- Time needs to be provided to communicate with the student(s) in private outside of the regular classroom. Otherwise it is likely that instruction will result in numerous unforeseen problems both in learning and in relationships. A critical aspect of learning is a caring teacher, one who understands students' issues and concerns, one who provides the necessary supports for success, and one who holds high expectations.

- Providing prior exposure works more effectively than remediation. Prior to introducing the unit to the entire class, it is important that the ELL student(s) have an opportunity to preview key concepts and vocabulary. When possible, it is advantageous if this can be done in students' primary language, but it can also be done in English.

- Sharing the desired learning outcomes and vocabulary prior to instruction is valuable to both the teachers and students. Pinpointing vocabulary, posting webs, and framing concepts and applications on charts and word walls can provide a reference and reinforcement. Pre-assessment of all students using language "buddies" is often a helpful strategy. In this strategy, it might be possible to pair the student with another student who has bilingual proficiency and can translate and converse in the native language. If this is not possible, parent volunteers or teachers aids might be able to assist.

Krashen (1994) offers Specifically Designed Academic Instruction in English (SDAIE) strategies for helping English Language Learners in the science classroom. These strategies include speaking clearly and at a slower pace, using gestures and facial expressions, using concrete materials and visuals, avoiding idiomatic expressions, and using student-centered activities.

Exploration using heterogeneous cooperative groupings is critical. Having students work together enables the English Language Learner to tap into the strengths of other learners. Lessons should be organized so that students can express themselves through drawings, short phrases, or mathematical data reporting where the English Language Learner is less likely to be marginalized.

When developing a concept, try to "chunk" the information into 10 minute segments, following each "chunk" with a short time of discussion with a neighbor to share what was learned. Allowing students to speak out enables them to work out an understanding of the material and remember the content (Hansen, 2006). This can be supplemented with multi-media opportunities such as videos or interactive software to help scaffold student learning. For older students opportunities to use the internet and investigate sources in their native language can be very helpful.

Curtin (2006) shared numerous suggestions gathered from in-depth conversations with adolescent English Language Learners. They described good teachers as ones who used examples, explained a lot, did not give too many directions, and spent a lot of time focusing on their actual teaching strategies. They did not "blame" students for not learning and were always seeking new teaching strategies. They incorporated games, used hands-on approaches, and had knowledge of multiple intelligence theory. They walked around the classroom and sought out students instead of waiting for students to raise their hands. They focused on faces and non-verbal communication from students.

When Curtin (2006) asked students about teaching practices they preferred, they noted teachers who knew their names and sometimes incorporated elements relating to their culture in their teaching. The students enjoyed group work and opportunities to seek help from other students without getting in trouble. They especially appreciated models and concrete examples and visual supports. Examples and opportunities to practice were often mentioned by students as desirable. They perceived teachers who used interactive instructional approaches as being much more congruent with their leaning needs than teachers who employed more didactic practices.

One element that emerged from Curtin's (2006) research with English Language Learners was a desire by students to be "walked through" a problem rather than being required to figure it out on their own. This poses an interesting dichotomy that science teachers in general face. Students prefer inquiry strategies, cooperative heterogeneous learning groups, and hands-on learning but also want the teacher to guide them through problem solving. This poses the universal challenge of how do educators develop higher-order thinking and independent learning skills in students and at the same time sustain a connectedness with the students in the process.

Assessment and grading often become especially difficult for English Language Learners. In traditional forms of objective assessments, the students do not have an opportunity to clearly communicate what they have learned and are able to do. It doesn't take long before motivation wanes when there is incongruence between one's understanding and performance as perceived by an external evaluator (teacher). The teacher must always look for ways that English Language Learners can demonstrate performance. Authentic assessment through a hands-on inquiry experience is a good strategy as a culminating activity. Other suggestions noted by Hansen (2006) are projects, drawings, labeled diagrams, posters, and products.

African American Students

African Americans are an ethnic group within mainstream America with their own culture that may affect their performance in science in unique ways. There may be special challenges in connecting the home, community, and classroom science learning.

Teacher expectations, particularly for African American youth living in low socio-economic environments, are lower than those held for other ethnic populations (Diamond, Randolph, & Spillane, 2004). The danger exists in how teachers approach the learners. When students are approached as if they are less capable than their peers, they achieve less, are absent more often, and are more likely to drop out of school. A particular danger is found with grouping or tracking students. Tracking does not increase student performance but, in contrast, increases the potential for school failure and dropout (Pettit, 2006, p. 107). Diamond, Randolph and Spillane (2004) found that when African American children performed high academically compared with white counterparts they were considered an exception to the rule. Whereas, if an European American performed poorly, he/she was considered an exception. When teachers have low expectations of students' academic ability they tend to give them less challenging coursework (Farka, 1996). These become coupled -- teachers emphasize student deficits and students perceive a reduced sense of responsibility.

In her study, Pettit's (2006) data suggested that teachers in a school with a high percentage of African American children cited by the government as a school in need of assistance according to the NCLB blamed students for poor performance in order to deflect professional blame away from themselves. She concluded that the school engaged in a faulty testing curriculum that guaranteed poor student performance: 1) teachers felt the focus of the school was raising test scores, 2) teachers felt under tremendous scrutiny and were afraid of professional repercussions and embarrassment, and 3) teachers felt they must teach to test and find ways to produce higher test scores. Pettit (2006), in expressing concerns about the impact of NCLB on student achievement, suggests that students in schools in need of improvement are receiving a canned curriculum that encourages shallow and low ability thinking (p. 86). She also concluded that the "blame game" supports a culture of failure in both students and teachers.

In her study of four adult African Americans with disabilities, Peterson (2006) illuminates the challenges and navigational techniques and adaptations that these individuals employed. They constantly struggled with low expectations by educators and guardians. They described acts of resistance that were "slightly oppositional" and "quietly subversive" in response or reaction to the dominant ideology in the classroom. Examples included purposefully ignoring directions, intentional lack of participation, engaging in distracting techniques, and intentional tardiness particularly after physical therapy (p.150). Collins (2000) describes adaptive behaviors of persons located in an oppressive culture as "working the cracks" to initiate change through pecking at "cracks and fissures that represent organizational weakness" (p. 282). Peterson notes that in her research the individuals exhibiting semi-conscious acts of resistance possessed a developing understanding of the oppressive nature of their circumstances, but were unable to fully explain their intent or articulate a desired outcome at the time the experience occurred (p.153).

A study conducted by Neuman et al. (1995) involved interviews with 19 African American parents regarding learning. They found three very different views of family perspectives about learning. One group believed knowledge was finite and the school's responsibility was to disseminate that knowledge to learners. Another group believed that knowledge included tangible skills and students made their own mind up about when and what they learn. The third group thought that learners were active constructors of knowledge and greatly valued connecting the learner within the instructional process. When there is a difference about beliefs the discontinuity is more pronounced (Weigel, et al., 2005). Anderson and Stokes (1984), reported that Anglo families were much more likely to initiate educational interactions, where African American families waited for the child to initiate.

In investigating the thoughts, ideas, and perceptions of an African American adult with a vision disability Peterson (2006) described her frustration with a domineering guardian who felt she had a right to unapologetically interject her ideas, thoughts, and opinions in a manner that overshadowed and contradicted what the individual was attempting to say (p.84). She stated, "thus I came to understand Shana's inarticulateness not simply as a result of limited language skills, but generally overlaid by other factors including a lack of self-esteem, learned habits of compliance, social isolation, loneliness and the experience of oppression" (p.87).

Family plays a very important role in the learning process. A positive attitude by families improves the learning process (Pretzlik & Chan, 2004). Phillips (1987) reported that parents' perceptions of their child's academic competence were a better predictor of a child's self-perception than academic indicators, such as grades or test scores. An effective science teacher has a responsibility to engage in activities that bring about a shared understanding and agreement about the respective roles of each party in the learning process (Sonnenschein & Schmidt, 2000). Reese et al. (2000) indicates that there is an increased likelihood of a mismatch between a teacher's perception and family values, expectations, priorities, and perceptions with students from other cultures. In a study by Linek, Rasinski, and Harkins (1997), over 90% of teachers recognized the importance of involving parents, yet less than 5% supported involving parents as partners.

The social context of the science learning experience may be an important factor for the African American student. This might be particularly important during the ages of 7-14 where a child grows in complexity as a person, where there is an increase in competency in many domains, and where there is a progressive integration into the society or culture (Serpell, Baker and Sonnenschein, 2005). Differences between the language of the home and school can vary in conversational behavior (turn taking between an adult and child when conversing), motivation (whether a child feels rewarded by either the family or teacher), and learning style (learning by observing before performing), (Reese et al., (2000). A lack of consideration and communication often results in consternation and confusion that inhibits the educational process. Information flow from the teacher to the student and to the family members working toward consensus is vital. Teachers who do not make an effort to know the family are failing to know the student.

Confusion is particularly paramount in an inquiry-based science curriculum where teachers focus on process while the student and parent believe that a good deal of rote learning is needed to develop proficiency. Eccles and Harold (1996) noted that while teachers claimed to frequently encourage parents to assist children in learning, they seldom offered suggestions on what parents should do. This often resulted in parents being unsure of teachers' expectations for their child's science learning. There also tends to be little consideration of children's ideas regarding home-school science connections (Shields et al., 1983). There is a need throughout the school years to promote science connections between the home, school, and community context.

An element associated with fewer African Americans in science fields is African American student performance and participation in the mathematics curriculum. As a group, they perform less well on standardized measures and are less likely to select advanced mathematics courses or electives in mathematics at the high school level. Mathematics is often a "gatekeeper' for advanced science courses. African American students often find mathematics more difficult than students from other ethnic groups. Some associate this as due to language and learning style differences (Orr, 1987; Delpit, 1995).

A study by Msengi (2006) summarizes the idea that triangulating information between the adult family member, the student, and the associated teacher can be a tool for a shared understanding leading to improved home-school relationships. He states further that these efforts can build on family strengths and provide flexible venues for exploring alternatives rather than dwelling on conflicts between the adult family member, the student, and the teacher. Misunderstandings are often a result of limited communication.

The following are classroom suggestions for addressing the unique needs of African American children:

- Children achieve more when teachers provide hands-on experiential learning opportunities for students in science (Simpson, 2002).
- Higher student outcomes are achieved when students are allowed to work together in cooperative groups (Hilberg & Tharp, 2002).
- The availability of a mentor to help the teacher address circumstances unique to the cultural context of the community is beneficial to student learning (Starnes, 2006).
- Walking through investigations on occasion to guide students through the thinking process can improve student motivation and engagement (Curtin, 2006).
- Initiating family engagement and providing guidance on what parents can do to help in science learning yields improved student performance (Sonnenschein & Schmidt, 2000).
- Using examples, taking time to explain, and not giving too many directions have been found to improve the student-teacher relationship (Curtin, 2006).
- Exposure to key concepts and vocabulary is important early in the lesson. More effective teachers work to bring in language connections and student experiences associated with the concepts (Krashen, 1994).
- Time to practice particularly through games and exposure to multiple intelligence activities resulted in improved student engagement and improved student attitudes towards their teachers (Curtin, 2006).
- Walking around the classroom, seeking out student responses instead of waiting for students to raise their hands, and encouraging students often are effective strategies (Starnes, 2006).

Lesbian, Gay, Bisexual, Transgender, or Questioning

It is important that educational environments accept the responsibility of all of the students in their care. One aspect of uniqueness that is unsettling for many, sometimes because it may transcend religious or moral convictions, is the issue of homosexuality.

Persons with disabilities who develop new feelings based upon their sexual awakening and physiological development can often feel that they are in love. These feelings can make them feel uncomfortable and confused, not knowing how to act or react. This becomes even more complex when associated with being identified as gay or lesbian,

The responsibilities of teachers and educators cannot be ignored in this regard. In addition to issues of social adjustment and mental health, there are significant issues regarding safety and wellness. While some educators may feel uncomfortable addressing these issues based upon their own fears or beliefs, it is a professional responsibility of educators, in all positions and at all levels, to provide a safe and supportive environment for all students.

In a survey conducted by the Gay, Lesbian, and Straight Education Network (GLSEN) in 2003, 64.3% of Lesbian, Gay, Bisexual or Transsexual (LGBT) students reported feeling unsafe at school because of their sexual orientation. In the same survey 82.9% indicated that faculty or staff failed to intervene when homophobic remarks were made. In terms of violations, 84% of LGBT students reported being verbally harassed, 91.5% hearing homophobic remarks frequently or often, and 39.1% reported being physically harassed because of their sexual orientation (Sims, 2003).

The trauma, trials and tribulations can be a summed up in a statement in an article by N.J. Bailey (2005):

> The shame and ridicule and the fear of physical attack make school a fearful place, resulting in frequent absences and, too often, academic failure. These youth spend an inordinate amount of energy determining how to get safely to and from school, how to avoid the hallways when other students are present so they can avoid verbal and physical harassment, figuring out where they might be safe in the lunchroom or the locker room, and which restroom they can use and when.

Schools must represent the social and academic mores we want society to emulate and must provide a safe and equitable environment for all students and all adults. Teachers and administrators have a professional responsibility to oversee all aspects of the educational context and when they do not intervene, they give tacit assent to perpetrators and they marginalize the victims. A few suggestions offered by N.J. Bailey (2005) are:

- ➢ Provide and require professional training for all adults in the school to learn and understand about LGBT needs, to become aware of responsibilities concerning their rights and well-being, and to develop skills to meet their needs.
- ➢ All professionals must act assertively to prevent harassment, demeaning statements, demeaning gestures, or isolating maneuvers by individuals in the school regardless of the place or time.
- ➢ Ensure that there is at least one person in the school who is a well-trained safe person to whom students can turn and get accurate information abut sexual orientation or gender identity. In some cases this may be a person outside school, but all professions in the school should be knowledgeable about this human resource.

- Examine the school curriculum to look at ways to appropriately incorporate history, literature, and role models from the LGBT community to forward a message, just as we need to do with all other marginalized groups, that in America everyone can live a successful and productive life.
- Examine libraries and multi-media resources to ensure that there is a solid and age-appropriate body of information and literature, both fiction and non-fiction relating to sexual orientation.

In schools where there are initiatives related to alleviating discriminatory actions towards students with disabilities, there are significant differences. The average grade point of LGBT students is more than 10% higher. They are 40% less likely to skip school and twice as likely to report that they intend to go to college. Equitable education ensures that everyone is valued and appreciated for the qualities they have without consequences by those who might be hypocritical, prejudiced, or biased because of their own beliefs.

Gifted and Talented

With the implementation of state-wide testing mandates and No Child Left Behind legislative policies, one of the most vulnerable groups are the students with above average abilities and giftedness. They may encounter being exploited as aids and tutors for less able students, being marginalized because the elements in the curriculum reflect things that they already know and are able to do, and finding difficulties in the way they are perceived by peers and teachers.

Gifted students often have to balance differences in development from social norms. For example, their intellectual understanding and problem-solving abilities may be much better developed than their social skills and physical maturation. Scholastic achievements may result in more busy work by the teacher or isolated study that alienates them from classmates and peers. Teachers might resent domination in discussions or distractions because the student finishes assignments too quickly. Gifted students may resent additional demands particularly if they come from multiple classes where teachers do not communicate among themselves.

The most important element in creating an appropriate balance is honest and substantive conversation with the student. A teacher needs to assess the current level of student performance, engage in dialog about learning experiences that are compatible with the student's skills and that he/she is willing to do, and develop a plan so that an appropriate level of challenge continues throughout the year. Most importantly is to discuss the balance between empowerment and responsibility with the student, with frequent checkpoints to insure that the outcomes are positive for the student and compatible with the educational program of the school.

Common practices include compacting the curriculum to avoid boredom, allowing the student freedom to enrich his/her learning experiences, presenting an educational program with different levels of challenge where students have some freedom of choice, using cooperative learning, and allowing groups to engage in more sophisticated problem solving or creative endeavors.

Lynne Bailey (2005) offers an engaging narrative of challenges and opportunities associated with a gifted early adolescent student. She shares some of the dilemmas in his personal experiences to balance academic and social relationships. She says she set high expectations and was proud of the impeccable work of the student. However, at a time when she was feeling a sense of pride about shaping a challenging curriculum, she received an e-mail from his mother expressing concerns about his workload and that he had no time to play, run, or spend time with his family. In following up, Bailey found out that several of his teachers had also added multiple end-of-the-semester projects and reports. Bailey says she became alarmed and frightened about the intense young man who was involved in so much activity, both curricular and extra-curricular.

Bailey took time to interview the student and get his view on the situation. Through conversation she was able to resolve elements with the student and achieve a level of moderation with the student. She states, "Only after much clarifying conversation was I able to attempt to address some of his instructional needs in a productive manner." She referred to Kaplan (2003) who noted that we should avoid thinking about one pedagogical approach for students with special talents. Each student and each context involves different considerations that relate to the context of the school, the nature of the subject matter, and the attributes and needs of the student.

However it is always beneficial to build on the research of others when planning appropriate interventions. Following are some suggestions by Watters and Dizmann (2003) for gifted and talented students in science and technology:

- Modifying Content
    - Modify content by allowing students to learn new concepts at their own pace.
    - More complex content should be introduced as students master concepts.
    - Include thematic, broad-based, integrative content beyond the single subject content.
    - Address students' sense of social responsibility by introducing real-world problem solving and inquiry tasks.
- Modifying Process
    - Applying a cognitive apprenticeship approach (Collins, Brown & Newman, 1989) that features:
        - Modeling: Demonstration of thought processes.
        - Coaching: Helping with problem-solving process.
        - Scaffolding: Providing temporary problem-solving support.
        - Articulation: Students demonstrate their own knowledge and thought processes.
        - Reflection: Students compare their problem-solving processes with peers or adult mentor.
        - Exploration: Students seek out new problems.
- Modifying the Environment
    - Encourage risk-taking, diverse ideas, independence, creativity, and autonomy

Students with Disabilities

People with disabilities are from all societal classifications, yet more are disproportionately identified from disfranchised groups. Federal regulations mandate the use of supplemental aids and resources if an alternative placement needs to be considered. To teach in an inclusive setting, preservice teachers and practitioners need training and professional development for teaching all students. Although some progress has been made in greater uses of technology, little has been done to help general classroom teachers understand their responsibilities toward meeting the needs of all students. Interventions are lacking, such as creating and using adaptive materials, modifying lessons, selecting from alternative instructional strategies, modifying laboratory equipment to allow full participation of all students, and adapting evaluation materials for students with special needs.

Special education continues to be considered as a sound alternative and caring placement for low performing students (Pettit, p. 125). Pettit (2006) states, "When students performed poorly they were perceived as incapable without being able to connect to the regular curriculum. Teachers felt they were doing the students and themselves a favor by pushing hard for special education placements." However, when placed, students face a new world of labels. This world is described as a different world, an exiled world that will ultimately stigmatize and limit the academic future of the identified students (Brantlinger, 2004; Kliewer & Biklen, 1996).

Motor/Orthopedic Disabilities

The term "motor/orthopedic disability" encompasses a large number of impairments that have a significant impact on a person's life as a result of problems with the functional or structural aspects of one or more body systems or structures.

Many classify these conditions according to neuromotor impairments (damage to the brain and/or spinal cord) or muscular/skeletal impairments. The conditions can result from congenital abnormalities and acquired diseases or be related to injuries or other causes. Further classification typically describes the impairment as mild, moderate, or severe, but as Best (1992) concludes, these terms must be understood only as guidelines and are far from universally applied.

Examples of neuromotor impairments include cerebral palsy, polio, muscular dystrophy, multiple sclerosis, and spinal cord disorders. Those relating to problems in muscular/skeletal function include arthritis, malformed or absent limbs, and scoliosis. Often concomitant conditions are associated with a number of the neuromotor impairments. Many students with motor/orthopedic disabilities need various types of physical therapy on a regular basis and may miss many hours of school. This is also true in the most severe cases when the student is in a school program specifically designed for these special needs. In these circumstances, sometimes specialized educators and therapists are used in home or hospital settings (Smith, 1998).

Science educators can gain information from several school staff sources to help students with motor/orthopedic disabilities succeed in the science classroom. For instance, take time to analyze the physical setting of the school and other learning locations. With input from student(s) with disabilities, you can determine barriers and hazards that could potentially impede students with motor/orthopedic disabilities. The school nurse and student(s) with disabilities can provide information on the constraints and side effects of medications to help science teachers understand any variance in student behavior. Special education personnel and other school specialists can help science teachers set appropriate expectations for academic and social tasks for the students. These resource people also often know how and where to obtain assistive technologies or access devices. However, if science teachers contact assistive technology agencies directly, they can become familiar with the specialized equipment.

Three categories of assistive technologies are described below.

Mobility devices: Power wheelchairs, sonic guides, visual enhancement devices, and devices that can manage muscle movement through electrical stimulation can allow for greater student independence. Robotics or computer interfaces for data collection and recording can provide opportunities for laboratory participation and, in many cases, laboratory independence for students who were previously denied access.

Augmentative communication systems: Technologies that modify speech output or display words for persons with limited or unusable speech, closed captioning technologies, descriptive video, and multimodality output devices can enhance both receptive and expressive communication . Alternative mice, sip-and-puff mouse code controls, head controlled pointing systems, blink switches, skin switches, trackballs, and sticky keys, can provide a means for expressive communication for students with orthopedic/mobility impairments.. IntelliTools that include multiple means of representation, expression and engagement can help struggling students. Prentke Romich Company and Freedom Scientific Learning Systems Group have an assortment of alternative, augmentive communication devices and computer access solutions designed for adults and students.

Sensory devices: Science probes and other data collection tools with digital output can allow students with mobility impairments opportunities to be active and sometimes independent in the process of data collection.

Resource people in the community and at institutions of higher education are often helpful in providing special equipment, obtaining volunteers to assist in the classroom or on field trips, making recordings, and preparing instructional materials. Such partnerships benefit all involved. Students with motor/orthopedic impairments who have adult role models who talk to them and serve as mentors are much more likely to experience success at school. In addition, their mentors can help teachers gain experience working with special needs students. These volunteers can help students take a serious approach to their studies as an important element in meeting their aspirations.

Providing a Supportive Learning/Social Environment

Problems related to learning conditions for students with motor/orthopedic impairments generally fall into two categories: time and space.

Time:

- The student may work more slowly.
- Assistive technologies may require thinking time in addition to working time.
- Certain combinations of motor tasks may become difficult or impossible.
- The student may tire easily.

Space:

- Abnormal motor patterns may be needed to accomplish a task and may thereby require more space or modifications of the work space.
- Special positioning may be required for certain tasks or activities.

The following measures may help to meet needs resulting from motor/orthopedic impairments:

- Provide more time to complete activities.
- Provide extra hours outside of the regular school day for the student to work in the laboratory.
- Provide partial outlines or data-recording sheets to minimize the time needed for recording data. Use peer support.
- Be knowledgeable of comfortable positioning or physical assistance, and provide assistance when necessary.
- Get to know the student(s) and challenge them to do what they can do on their own.
- Work as a member of a collaborative team (Keller, 2007).

Classroom interactions should model the behaviors we want students to assume when an adult is not monitoring their behavior. Treating others with dignity and respect, providing positive interactions, working cooperatively toward a common goal, helping others succeed, and drawing out the unique contributions of each individual are learned behaviors.

Common social/emotional limitations may include lack of connectedness to other persons or to a social role; needs of autonomy, accomplishment, and identity; and, needs of security, affliction, and intimacy. These limitations may be minimized if the teacher keeps the following guidelines in mind:

- Become aware of the social dynamics of the classroom, and seek ways to help the student gain peer acceptance.
- Reflect on your own modeling and disposition in working with students; it can be a powerful influence in the classroom.
- Be aware of mismatches in selecting peer helpers and cooperative working groups.
- Observe student behaviors that reflect learned helplessness or passivity.
- Be cautious about stereotypical attitudes among colleagues and peers.
- Always be clear that management interventions are directed toward behavior, not the individual.

Oversee the actions of classroom aides to ensure that their role is one that allows for maximum opportunities for student development.

Classroom Accommodations for Students with Motor/Orthopedic Disabilities

Often, classroom accommodations do not require elaborate modifications but merely a few well-planned adaptations, as the following suggestions demonstrate.

- Examine accessibility to materials and movement needs of the student.
- Adapt his/her workstation for minimal physical effort and comfort.
- Provide a supportive peer assistant (preferably someone that has had the class previously) or adult aide.
- Allow extra time for student and peers to continue with activities of choice outside of regular school day or at home.
- If student has limited motor control, consider tools or supports to serve as aids; have students work in groups.
- Provide a computer with software for the student to record observations and responses.
- Ensure that all aisles are at least one meter wide.
- Review work areas for appropriate height and accessibility of supplies and equipment.
- Examine trafficking needs of the student.
- Review classroom environment to ensure the student has appropriate access to peers for socialization and cooperative learning groups.
- Provide accessible means of reviewing drawings, charts, graphs, and/or models.
- Examine testing area for comfort of the student.
- If physical response is difficult, provide an assistive responding device.
- Provide low-force micro-switches for lighting, if appropriate.
- Look for adaptive software, keyboards, special switches, touch screen, and other special equipment.
- Alter size of equipment and provide handles or supports on supplies.
- Be especially careful if the student does not have good tactile sensory receptors. Severe burns can occur from hot water, chemicals, heat sources, etc.
- Plan appropriate breaks(Keller, 2007).

Science Lab

The student with impaired mobility needs to have easy access to equipment including computers, materials, safety devices, and other services such as restrooms, ramps, elevators, telephone, and accessible doors and exits. The student also needs enough aisle space for lateral movement and maneuverability. Positioning a wheelchair parallel to the lab bench and fume hood is generally restrictive, although some students prefer it. Ideally, a workbench should have an opening underneath that allows a student in a wheelchair to be closer to the work surface. A platform could also be used to raise the student to a more compatible height with the bench top.

Every teaching laboratory should have at least one adapted workbench. The basic requirements for a laboratory work station for a student in a wheelchair are listed below.

- Work surface 30 inches from floor
- 29-inch clearance beneath the top to a depth of at least 20 inches and a minimum width of 36 inches to allow leg space for the seated individual
- Utility and equipment controls within easy reach
- Clear aisle width sufficient to maneuver a wheelchair (recommended width is 42 to 48 inches). If the aisles are too narrow, a lab station can be set up at the end of the bench, or a portable station can be designed or purchased.

If the student can transfer from the wheelchair, another alternative is to design a more maneuverable chair for use in the lab only. An adjustable-height wheelchair may include a tray that can be snapped onto the chair's arms to carry equipment such as flasks and crucibles, leaving both hands free to operate the chair.

The science laboratory can be more accessible to students with impaired mobility by making various modifications. First, work with the student to anticipate areas that may be difficult to access. Figure out alternative procedures, using as much student input as possible. Other modifications may include the following:

- Adjust the height of storage units, or provide alternative storage space like a portable lazy Susan or cabinet on casters.

- Provide a chemical resistant laboratory apron and other appropriate coverings for exposed body parts.

- Provide work space for special equipment.

- Supply counter tops for auxiliary use in science labs.

- Lower shelves to lap-board height to hold instruments for students in wheelchairs.

- Provide single-action level controls or blade-type handles rather than knobs.

- Assign a lab partner who can help reach or manipulate objects as needed. Students whose disabilities affect the use of both upper and lower limbs may need a lab partner to perform experiments under the student's direction. The student should be able to observe the data acquisition and direct the experiment.

- Modify built-in lab tables (or use small ramp/platforms or table-type desks) that can be adjusted for various heights of wheelchairs.

- Provide an easy means for recording data, charts, or graphs.

- Use electric hot plates instead of Bunsen burners as heat sources.

- Use nonmanual types of laboratory teaching techniques (electronic probes vs. pipette bulbs) for students with arm/hand impairments.

- Place operating knobs and switches on laboratory hoods for easy access. The portable hoods meet safety standards and are accessible.

- Have accessible water, gas, and electric facilities.

- Increase the size of wheels, dials, handles, and buttons on lab equipment.

- Change the aisle width by relocating desks and/or chairs as needed for wheelchair access.

- Use lab sinks that are accessible from three sides for those who are single-side paralyzed.

- Use low-force electric micro-switches for lights and equipment.

- Use wider/bigger lids on the tops of containers.

- Have a portable eyewash available.

- When information gathering involves a physical action that the student cannot perform, try using a different type of experience that will yield similar information.

- Plan for class/lab times when a student with a mobility impairment may be late for class if breaks between classes are short (10 minutes or less). This way, the student won't miss important aspects of the science activity.

- Explore alternative ways for students who cannot fully use a computer because of physical limitations. Adaptations may include adaptive access software, altered keyboards (including Unicorn keyboards), special latching devices or keylock switchers, Power Pads, eye-controlled input systems, touch-screens with light talkers, trackballs, and footmice.

- Be aware of and prevent overheating for students with poor heat regulation(Keller, 2007).

Field Experience

Discuss and anticipate areas of difficulty with students who have a physical disability so you can work out alternate activities/experiences together for fieldwork or field trips. Many students using a wheelchair will probably need other travel arrangements because they often need to rely on attendants and ramp-adapted vans or power-lift vans for transportation to and from field activities.

In the field, provide assistance, but also provide positive reinforcement when the student shows the ability and willingness to do something unaided.

- Increase size of wheels, dials, handles, and buttons on field equipment.
- Use a peer-buddy system.
- Use wider/bigger lids on the tops of containers(Keller, 2007).

When information gathering involves a physical action that the physically impaired student cannot perform, try a different experience yielding the same information.

Make special advance arrangements with curators for field trips checking to ensure that facilities are accessible to students with disabilities. Ask questions such as the following:

- Are there nearby parking spaces reserved for persons with disabilities?
- Is there a ramp or a step-free entrance?
- Are there accessible restrooms?
- If the site is not on the ground floor, does the building have an elevator?
- Are water fountains and telephones low enough for a student in a wheelchair?

Arrange with curators of museums, science centers, etc., for alternate activities if it is not possible to have the student in a wheelchair do the activities. Ask if objects can be moved or positioned to provide the student with visual or tactile access. Discuss any needs, problems, or alternatives with the student.

Visual Disabilities

People with visual impairment have either low vision or blindness. If they have low vision, they use whatever visual perception they possess to access information. People with blindness are not able to gather information visually. Visual disabilities present at birth, unless they are the result of injury, are referred to as congenital disabilities. Visual impairment that occurs later in life as a result of an accident or injury is called adventitious (Ward, 1986).

Visual disabilities are classified based on two quantifiable parameters: visual acuity and range of peripheral vision. Visual acuity refers to the resolution capability and its variation with viewing distance. Range of peripheral vision refers to the angle within which vision is effective. Legally, people are considered blind if their visual acuity is 20/200 or less or if their range of peripheral vision is 20 degrees or less (Smith & Luckasson, 1995). In general, children are eligible for special services (resource or itinerant teacher) if their measured distance visual acuity is 20/70 or less in the better eye with corrective lenses.

Visual impairments may include an inability to see peripherally, high or low sensitivity to normal light, blind spots in the visual fields, color blindness or an inability to see contrast, or a combination of these problems. With some vision disorders, vision may fluctuate and be affected by fatigue, emotions, or lighting.

Besides having several vision problems, many visually impaired individuals also have more than one disability and may require additional help to meet their needs. For example, for a student with a visual perception problem, the visual image is inaccurately processed by the brain even though an accurate visual image is received. This student may need help from a specialist in learning disabilities or may require expanded staffing for learning needs.

Although there is no established correlation between intelligence or academic potential and visual impairment, persons with such conditions often are less skilled than their nondisabled peers in physical development, academic achievement, and social skills. However, most people with visual impairment want educational activities that help them grow in these areas and lead more independent, autonomous lives.

Another goal is to provide a curriculum that gives visually impaired students the largest number of experiences they can reasonably explore (Gough, 1981). If these experiences are to provide the most benefit, they must be highly varied. However, visual impairments tend to restrain individuals from having this wealth of experiences.

Science can potentially be especially beneficial for improving the cognitive abilities of students with visual impairments. Good science teaching involves the frequent use of manipulatives and the ability to use tactile sensory input in broadening the experience base of students with visual impairments. By including visually impaired students in handling equipment, conducting investigations, and collecting data, teachers are enabling them to draw from a variety of schemata in cognitive processing. This is especially important in the development of abilities to utilize higher order reasoning.

The regular classroom teacher can often help identify vision problems, particularly in cases of gradual vision loss. Physical changes in the student's eyes and face are often indicators of vision loss. Frequent indicators are head tilting, covering one eye, squinting, excessive rubbing or watering of the eyes, and wandering eyes when visual aids are used. Some students may complain of dizziness, headaches, or nausea. Look for students who hold a book close to their eyes or demonstrate coordination problems that might be vision related. In some cases, this may be due to bad habits or clumsiness, but it may often be that a student is "masking" a vision problem for personal reasons (e.g. perceptions on how it may influence social relationships).

Many of the more common vision problems can be corrected with treatment or eyeglasses. For instance, myopia (nearsightedness), hyperopia (farsightedness), and astigmatism (blurred vision caused by an irregular curvature of the refractive surfaces of the eye) are troublesome to learning and often develop during the school years.

Teachers may also help recognize amblyopia (when the two eyes do not work together), strabismus (when the eyes do not focus on the same object due to imbalance of the muscles on the eyeball), and nystagmus (small involuntary movements of the eyeball from side to side). These conditions often produce difficulty in reading because students may lose their place. They may also have trouble with handwriting and difficulty working on a detailed project.

Observant teachers might also recognize early on conditions requiring medical treatment such as cataracts (lens becomes cloudy or opaque), glaucoma (high fluid pressure inside the eye), retinitis pigmentosa (hereditary degeneration of the retina), or optic atrophy (degeneration of the optic nerve). When you even remotely suspect that a student may have a vision problem, try to alert parents, vision screeners, or a school nurse to the need for an appropriate medical examination.

Special Devices Used by Students with Visual Disabilities

Regular classroom teachers need to be aware of vision-aiding devices and their proper operation when working with a student with visual impairment. This will often include consultation with the resource or itinerant teachers, the parents, specialists in orientation and mobility, and others involved in a student's education. Students must be taught to use all of their senses to determine and maintain an awareness of the structure of the environment and how to move safely, efficiently, and independently. The skills and devices will depend upon the individual student's concept development, personal attributes, and limitations.

Science teachers should help prepare the student's Individualized Education Program (IEP) because they know the type of equipment needed for active participation in science classes and labs. The cost of some specialized equipment may be too expensive for some schools or individuals; however, funds are available from some rehabilitation, state, or local education agencies when a device is mandated on a student's IEP.

Optical devices. Optical devices for the individual are usually prescribed by an eye specialist; however, special adaptations are often necessary for visually impaired students in the science laboratory. Glasses with special prescriptions, magnifiers, and small telescopes are common optical aids. In the science laboratory, the science teacher needs to communicate with the orientation and mobility (O&M) specialist for adaptations that will allow the student to be an active participant. For example, a microscope or specialized optical aids could help the student collect data when using equipment in experiments or in outdoor field activities. It is unlikely that the O&M specialist will have a sufficient science background to know when and where optical aids are necessary, which means close collaboration between the science teacher and the O&M specialist. Most microscope suppliers now have adaptive equipment that will allow projection on a monitor, television or screen.

Nonoptical devices. Lamps, bookstands, large-type books, sun visors and other shields, acetate, page markers, and reading windows are important in reducing glare, visual discomfort, and postural fatigue for students with low vision. Adapted measurement tools and bold-line paper, including graph paper, are available to increase the student's level of participation.

Computer related resources. Text to speech software is available from multiple sources, (i.e. JAWS, Kurzweil, WYNN). Voice, internet voice and Braille are can be used as output options on computers. Refreshable Braille displays, Braille embossers, screen enlargers, and closed circuit TV with Zoom capabilities can improve access. There are adapted and large print keyboards available. Screen enlargement and alternative backgrounds can ease the effort required of the learner. Accessible software, (i.e. Digital Frog or Digital Field Trips) is becoming more commonplace.

Devices for enhancing tactile functioning. Braille, braillewriters, raised-line drawing boards, templates, braille and raised-marking measurement tools, and specialized markers that create raised lines or dots are tools especially designed for visually impaired students. The Cubarithm Slate and Crammer Abacus are specially designed devices to facilitate mathematical computation. The Mowat Sensor, Polaron, and Sensory 6 are other specialized devices that provide tactile or auditory feedback about obstacles in the environment. They can be handheld or worn around the head or neck.

Devices for enhancing auditory functioning. Advances in technology, along with discoveries that recordings are commercially feasible, have greatly increased the availability of both learning materials and leisure-reading materials for individuals with visual impairments. Cassette tape recorders with variable speed components allow individuals to adjust the recording to comfortable levels. Science teachers can often obtain materials such as beeper balls and adapted gym equipment for use in science investigations. There are also electronic and computer accessories that can utilize measuring devices with variable auditory output for doing science experiments and research projects.

Electronic devices. Talking calculators, computers, speech synthesizers, and adapted software are available from many sources. The design of access technology for individuals with visual impairments is an ongoing endeavor, and several hardware and software devices can give students access to the computer screen. A speech synthesizer allows the student to hear what is presented on a computer screen via a speaker or earphone. A display processor allows the student to control the size, contrast, and brightness of a computer screen. Refreshable Braille displays provide a small tactile Braille version of what is on the screen. Braille embossers are special printers that produce materials in Braille.

The American Printing House for the Blind maintains an educational research and development program that is concerned with educational procedures and methods and the development of education aids. The American Foundation for the Blind maintains six regional centers across the country and operates a toll-free information hotline.

Teaching Science to Students with Impaired Vision

Many students with severe visual disabilities have mastered science laboratory work. Blind students who have been accommodated in the laboratory testify that the work is not only educational, but enjoyable; for them, the hands-on experience was vital. Some students with impaired vision have completed laboratory sessions, possibly using only a magnifying glass or relying informally on a partner or nearby classmate to read numbers or confirm observations. Other students with impaired vision require more help. The degree of disability determines the policy to be adopted. Computer-interfaced devices are one way to provide an intermediate level of accommodation that allows blind students to work in the laboratory more independently.

Some students who are visually impaired may require a full-time laboratory assistant. In schools that allow or use the lab partner system, the instructor should help the student find a suitable partner. The assistant should not be taking the course simultaneously, but it is useful to have someone who has completed the class previously and knows the equipment and terminology. The science student does the thinking and directs the assistant to give a response. It is helpful for the student to have the opportunity before or during the lab session to feel and visualize how the equipment is set up. The student should be encouraged to be as independent as possible. In some cases, it may be necessary for the assistant to manipulate the equipment. The instructor should confirm that the assistant functions properly. When questions arise, the student with visual impairment should take them up directly with the instructor, not through the assistant, and vice versa.

Blind students negotiate best in familiar surroundings. Even though they may never need to visit remote parts of the laboratory, they should familiarize themselves with the entire setting. A short lab tour with the lab instructor locating sinks, reagent shelves, hoods, safety showers, and other equipment will orient the student and help to determine the best place to work. The student needs to find the exits, learn the bench configurations, memorize the positions of the utilities, and so forth. In this way, the laboratory becomes familiar and comfortable. This orientation session can also be used to explain the safety rules, outline fire drill and other procedures, and to explain what locations in the laboratory pose the greatest potential hazards. Blind students who have guide dogs may decide not to take the dogs into the laboratory. Finding an office or another nearby location may be necessary. Guide dogs are obedient and accustomed to waiting.

Students with partially impaired vision may require no special laboratory assistance at all. However, one lab station may be better than another because the lighting is better. Some students with partial sight may need larger letters on reagent bottles, a magnifying glass to read burettes, or a larger notebook than prescribed for the course. Such requirements can often be met utilizing input from the student. The development of special equipment to facilitate laboratory work for students with impaired vision is a relatively new area of research, but progress is being made rapidly.

Classroom Suggestions Concerning Visual Impairments

- Get to know each student and be sensitive to his or her feelings and wishes. It is generally best to be open and honest about visual disabilities. Other students usually adjust well when they understand the visual limitations of a peer. However, particularly early on, if the student wishes, sensitivity and discretion should be practiced. Introduce the student with a visual disability as you would any other student. Encourage the student to answer questions from adults and other students in a direct and straightforward manner.

- Apply the same general rules in regard to praise and discipline. However, because visual expression is a very common form of praise, special efforts should be directed to give verbal encouragement or a pat on the shoulder.

- Look at traffic patterns and access to materials in the classroom and laboratory. Provide additional work, desk, aisle, and locker space to accommodate movement and special materials.

- If students have adaptive devices, be sure they are using them and that the devices are working properly. Watch for apathetic and dependent behaviors, and work with the students to ensure that they are engaged whenever possible.

- If the student exhibits certain mannerisms that affect peer relationships and interfere with learning in the classroom, work with the student and itinerant teacher in dealing with this behavior.

- Model acceptance, provide encouragement, and maintain high expectations. Workload and time expectations should approximate those of other students in the class.

- Use tactile stimuli, provide printed directions in large print or Braille, adjust light levels, and provide auditory directions with appropriate pacing.

- Work closely with the resource teacher, itinerant teacher, and orientation and mobility specialist to design lessons that will enable the visually impaired student to be active in all activities.

- Don't hesitate to use peer helpers and plan lessons using cooperative learning strategies.

- Encourage independence, and seek out ways the student can reciprocate assistance to others.

Managing Instructional Activities for Students with Visual Impairment

Common areas in which accommodations may be needed, as well as strategies for dealing with each, are presented below.

Deficit: The student requires accommodation for printed class materials.
Strategies:

- Lend any transparencies, notes, and print materials to the resource or itinerant teacher to enlarge, darken, or make into Braille.
- Use a magnetic board and Playschool Magnetic Letters and Numbers for Chemical Elements and Formulas
- Use materials with magnetic backing (like magnetic business cards) to cut out symbols for mathematic operations, electron configuration or different types of chemical bonds. Use on a magnetic board.
- If the student has low vision, work with the student for the best seating placement for visual comfort. If the student is using a prescribed telescopic device, be sensitive to placement and time considerations.
- Assign a classmate to make photocopies of notes and diagrams.
- Speak the notes or transparency text aloud and allow sufficient time for the student to take notes.
- Investigate ways to use an adapted laptop or portable computer.
- Use recordings with earphones when appropriate. Compressed speech devices are also available that will enable the student to progress through the text at a rate approximating silent reading.

Deficit: The student requires accommodation for information presented through visual aids.
Strategies:

- Make tactile or raised line drawings by hand or through thermoforms
- Make tactile illustrations using fabric paint
- When using maps and charts, raised maps or "sound maps" may be used.
- Get charts and maps to the resource or itinerant teacher in advance. It may be possible to enlarge, modify, or simplify the materials so the student can use them.
- Make arrangements with the resource, itinerant teacher, or aide to show a videotape or film to the student in advance or after class to aid the student in learning the visual concepts presented. Make advance arrangements for descriptive video enhancement for multimedia materials used in the classroom.
- Investigate other resources on the same concepts that can allow alternative ways to learn the material.

Deficit: The student requires accommodation for classroom demonstrations.
Strategies:

- Examine the demonstration area to provide maximum visual comfort by reducing glare, using large models, and conducting the demonstration in a location with maximum contrast (e.g. a dark background).
- Allow the student to handle the materials before and/or after the demonstration period. Have the student assist in the demonstration (as an accommodation to the visual limitation rather than as a special privilege) whenever it is reasonable.
- Consider videotaping the demonstration or closed circuit television to provide a means of magnification and/or subsequent review.
- Investigate the availability of audio-taped descriptions of demonstrations and visual presentations.

Deficit: The student requires accommodation in evaluation and testing.
Strategies:

- It is normal for a student with a visual impairment to require additional time to complete tests. Time and a half is a good general rule of thumb. Do not overuse oral testing when there are other options. Visually impaired students need to maintain print and Braille literacy. Often a tape recorder with earphones along with a portable computer will allow the student to take tests independently.
- For low vision students, enlarging the text on a copy machine may help. A yellow acetate filter will often help to provide better contrast when reading.
- Work closely with the resource and itinerant teacher to plan evaluation strategies. When visually impaired students develop adaptive skills, your expectations should approximate those for other students. It is important to instill confidence in their competence.

Deficit: The student requires accommodation in homework.
Strategies:

- When thinking about work outside of class, think in terms of time rather than common assignments. It is unfair to take away an individual's childhood or free time in order to meet the same homework expectations of others who can work more quickly.
- Consider allowances for extra time to repeat laboratory exercises outside of the school day and to review lessons using visual and print materials in class.
- Work with the itinerant or resource teacher on advanced concepts. Many times these individuals have very limited science backgrounds, particularly at higher levels.

- Set aside time for you to work with the student outside of class to help with difficult concepts or unfamiliar vocabulary. In class, use cooperative learning and peer assistance when appropriate.

Deficit: The student requires special accommodations for laboratory and field trip activities.
Strategies:

- Make the work area accessible for the student. Work with the M&O specialist and the resource teacher to help the student become familiar with the instructional materials and laboratory equipment. Investigate equipment adaptations that can be made locally, and place supplies so they are accessible to the student.
- Contact the American Council for the Blind and the American Foundation for the Blind to obtain information about special devices, laboratory equipment, and appliances for individuals with visual impairments. Seek out suppliers of specialized equipment, and examine resources with the student and other specialists.
- Establish a buddy system in which the visually impaired student can work cooperatively with a seeing peer to conduct investigations.
- Make the laboratory accessible before and after class sessions devoted to experiments. A visually impaired student will need some advanced exposure to the materials and the procedures. Normally they will need extra time to carry out the investigations and additional time in the laboratory to review their results.
- Think through your directions and plan out your verbal instructions to ensure they are complete; get print materials to the resource teacher prior to the activity.
- Keep in mind the principle of partial participation when it is impossible to have full involvement because of safety or mobility factors. If the student cannot actually collect samples, plan out strategies to get the materials to the student.

Laboratory Modifications

- Describe and tactually/spatially familiarize the student with the lab and all equipment to be used.
- Use an enlarged activity script, directions, or readings for a low-vision student (or taped script for a student who is blind) for use with tactile 3D models.
- Make all handouts and assignments in the appropriate form for the students: e.g., regular print, large print, Braille, or tape depending on the student's optimal mode of communication.
- Provide assistance when needed for converting certain laboratory materials from a visual to a tactile format.
- Have the student with a vision impairment do a trial run on the equipment before the activity.
- Allow more time for the laboratory activities.
- Always try to keep materials, supplies, and equipment in the same places.
- Use a microprojector or similar device to help the visually impaired student examine images from a microscope.
- Place the student and/or tape recorder an appropriate distance from the activity to permit hearing and/or the recording of results or observations.
- Use an overhead projector or opaque projector to show step-by-step instructions. Mask all the instructions except the one(s) that you want followed for students with vision impairments.
- Use Descriptive Video for videos or laser disks. If Descriptive Video is not available, use a sighted narrator to describe movies, videos, laser disks, or slides.
- Provide means for the acquisition and/or recording of data in an appropriate mode for the student.
- Use tag shapes for showing relationships (such as distance comparisons), buttons, or other markers on a "layout" board.
- Use braille label maker for identifying materials and containers in the laboratory for students with a vision impairment who read Braille.

- Provide accessible equipment that the student with a vision impairment can use to interpret and understand the results of laboratory exercises (e.g., audible readout voltmeters, calculators, talking thermometers, talking compass, magnifiers, etc.).
- Use a hot plate for heating instead of Bunsen burner.
- Label material, supplies, and equipment with regular print, large print, and/or Braille, as appropriate for the vision-impaired student.
- Use chemistry stencils to make foam or magnetic cut outs.
- Pair the student with a visual impairment with a sighted student. Then have the non-impaired student describe the activities and outcomes as they are observed.
- Use a low-vision projection screen to magnify images up to 720X.
- Use a portable communication board to provide auditory scanning of laboratory materials such as pictographic symbols, letters, and/or words.
- When using a computer, have the student with a visual disability use a voice input device or a remote voice system to verbally enter commands.
- Prior to the enrollment of a student with a visual impairment in class, obtain laboratory equipment that has available ability to produce adaptive outputs such as a large screen, print materials, or various audio output devices.
- Use various Braille devices to assist vision-impaired students when reading.
- Consider alternate activities/exercises that can be utilized with less difficulty for the student, but have the same or similar learning objectives(Keller, 2007).

References to such equipment can be located easily on the Internet or through science organizations such as the American Association for the Advancement of Science or the National Science Teachers Association. Examples of equipment now available include:

- Voltmeters and multimeters with audible readout
- Graduated cylinders with floats.
- Talking thermometer
- Light probes (used as part of readout devices; it emits a tone that increases in pitch proportionally to changes in light intensity)
- Liquid-level indicators
- pH meter
- Talking balance
- Spectroscope
- Electronic calculators with Braille printout
- Braille labelers
- Braille rulers and meter sticks
- Braille thermometer
- Laboratory glassware with raised numbers
- Laboratory plastic ware as a substitution for glassware
- Sandpaper labeling for hazardous chemicals
- Spoons with sliding covers
- Electronic calculators with both voice and Braille output
- Microcomputers equipped with interfacing cards to control a variety of instruments

Field Experience Adaptations

- Make all handouts, safety information, and assignments available in an appropriate form (e.g., regular print, large print, tactile Braille, or cassette).
- Provide models that can be used in the field for comparative study with the actual specimen.
- Use a sighted guide.

- Do detailed description and narration of objects seen in science centers, museums, and/or field activities.
- Provide a laser cane or Mowat sensor to assist the student in unfamiliar surroundings.
- Use an enlarged activity script, directions, or readings for descriptions of a field/activity for a low vision student.
- Suggest that the student use a standard tape recorder.
- Consider alternate activities/exercises that can be utilized with less difficulty for the student, but have the same or similar learning objectives (Keller, 2007).

Deaf and Hard of Hearing

Persons with hearing impairments fall into two main categories--those who are hard of hearing and those who are deaf. Individuals who are hard of hearing still have some degree of hearing, which may or may not be enough for them to use auditory information in communication. Deaf persons have no ability to hear. Hard-of-hearing conditions are sometimes labeled as a mild or moderate disability, while the terms severe or profound disability describe the condition of deafness. About .12% of students are identified as hearing impaired.

Another system of classifying hearing impairments describes the hearing loss in decibels. Mild hearing impairment corresponds to a loss of between 26-54 decibels, while moderate, severe, and profound hearing impairments are described as a loss of 55-69, 70-89, and more than 90 decibels, respectively (Mastropieri & Scruggs, 1993). Among the causes of hearing disabilities are the effects of disease, heredity, and exposure to loud sounds.

Deafness is further characterized into pre-lingual or post-lingual deafness, depending upon whether the disability was incurred prior to or after the ability to use speech. Research indicates that as many as 95% of deaf children are pre-lingually deaf (Smith & Luckasson, 1995).

Though there is no relationship between intelligence and hearing disabilities, persons with auditory disabilities do show substantial academic deficits when compared with their hearing peers. Goals of the educational community relate to reducing these performance gaps and improving speech and language skills.

Instructors can typically achieve a good deal of progress in their ability to teach hearing-impaired students by remembering a few simple suggestions. For example, hearing-impaired students cannot usually interpret verbal descriptions given during a demonstration and also pay attention to the demonstration. Thus, the simple change of describing a demonstration and then carrying it out may significantly improve the ability of a student with a hearing impairment to assimilate the content of the demonstration (Vaughn, Bos, & Schumm, 1997).

Hearing impairments are often labeled as one of the "invisible disabilities" because the disability is not apparent by visual observation. However, deafness is in many cases a more severe disability than being blind. In addition to severe problems with language development and academic achievement, a hearing impairment often affects a student's social and personality characteristics. Given the severe communication problems students with hearing impairment have, they often seek out friends with the same disability.

Hearing disability is affected both by the level of hearing impairment and the time of onset of the disability. Individuals who are born deaf or acquire deafness before developing language usually have much more difficulty acquiring spoken language and performing academically. Because communication is so dependent upon auditory stimulation, hearing-impaired students lack inferential stimulation from the onset of the disability. Much of our developmental reasoning is nurtured through sounds we hear, from hearing a door close to making judgments about people on the basis of how they interact orally. In addition, many individuals may have hearing impairments due to cognitive processing difficulties or a limited range of hearing (e.g., an inability to receive or process the frequency range of normal hearing).

As with other disability areas, positive social adjustment has much to do with how others accept the disability. A teacher who models a cheerful, positive, accepting individual with high expectations can greatly influence the socialization of the student with a hearing impairment. The classroom teacher must reflect confidence in the competence of the student in all aspects of performance: physically, academically, emotionally, and socially.

Today about two-thirds of hearing-impaired students are taught by total communication in which the use of sign language is paired with oral techniques. About one-third are taught by oral techniques and learn speech reading and how to effectively use the hearing they do possess. With patience and careful listening, they can understand the majority of the students who are not deaf. Hearing-impaired students who have received the benefits of excellent instruction, particularly those with strong and stable support from home, may exhibit good language and academic skills.

General Accommodations for Students who are Deaf or Hard of Hearing

- Locate student in the classroom seating for direct eye and lip visibility.
- Secure student eye contact before speaking.
- Keep your face and lips visible to the deaf student when speaking.
- Slow your speech and speak clearly.
- Repeat responses of other students, or delay individual responses until the student has good eye contact with the speaker.
- Pre-teach vocabulary and allow student to explore the materials prior to the lesson.
- Provide a supportive peer assistant during the activities.
- Allow extra time for student and peers to engage in activities of choice outside of school day and at home.
- Prepare printed directions in advance and laminate a copy so the direction sheets last longer.
- Have interpreter accessible if desired.
- Review directions with the student.
- Review lighting and background for appropriateness.
- Communicate with the student concerning any interference from background noises.
- Search out adaptive equipment and supplies and make them available to the student (i.e., probe-ware, oscilliscopes, etc.)
- Maximize availability of visual media and/or models.
- Allow for direct manipulation of material when appropriate.
- Clearly label items or equipment.
- Get feedback from student.
- Allow more time.
- Use a handling device "microphone" for any student who speaks during cooperative group activities (Keller, 2007).

Classroom Suggestions

- Get to know the student and be sensitive to the student's feelings and wishes. It is generally best to be open and honest about the hearing disability and adaptations necessary for communication. Other students usually adjust well when they understand the hearing limitations of a peer. However, because speaking is such a continuous process, it may be necessary to remind classmates to interact in ways that include everyone. Particularly early on, be sensitive and discreet if the student wishes. Introduce the student with a hearing disability as you would any other student. Encourage the student to answer questions from adults and other students in a direct and straightforward manner.

- Work with the student on seating location, background, appropriate ways to get attention (e.g., tapping on the shoulder), visual accessibility to other students, and alternative modes of communication if there is limited language development.

- If the student uses an interpreter, work on an arrangement in which the student can see both you and the interpreter.

- Arrange for a note taker. A student cannot speech read or use an interpreter while taking notes or watching a demonstration.

- Draw the student's attention before speaking, face the student when you speak, and keep your face visible and well-lit. Speak clearly and naturally.

- Provide instruction to classmates to model the same behaviors (i.e., face the hearing-impaired student when speaking, keep your head up, keep your hands from your face, speak clearly and naturally with good lip movement). When appropriate, repeat the questions and comments of others in the room. If possible, seat students in a circle or partial circle to enhance visibility. To provide the hearing impaired student with an opportunity to locate the speaker in cooperative groups or during class discussions, require that student who is speaking has a device in hand (i.e. paper towel end roll) before speaking.

- Apply the same general rules in regard to praise and discipline. However, because oral expression is a very common form of praise, special efforts should be directed to give visual encouragement.

- Watch for apathetic and dependent behaviors and observe students to ensure that they are engaged. Be sensitive to fatigue. Students with a hearing impairment must rely on visual input and must process the information. This is often very exhausting, and breaks must be built into the schedule so they can rest.

- If the student has adaptive hearing devices, be sure the student is using them and that they are working properly.

- If the student exhibits certain mannerisms that affect peer relationships and interfere with learning in the classroom, work with the student and itinerant teacher in dealing with this behavior. Assisting in student socialization is an important part of your teaching responsibilities.

- Model acceptance, provide encouragement, and maintain high expectations. Check for comprehension often. Workload and time expectations should approximate those of other students in the class.

- Use visual and tactile stimuli. Provide printed material for directions, assignments, and test schedules. Provide auditory directions with appropriate pacing. Use an overhead and visual aids as much as possible.

- Whenever possible, use captioned films or videos. Investigate the availability of real-time captioning devices or assistive listening devices.

- Work closely with the resource teacher to preview new concepts. Vocabulary in science is particularly difficult because hearing-impaired students lack the experiences and exposure to many science concepts that have been repeated and reinforced for hearing students.

Managing Instructional Activities

Common deficits and strategies for helping students with hearing impairments are presented below.

Deficit: The student requires accommodations for information presented by means of lecture-recitation.
Strategies:

- When possible use a resource teacher or aide to preview the concept with the student.
- Ensure that the background is dark and uncluttered. Wear clothes that contrast with your hand and face color.
- Use a visual or tactile signal to get the student's attention before beginning.
- Face the student directly; make sure the student can see your face. Keep objects and hands away from your face while speaking. Speak clearly and directly.
- When reading, keep the book or paper down and your head up.
- Use visually stimulating learning materials.
- Provide written or pictorial directions.
- Check for comprehension.
- Limit your presentation time and watch for fatigue.

Deficit: The student demonstrates delayed performance in basic skills. Written work appears disorganized or lacks proper construction. Mathematics skills are below those of most students. Reading difficulties are quite pronounced.
Strategies:

- Much of language is reinforced and developed through oral discourse, so developmental delays are to be expected, particularly in the use of prepositions, verb tense, and articles. The hearing impaired student will need special guidance and understanding. Select one or two skills and make corrections, then follow through with additional refinements. Collaborate with the resource teacher and aid to get additional assistance at the student's performance level.
- Mathematics achievement is the strongest overall area for most students with hearing impairments, but it is often below that of most other students. Allow the resource teacher and student to preview mathematics exercises used in experiments and investigations requiring quantitative calculations. Provide a guide to help the student through the process of recording data and carrying out the calculations.
- Science is often a particularly difficult subject because it is very laden with special vocabulary and builds on assumed experiences that many hearing-impaired students do not have. Provide language cards to help in vocabulary: Try to provide a picture or other visual aid that represents new vocabulary terms. Keep folders containing relevant words and concepts to share with a resource teacher or aide to reinforce the material presented through instruction.
- Investigate high-interest, low-vocabulary reading materials that cover the same content and can be substituted for, or augment, the regular text. This includes many trade books.
- Investigate possibilities of having a shortened summary prepared that covers the same information as that presented in the science textbook. At upper levels these can sometimes be prepared by the student or a peer assistant.

Deficit: The student requires accommodation for classroom demonstrations.

Strategies:

- Examine the demonstration area to provide maximum visual comfort by reducing glare, using large models, and conducting the demonstration in a location with maximum contrast (e.g., a dark background).
- Allow the student to handle the materials before and/or after the demonstration period. Consider videotaping the demonstration or using closed circuit television with captioning where the student can review the demonstration.

Deficit: The student requires accommodation in evaluation and testing.
Strategies:

- Investigate performance-based assessment in which the student can demonstrate knowledge and understanding by interacting with science materials.
- Work closely with the resource teacher in planning evaluation strategies. If the student has an interpreter present, spend time with the interpreter to ensure that the latter can sign appropriate information.
- Use illustrations in test construction, and allow the student to share knowledge using illustrations or labeling (e.g. cell parts, plant parts, etc.).
- Set up evaluations using the computer. The computer has become a tremendous tool for including students with hearing impairments.

Deficit: The student requires accommodation in homework.
Strategies: For visually impaired students.

- When thinking about work outside of class, think in terms of time rather than common assignments. It is unfair to take away an individual's childhood or free time in order to meet the same homework expectations of others who can work more quickly.
- Consider allowances for extra time to repeat laboratory exercises outside of the school day and to review lessons using visual and print materials in class.
- Work with the itinerant or resource teacher on advanced concepts. Many times these individuals have very limited science backgrounds, particularly at higher levels.

Laboratory Modifications

Students who are deaf or hard of hearing require few specific physical accommodations in the science laboratory. However, there are important laboratory safety considerations: (a) Use electrical devices or power strips with visual indicators, (b) install visual or sensory alarms, and (c) install an accessible telephone with a telecommunication device for the deaf (TDD). The following are suggestions for maximizing the effectiveness of laboratory experiences for hearing-impaired students.

- Plan lessons using cooperative learning strategies. Encourage student interdependence, and look for ways the student can reciprocate assistance to others. Be sensitive to selecting laboratory partners who will be patient and responsive in communication.
- Avoid seating the student in heavy traffic areas.
- As you demonstrate a procedure or technique, deliberately alternate between speaking (use FM audio trainer for hard of hearing) and manipulating the materials. This allows the student who is hearing impaired to look at one thing at a time.
- If the student does not understand, try repeating; if the student still does not understand, rephrase a thought or use a different word order. Be patient; the interpreter may not have science knowledge. You may need to demonstrate or display apparatus.

- Keep visual pollution on the chalkboard to a minimum. Leave only what you are discussing.
- Write new vocabulary words on the chalkboard before the laboratory experience.
- Make chalkboard notes legible.
- Do not talk while writing on chalkboard.
- Maximize the use of visual media and demonstrations.
- Repeat new vocabulary in different contexts for reinforcement.
- Assign students with hearing impairments to a laboratory station that allows an unobstructed view of the chalkboard and the instructor and/or interpreter.
- Begin explanations with concrete examples, working from the concrete to the abstract.
- Write on the board or on paper any changes in experimental procedures, assignments, exams, due dates, or special events.
- Label equipment and materials to aid in the learning of new vocabulary items.
- Provide concise, step-by-step directions prior to the laboratory activity and preview it with the student, if possible.
- Provide indicator lights for the on/off status of equipment.
- Obtain feedback from your hearing-impaired students at every opportunity as an indicator of the level of understanding.
- Use signaling devices to alert the student to a significant sound in the lab.
- Use an overhead projector to show step-by-step instructions. Mask all the instructions except the one that you want followed next.
- Provide an outline of the lesson/activity/handout to the student in advance, and give your expectations.
- Present only one source of visual information at a time.
- If non-captioned videos or movies are shown, a dim light is needed so that the student who uses an interpreter can see the interpreter's signing.
- Provide or adapt reading materials at appropriate reading levels and provide resource material at these same reading levels.
- Use highly visual materials (e.g., many figures, pictures, diagrams) in reading assignments.
- Consider alternate activities/exercises that can be utilized with less difficulty for the student, but have the same or similar learning objectives (Keller, 2007).

Field Experience Adaptations

- Adapt as many activities as possible to a visual mode.
- Consider alternate activities/exercises that can be utilized with less difficulty for the student, but have the same or similar learning objectives.
- Whenever possible, allow for direct access to and manipulation of materials.
- Use flash cards for clarity in field exercises.
- Use an interpreter.
- Use a "buddy system" and be sure the buddy is alert and sensitive to any dangers relating to auditory stimuli (Keller, 2007).

Learning Disabilities

Definition

Persons described as learning disabled can suffer from one or more of a number of diverse conditions. Cartwright, Cartwright, and Ward (1995) have offered examples including brain injuries, deficiencies in attending behaviors, dyslexia, dyscalculia, and a host of others. These authors report that, as with some other disability categories set out in the IDEA, the definition of learning disability varies between states and between researchers and remains contentious. Common to most definitions of learning disabilities is the idea of a significantly diminished ability to communicate with and understand language in spoken and written forms (Vaughn, Bos, & Schumm, 1997). The disorder is intrinsic to the individual, presumed to be due to a central nervous system dysfunction, and may occur across the life span (National Joint Committee on Learning Disabilities, letter to NJCLD member organization, 1988, p.1). Students with learning disabilities tend to interact with both teacher and other students at a lower rate than their peers. The inability to understand and perform mathematical calculations, speak, write, and read are included in this learning difficulty.

The definition excludes persons whose difficulties are the result of other disabling conditions such as impairments of vision, hearing, and articulation, as well as severe emotional disturbances. Additionally, as Smith (1998) has reported, persons who have significant developmental disabilities, such as mental retardation, are likewise not covered under the definition of learning disability; average or above average intelligence is a requirement for classification as learning disabled. Smith also noted the fact that reading difficulties form the most common manifestation of learning disability, outnumbering mathematical difficulties by about two to one. Males are also more likely than females by a ratio of approximately four to one to experience a learning disability (Vaughn, et al., 1997).

Learning disabilities have become the most frequently reported disability served under the IDEA provisions. The United States Department of Education's National Center for Educational Statistics (2004) indicates that 42.7% of the children diagnosed with a disability have learning disability as their primary disabling condition.

Causes of learning disabilities are varied, and different researchers have reached very different conclusions on this topic. Some cases have readily identifiable causes such as trauma to the brain or disease, while others lack any indication of cause, neurological or otherwise. While individuals with learning disabilities are of average or above average intelligence, the disability creates a gap between ability and performance. Without early and adequate identification and intervention, learning disabilities can lead to serious consequences for individuals and society, including loss of self-esteem, school dropout, juvenile delinquency, illiteracy, and other critical problems.

According to the National Joint Committee on Learning Disabilities (letter to NJCLD member organizations, 1988, p.1), problems in self-regulatory behaviors, social perception, and social interaction may exist with learning disabilities but do not by themselves constitute a learning disability. Although learning disabilities may occur concomitantly with other handicapping conditions (for example, sensory impairment, mental retardation, serious emotional disturbance) or with extrinsic influences (such as cultural differences, insufficient or inappropriate instruction), they are not the result of those conditions or influences.

Learning disabilities typically affect five areas:

1. Spoken language: delays, disorders, and deviations in listening and speaking
2. Written language: difficulties with reading, writing, and spelling
3. Mathematics: difficulty in performing arithmetic operations or in understanding basic concepts
4. Reasoning: difficulty in organizing and integrating thoughts
5. Memory: difficulty in remembering information and instructions

The following are types of specific learning disabilities and their characteristics (Fogarty, 2000):

Memory disorder: An inability to store and retrieve upon demand previous experiences, sensations, and perceptions when the original stimulus is no longer present (referred to as "imagery" or "recall"); may not be able to remember stimuli heard (auditory memory) or stimuli seen (visual memory).

Characteristics:

- Has difficulty remembering directions or explanations.
- Has difficulty remembering names of objects, people, or places.
- Has difficulty remembering faces.
- Has difficulty remembering the rules of the game.
- Doesn't remember common works taught; may have immature speaking vocabulary and/or poor sight vocabulary in reading.
- Has difficulty remembering math facts; counts on fingers to solve basic math problems.
- Doesn't remember the details or ideas of a story heard or read.
- Doesn't remember the spelling of common irregular words; attempts to spell phonetically (e.g., "sez" for "says").

Sequential processing disorder: An inability to remember or organize a series in its proper order.

Characteristics:

- Has difficulty following more than one direction.
- Has difficulty learning the days of the week or months of the year.
- Has difficulty learning the alphabet in sequence.
- Has difficulty learning phone number and address.
- Confuses the order of letters in words in reading or spelling ("was" for "saw").
- Omits or adds letters to words when reading.
- Omits or adds words to sentences when reading or spelling.
- Learns isolated sounds but has difficulty blending them to read words.
- Transposes the order of numbers; writes "13" for "31."
- Has difficulty telling a story in sequence.
- Has difficulty writing ideas in an organized sequence.
- Often has difficulty with language syntax (understanding or expressing the rules of word order).

Auditory perception or auditory processing disorder: An inability to identify, understand, organize, and/or interpret stimuli received from the auditory sense.

Characteristics:

- Has difficulty understanding or following directions.
- Has difficulty understanding instructions orally in class; may become distracted during teacher's lectures.
- Has poor word attack skills; difficulty blending sounds; often reads by guessing at word from first letter (e.g., "best" for "bed").
- Has difficulty spelling words phonetically but may be able to spell common sight words (e.g., difficulty spelling "plant" but can spell "the").
- Often has language problems (see characteristics of receptive and expressive language disorders).
- Often has sequencing problems (see characteristics of sequential processing deficit).

Receptive language disorder: An inability to understand the spoken word.

Characteristics:

- Has difficulty understanding the meaning of common words; poor vocabulary development.

- Has difficulty discriminating parts of words such as plurals, suffixes; doesn't realize the meaning changes with these word units.
- Often understands the meaning of single words but has difficulty understanding sentences.
- May understand a word in one context but not another (e.g., may understand "palm" as part of a hand but not as a tree).
- Often responds inappropriately to questions.
- Has difficulty understanding and following directions or instructions.
- Does not enjoy hearing stories but prefers looking at pictures in books.
- Doesn't understand jokes or puns.
- Often has difficulty understanding abstract concepts, inferences, subtleties; remains concrete and literal.
- Often has difficulty with reading comprehension.

Expressive language disorder: An inability to communicate verbally with others.

Characteristics:

- May be very quiet; offers minimal conversation or speaks in short phrases rather than complete sentences.
- Often becomes frustrated when trying to communicate with others.
- Spoken vocabulary seems immature.
- Has difficulty finding the correct word to express an idea; may substitute words such as "thing" or "stuff"; may describe words.
- Often uses words incorrectly.
- Jumbles word order when speaking.
- Has difficulty stating ideas in an organized way; difficulty organizing words appropriately to ask a question; may begin speaking in the middle of an idea.

Visual perception or visual processing disorder: An inability to identify, understand, organize, and/or interpret stimuli from the visual sense.

Characteristics:

- Often has difficulty with spatial relationships; confused by concepts of up-down, over-under, top-bottom, etc.
- Has difficulty perceiving geometric shapes.
- Rotates or reverses letters or numbers when reading or writing such as "b" for "d," "n" for "u," "6" for "9".
- Loses place on a page when reading.
- Has difficulty with left-to-right orientation when reading or writing.
- Often reads without expression or ignores punctuation because written symbols are not meaningful.
- Has difficulty understanding concepts shown in pictures.
- Has difficulty associating letter name or sound to the visual symbol.
- Has difficulty understanding maps, graphs, etc.
- Math is often weak because of the spatial concepts and written symbols involved.
- Often can't perform math operations in written symbolic form but can verbally explain math concepts.

Visual-motor integration dysfunction: Uncoordinated movements of the eye and hand in which the eye inaccurately guides the hand when completing tasks.

Characteristics:

- Slow to complete written work.
- Copies geometric shapes incorrectly.
- Copies material (letters, numbers, words, etc.) incorrectly; omits, adds, reverses letters, numbers, words.
- Has difficulty copying from the board.
- Has difficulty maintaining straight columns to solve math calculations.
- Has poor handwriting; doesn't form letters correctly; poor spacing, writes above or below lines.
- Often writes very small or very large.

Simultaneous processing disorder: An inability to integrate stimuli in order to recognize a gestalt (whole).

Characteristics:

- Has difficulty with spatial relationships; has difficulty perceiving geometric shapes.
- Has difficulty understanding a picture if part is missing; may not recognize as shape, letter, number, etc., if all lines are not connected.
- Has difficulty remembering faces.
- Often has difficulty with matching activities; copying designs; working puzzles.
- Has difficulty deriving meaning from pictures.
- Has difficulty learning the shapes of letters, numbers, or words.
- Has difficulty understanding the main ideas of stories.
- Often has difficulty developing a sight vocabulary, learning words that don't fit a phonetic pattern.
- Doesn't read in meaningful phrases.
- Has difficulty with place value in math.
- Has difficulty with simple addition/subtraction tasks.
- Has difficulty with complex math concepts.

Disorder of written language: Inability to communicate through written form.

Characteristics:

- Written vocabulary seems immature; uses small, concrete words.
- Does not write with complete sentences.
- Has difficulty writing an organized, integrated story; story doesn't have an introduction or ending; doesn't write in paragraphs; ideas don't connect.
- Writing is unreadable due to gross spelling errors.
- Uses words incorrectly in writing; doesn't apply grammar rules.
- Doesn't use capitals or punctuation with writing.

Abstract thinking deficit: An inability to deal with words and ideas that have no concrete determinants, ideas that can't be known directly through the senses.

Characteristics:

- Has trouble seeing similarities and differences and relationships.

- Has difficulty understanding cause-effect relationships.
- Has difficulty classifying or categorizing.

Attention deficit disorder: Inability to attend to tasks for any length of time; susceptible to distractions. Some people with ADD are quite under active, and their problem may go unnoticed. Others are hyperactive and fall under the ADHD category (Attention Deficit Hyperactivity Disorder). They are restless and fidgety with excessive movements that appear aimless.

Characteristics:

- Is easily distracted.
- Has difficulty concentrating.
- Has short attention span, especially with low-interest activities.
- Is impulsive.
- Frequently interrupts.
- Has enthusiastic beginnings, but poor endings, due to inability to remain focused on tasks.
- Has low tolerance for frustration and stress.
- Frequently offers inappropriate responses.
- Is disorganized.
- Spends excessive amount of time at tasks due to inefficiencies and/or poor organizational and/or time management skills.
- Exhibits poor listening skills.
- Has difficulty following complex directions.
- Is overwhelmed by too much noise or too much visual distraction.
- Shows deficits in social skills.
- Is forgetful.
- Has difficulty generalizing ideas and experiences; each experience is an isolated event; doesn't transfer learning from one lesson to another; concepts need to be relearned for each new situation.
- Has difficulty summarizing.
- Often has difficulty with mathematical reasoning; may memorize facts or processes but not understand math concepts or accurately apply concepts.

Classroom Accommodations

The learning disabled student often has a number of limitations that require accommodations in learning materials, time, support, strategies, and methods. Good science is by its nature rigorous, and the trauma for learning disabled students of repeated failure often results in uncontrollable withdrawal. Learning disabled students often come to believe that their fate is unrelated to their behavior. Even when students are subsequently placed in a situation where their responses might be instrumental in providing a successful learning experience, they nevertheless cannot perceive the possibility of gaining control due to their past history (Gentile & Monaco, 1988). This ensuing lack of educational preparation results in dumping able individuals with learning disabilities into a world where they cannot be successful in science classes and into occupations not commensurate with their talents, abilities, or interests.

In a majority of situations, the reactions teachers get from a student with learning disabilities is a result of alienation that occurred during the student's beginning school experiences. One type of learning disabled student in science is described as a dropout who is not identified because the student keeps coming to class. However, the student's presence is only physical, and it seems that it is impossible to motivate or engage the student into actively participating in the learning process. Our challenge as educators is not only to improve teaching, but to put into place mechanisms that elicit participation and responsibility on the part of all students.

New technologies now offer a wider range of products to help struggling students particularly those with deficits in basic skill areas. Word processing programs have spell check, grammar check and writing aids built into the programs. There are concept mapping, outlining and word prediction programs to help students who are struggling with challenging concepts. Text to speech and speech recognition software programs are available. Computers can be used to provide students with a common layout, screen readers that can remove distracting graphics, and test taking aids. Screen enlargement and alternative backgrounds can ease the effort required of the learner.

Clear expectations are critical, beginning with the teacher's first contact with students with learning disabilities. Students need to know the structures that define behavior in the classroom, and they must develop a sense of acceptance and belonging.

Students with learning disabilities often need to have a very specific understanding of what they should be doing. If expectations are vague, it is only natural that they will test the limits to find where the boundaries are. If limits are undefined or variable, the teacher can expect to be tested throughout the year. Wright (1993), in a study of effective teacher practices with inclusion, found practiced routines and relatively fixed schedules were manifested through modeling and teacher action.

Unconditional acceptance, including the right of every individual to be treated with dignity and respect, is an essential area of imprinting. On the first day of school students must be told, "You are going to be successful in this class. I will make accommodations to help you succeed. I am willing to get to know you as a person. I will provide appropriate opportunities for you, but to learn, you must accept responsibilities. We must be able to communicate in order to determine an appropriate program. Trust me."

These are easy words to say, but to establish credibility, actions must consistently support this position. Trust takes time, and the effective teacher must be willing to devote the personal time in order to establish a sense of trust and confidence from the students. Students with learning disabilities often feel out of place and often must deal with severe learning problems on their own outside of the classroom. These problems can often be overwhelming for a student, leaving little energy and desire to focus on the rigorous tasks associated with school.

The following are general accommodations that can assist the learning disabled student to stay focused and on task.

- Eliminate distractions.
- Review directions in advance.
- Give undivided attention to the student.
- Allow for signaled response.
- Don't pretend to understand if you do not.
- Focus on what the students says, not how well it is said.
- Listen patiently.
- Allow more time.
- Review lighting and background for appropriateness.
- Eliminate background noises.
- Maximize availability of visual media and/or models.
- Clearly label items or equipment.
- Allow for direct manipulation of material when appropriate.
- Get feedback from student.
- Provide a reader when appropriate.

- For students with perceptual problems, avoid computer answer sheets.
- Allow alternative response modes (e.g. circles or dictation).
- Consider pacing (Keller, 2007).

Laboratory and Field Experience Modifications

The modifications below deal with specific ways that laboratory and field experiences can be improved for learning-disabled students.

- Clearly label equipment, tools, and materials. Color-code them for enhanced visual recognition.
- Provide clear photocopies of your notes and overhead transparencies.
- Make cue cards or labels that tell the steps of a procedure to expedite student understanding.
- Use an overhead projector with an outline of the lesson or unit of the day.
- Plan for extended work time in the laboratory.
- Allow extended time for responses and the preparation and delivery of reports.
- In dealing with abstract concepts, use visual tools such as charts and graphs. Also, paraphrase and present concepts in specific terms, and sequence and illustrate them with concrete examples, personal experiences, or hands-on exercises.
- To minimize student anxiety, provide an individual orientation to the laboratory and equipment; give extra practice with tasks and equipment.
- Find areas of strength in the student's lab experiences; emphasize those strengths as much as possible.
- Allow students with learning disabilities the use of computers and spell-checking programs on assignments. Consider alternate activities/exercises that can be done with less difficulty for the student, but have the same or similar learning objectives (Keller, 2007).

Attention Deficit Hyperactivity Disorder

Attention deficit hyperactivity disorder (ADHD) is one of the most controversial categories of disabilities included in the IDEA. There is difficulty in definition, diagnosis, and treatment. Smith (1998) reports that from 10 to 20% of school-age children have some type of learning disability that can be related to an attention deficit problem. Other authors reported that smaller numbers of children can actually be diagnosed as suffering from the defined disability ADHD (Vaughn et al., 1997).

Many authors agree that among the key ingredients in diagnosing ADHD are heightened levels of inattention, characterized by a failure to correct mistakes of a casual nature; avoiding tasks that require concentration; and a susceptibility to distractions of various types. Additional requirements for diagnosis include hyperactive behaviors such as a propensity for fidgeting, difficulty in quiet play and activities, and excessive talking. Impulsivity is also common in many definitions and is usually described as typically impulsive behaviors such as blurting out answers in class and interrupting games or conversations.

Several distinctions between males and females have been pointed out by Vaughn, et al. (1997). They state that the disorder occurs approximately three times as often in males as in females and that males with ADHD typically exhibit symptoms that can roughly be described as hyperactive, whereas many females diagnosed with ADHD seem to be more withdrawn than is the norm. Barkly (1990) said that the affliction affects males in a rate of 6:1 in diagnosed cases and indicated that as many as 33% of males could be diagnosed as ADHD (p. 66).

Not all authors agree that ADHD is a real disorder, or at least that, in some cases, the label is undeserved and that other causes and circumstances may be responsible for students' behavior. A recent study concluded that the differing positions on the causes of ADHD can be grouped into two main categories. One is based on a medical model and the other on a behavioral model. The medical perspective supposes that the root cause is neurological in nature. The most common treatment is the use of prescription drugs containing methylphenedate, the most popular medical source being Ritalin. The growth of prescriptions increased 600% from 1990-95, with continued increases estimated at doubling every 4 to 7 years (Drug & Chemical Evaluation Section, 1995).

The other position states that ADHD symptoms are exhibited because of social conditions, such as the social environment found at schools, and that the disorder is essentially "constructed" (Davison, 2001). Several assessment instruments are commonly completed by parents, teachers, and/or other school personnel who interact with the child daily. These include: Connors' Parent & Teacher Rating Scales (Connors, 1989), Attention Deficit Disorders Evaluation Scale (Ullman, Seston, & Spragg, 1991), and the Children's Attribute and Adjustment Survey (Lambert, Hartsough, & Sandoval, 1990). Armstrong (1996) suggests that relying on subjective judgments by teachers and parents who have an emotional investment in the outcome may be one contributing factor in this increased ADHD diagnosis. It is apparent that the perceptions of those individuals completing the questionnaires have a definitive influence on whether the child will be labeled, and likely medicated, for the disorder.

Those who attempt to find educational strategies to help persons diagnosed with ADHD generally agree that more structured educational methods are best, such as the use of organizational aids and the construction of educational activities that are within the attention span of the student.

Classroom Accommodations

Classroom accommodations for students with ADHD are similar to those for students with learning disabilities.

- Eliminate distractions.
- Review medications and the effect on the student; consider this in planning any testing schedule.
- Be straightforward.
- Allow for time-out if a student needs it.
- Review directions in advance.
- Give undivided attention to the student.
- Allow for signaled response.
- Don't pretend to understand if you do not.
- Focus on what the student says, not how well it is said.
- Listen patiently.
- Allow more time.
- Review lighting and background for appropriateness.
- Eliminate background noises.
- Maximize availability of visual media and/or models.
- Clearly label items or equipment.
- Allow for direct manipulation of material when appropriate.
- Get feedback from student.
- Provide a reader when appropriate.
- For students with perceptual problems, avoid computer answer sheets.
- Allow alternative response modes (e.g. circles or dictation).
- Reflect on the pace of instruction (Keller, 2007).

Laboratory and Field Experience Modifications

- Establish and maintain consistent routines and consistent expectations.
- Gradually reduce the amount of assistance, but keep in mind that these students will need more help for a longer period of time than students without a disability.
- Use a daily assignment notebook as necessary, and make sure each student correctly writes down all assignments. If a student is not capable of this, provide assistance.
- When appropriate, provide a list of printed instructions in a sequential format. Keep instructions as simple and straightforward as possible.
- ADHD students may need both verbal and visual directions. You can do this by providing a visual model and a verbal description of what the student should be doing.
- You can give an ADHD student confidence by starting each lab assignment with a few questions or activities you know the student can successfully accomplish.
- To help with changes in assignments, provide clear and consistent transitions between activities and notify the student with ADHD a few minutes before changing activities.
- Make sure all students comprehend the instructions before beginning their tasks (the ADHD student will probably need extra assistance).
- Simplify complex directions. Avoid multiple commands.
- Help the students feel comfortable about seeking assistance (most students with ADHD will not ask for help).
- Assign only one task at a time.
- Modify assignments as needed for the ADHD student.
- Keep in mind that students with ADHD are easily frustrated and they need assurance of things that are common in science, e.g., when an experiment does not turn out as expected. Stress, pressure, and fatigue can help reduce their self-control and can lead to poor behavior.
- Consider using alternative activities/exercises that are less difficult for the student, but have the same or similar learning objectives (Keller, 2007).

Developmental Delays

Developmental disability, also referred to as mental retardation, includes a wide distribution of impairments, which hampers a precise definition. Cartwright, et al. (1995) report that in a review of such definitions published in 1978, over 30 distinct definitions were found. One of the difficulties associated with the imprecise definition results from the fact that it is extremely rare to find an individual with developmental disabilities who exhibits all of the descriptors in the definitions (Wood, 1998). In spite of the variability, several authors (Bullock, 1992; Cartwright et al., 1995; Smith, 1998) have referred to a significant negative impact on the general intellectual function, inappropriate behaviors relating to adaptation, and diagnosis before age 18 (often referred to as the developmental period).

Another variable used in the definition of developmental disability is the IQ score. A popular cutoff point is a score of less than about 70 to 75. Below this level, persons are often labeled as mentally retarded or developmentally delayed (Bullock, 1992). Bullock and Smith (1998) have both presented statistics that conclude that this cutoff indicated that 1 to 3% of the population is included under this definition of developmental disability.

A distinction cited by Geiger and Ringlaben (1992) concerns the causes of the disorder. Bullock (1992) states that two categories can be established: organic mental retardation and environmental/familial retardation. The former term is used to describe cases in which impacts to the brain, caused for example by genetic or chromosomal defects, infections, traumas, and other factors, can be identified as a causal agent. Environmental/familial mental retardation is used in descriptions when no such cause or causes can be identified. The mechanism in environmental/familial causes is debated, according to Bullock, essentially in terms of whether the mechanism is hereditary or due to environmental causes.

Although the actual percentage of students identified as mentally retarded is about 1.14%, a much larger percentage of the student population has difficulty learning science. Murnane and Raizen (1988) and Polloway and Patton (1997) have reported that science in elementary and secondary schools is taught largely through the use of textbooks by both regular and special education teachers. They also report that the number of words read by students with mild disabilities is half or fewer than the words read by normally achieving students. Cawley (1994) reported that a slow reading rate has a tremendous effect on mastery of material in the classroom, thus denying students with disabilities access to the content and processes of science, and denying them opportunities to demonstrate knowledge and process competencies in evaluation.

Persons with developmental disabilities display a wide range of abilities. Those with mild impacts may function well in independent settings, whereas those who are more severely affected require robust and continuing assistance with many or all life skills.

Classroom Accommodations

Special education teachers utilize a number of adaptive information-processing and mnemonic techniques (Mastropieri & Scruggs, 1994), adaptive instructional strategies (Woodward, 1994), and adaptive strategies for textbook modification (Lovitt & Horton, 1994). The majority of these are unfamiliar to science teachers. It is also unlikely that general classroom teachers, especially those at the secondary level, will employ these strategies without regular collaboration.

A common response received in workshops designed to train secondary teachers in the various methods of adapting textbook materials is, "I can see that it would really help my students, particularly the slow ones, if I modified certain of their materials, but when will I find the time to do it?" Admittedly, this is a troublesome issue. Exercises in textbook modification and lesson adjustment are important assignments for methods course students.

The following are six applications for modifying materials cited by Lovitt and Horton (1994, p. 115):

- Modify only textbook chapters or passages within chapters that have proven to be difficult for students or that clearly lack organization.

- Collaborate and work as a team to modify a textbook chapter. This can simulate how a teacher can work with other teachers to reduce the overall workload associated with adaptive instruction by dividing the modification load and sharing materials.

- As part of associated field experiences, have students use curriculum-based assessments prior to instruction to determine which students can interact with the text at an independent level and which students will need material modified.

- Include a class exercise in which methods students computerize the materials adaptation process by using commercial software, thereby developing a continuous store of materials.

- Coordinate methods courses to allow students to co-teach a science lesson and to modify the materials cooperatively.

- Examine science textbook series and review the total program. Have students look for study guides, graphic organizers, vocabulary exercises, computer programs, or other adaptations of material in addition to basic textbooks and supplementary materials.

Other classroom modifications for students with a developmental disability could include the following:

- Meet with the student and/or aide to discuss accommodations in private prior to each learning sequence.
- Preteach laboratory whenever possible.
- Review directions in advance.
- Provide a reader if necessary.
- Examine vocabulary in advance and consider options.
- Review lighting and background for appropriateness.
- Eliminate background noises.
- Maximize availability of visual media and/or models.
- Allow for direct manipulation of material when appropriate.
- Get feedback from student.
- Allow more time.

Behavioral Disorders

Smith (1998) implies that behavioral disorders, like ADHD, are very problematic to define. One of the aspects of behavioral disorders that makes their definition difficult is the fact that nonbehavior-disordered children often exhibit inappropriate behavior and that children who have been officially diagnosed as behavior-disordered often behave in quite reasonable, normal ways (Cartwright et al., 1995).

Schemes for categorizing the actions of students with behavioral disorders usually define two main types of aberrant behavior: externalizing behaviors and internalizing behaviors. Externalizing might be most readily understood in terms of behaviors such as hostility toward other students and toward instructors, physical aggression against other persons, and obscene gestures. The second main category, internalizing behavior, is typified by such affects as excessive shyness and more extreme forms of behavior such as anorexia and bulimia (Smith, 1998).

Bullock's (1992) more general definition describes behaviors that consistently do not meet the expectation of societal norms. While providing this description, Bullock points out that many students who are eventually diagnosed as having behavioral disorders are first referred to professionals for evaluation because of a perceived academic deficiency. However, Stiker (1997) believes teachers must understand that acts of resistance must be understood as cries of affirmation, belonging and support, not as acts of deviance, malice, or laziness. The development of a sense of self is a process arising from interactions with others. Sandstrom, Martin, and Fine (2001) report that individuals understand themselves through their continued engagement reacting and responding to their world. Within their world acts of resistance played a central role in social interactions and their ability to develop self-efficacy. When understood in this way, educators must create a classroom where the discourse of difference positions the students and their unique traits as positive, valued, and respected.

Approaches for educational intervention are many times categorized in the same way that Cartwright et al. (1995) have suggested. These authors recognize three basic approaches. The first, behavioral modification technique, stresses the "unlearning" of inappropriate behaviors by techniques such as positive reinforcement. A second approach is to use psychodynamic methods not dissimilar to those used in the psychoanalysis of patients. Lastly, some place hope on social, or ecological, approaches in which educators and other professionals look at the maladapted behaviors in the context in which they occur and seek environmental changes to facilitate improvement in the student's behavior.

Classroom Accommodations

Many of the following adaptations have been presented previously for students with ADHD and for those with learning disabilities.

- Discuss appropriate accommodations privately in advance.
- Provide a cooperatively determined "time-out location" where the student can go to after a signaled response from the teacher.
- Review directions in advance.
- Give undivided attention to the student.
- Allow for signaled response.
- Don't pretend to understand if you do not. Focus on what is said, not how well it is said.
- Allow for computer or written response.
- Listen patiently.
- Allow more time.
- Don't confront a confrontational child in public if possible to avoid.
- Whenever possible, allow a "cooling off" alternative.

Laboratory and Field Experience Modifications

- Establish and maintain consistent routines and consistent expectations.
- If unstructured activities must occur, clearly distinguish them from structured activities in terms of time, place, and expectations.
- Be sensitive when making team pairings for activities so that the student with an emotional disorder is supported.
- Use a wide variety of instructional equipment that can be displayed for the students to look at and handle.
- When an interest in a particular piece of equipment has been kindled, talk to the student about it and show him or her how to use it.
- Make activity instructions simple but structured.
- Monitor carefully to ensure that students without disabilities do not dominate the activity or detract in any way from the successful performance of the student with a behavioral disorder.
- Make special efforts to get students with behavioral disorders to interact in laboratory activities.
- If a student must be denied permission to use the equipment, do so on an impersonal basis so the student will not feel hurt or discriminated against.
- Plan for successful participation in the laboratory activities for students with behavioral disorders. Success is extremely important to them.
- To ensure success, consider the special needs and interests of each person; give friendly, patient instruction in the laboratory skills; and continually encourage a wider interest in activities.
- When a student reacts with dislike to the activities, allow a time-out option. Address the problem privately with the student. Avoiding an activity often stems from fear of the experience or factors inherent within the situation itself.
- Keep in mind that some students with behavioral disorders may go to great lengths to avoid class participation. Feigning their disorder is the method most frequently used, in hope of being excused from participation.
- Consider alternate activities/exercises that are less difficult for the student, but have the same or similar learning objectives (Keller, 2007).

Speech and Language Disabilities

Communication is basic to our lives; without it we do not fare well either psychologically or academically. Vaughn et al. (1997) stated that communication is necessary for the proper development of social relationships of all kinds and for the most basic of our actions, such as expressing our personal needs and desires. These authors have reported that approximately 7-10% of school-age children have some type of speech and/or language disorder, including mild disabilities, that affects their communication, while 2-3% of students with disabilities have speech and/or language difficulties as their primary disabling condition. Other authors have cited the IDEA as enumerating approximately one million school-age children who exhibit speech and language disorders; this accounts for about 2% of the total population of children and slightly more than 20% of students with disabilities. This does not include children who have speech/language problems secondary to other conditions, such as deafness (Cartwright et al., 1995).

Most authors categorize speech and language disabilities along fairly similar lines. In terms of speech, the disability can affect the qualities of the voice, the student's ability to articulate sounds, and the degree of fluency (Mastropieri & Scruggs, 1993). Examples of these types of problems include total absence of voice; disorders in pitch and resonance such as difficulties in pronunciation and inappropriate additions, substitutions, and distortions; and speech difficulties like stuttering (Bullock, 1992). Language disability relates more strongly to problems in the understanding and proper use of the structures of language such as sentence components and the more general understanding, sometimes referred to as semantics.

A language disorder is an impairment in the ability to understand and/or use words in context, both verbally and nonverbally. Some characteristics of language disorders include improper use of words and their meanings, inability to express ideas, inappropriate grammatical patterns, and reduced vocabulary and inability to express ideas or to follow directions. One or a combination of these characteristics may occur in children affected by language learning disabilities or developmental language delay. Children may hear or see a word but not be able to understand its meaning. They may have trouble getting others to understand what they are trying to communicate.

Speech disorders refer to difficulties producing speech sounds or problems with voice quality. They might be characterized by an interruption in the flow or rhythm of speech, such as stuttering, which is called dysfluency. Speech disorders may be problems with the way sounds are formed, called articulation or phonological disorders, or they may be difficulties with the pitch, volume, or quality of the voice. There may be a combination of several problems. People with speech disorders have trouble using some speech sounds. Listeners may have trouble understanding what someone with a speech disorder is trying to say. People with voice disorders may have trouble with the way their voices sound.

Causes of speech and language disorders are highly varied. They include problems in the structure of the organs used for the production of spoken language, such as problems related to cleft lips and palettes or their improper repairs, as well as brain damage due to disease or injury. Males are approximately four times as likely to experience such disabilities (Cartwright et al., 1995). The authors pointed out that important considerations from an educational standpoint include involving speech and language therapists and providing a low-stress environment for students with speech and language disabilities to practice their skills. Wood (1998) reminds educators that students at all ages are bothered by abnormalities in their speech patterns and that instructors should keep this in mind in designing situations for students with speech and language disabilities.

Classroom Accommodations

- Work with the speech language pathologist and the student to discuss appropriate strategies.
- Allow the student to meet in private before or after school about assignments.
- Discuss appropriate teaching interventions with the student in advance.
- Use computers with visual output.
- Use electronic mail.
- Investigate speech synthesis options.
- Consider Internet-accessible services/resources as alternative learning options.
- Review directions in advance.
- Give undivided attention to the student.
- Allow for signaled response.
- Don't pretend to understand if you do not.
- Focus on what is said, not how well it is said.
- Allow for computer or written responses.
- Listen patiently.
- Allow more time.

Laboratory Adaptations

- When possible, allow the student to use a technical output device (e.g., laptop computer).
- Be a good listener.
- Preplan for accepting laboratory partners.
- Allow more time for the student to complete activities.
- Anticipate areas of difficulty in access and involve the student in doing the same. Together, work out alternate procedures while trying not to disengage the student from the activity.
- Place the student within a reasonable distance from the instructor, so the instructor can meet his or her needs.
- If appropriate, provide assistance, but also provide support when the student shows the ability to do things unaided.
- Consider alternate activities/exercises with less difficulty for the student, but with the same or similar learning objectives.

Field Experience Modifications

- Discuss with students any needs, problems, or alternatives they anticipate in the field learning environment.
- Make special advance arrangements with curators during field trips to museums, etc.
- When information gathering involves a communication action that the impaired student cannot perform, try a different experience yielding the same information.
- In the field, provide assistance, but also provide support when the student shows the ability to do something unaided.

Autism

Autism is the fastest growing developmental disability with a 10-17% annual growth. It is perhaps the least understood disability category. The abnormality is reflected in 1 in 166 births and affects 1-1.5 million Americans (Autism Society of America, 2006). As recognized under the IDEA, diagnosis includes the demonstration of a persistent pattern of isolation that begins before the age of 3 years. This early onset of social and other difficulties is a main feature of the disorder diagnosis. Though the cause of autism is still a matter of contention, most now agree that the disorder is neurological and not the result of inappropriate experiences in early childhood, such as parental neglect, which was the original suspicion. The disorder is essentially characterized by various serious developmental and behavioral symptoms and occurs approximately four times as often in boys than girls (Simpson, 1992). The most prevalent symptoms are difficulty communicating and forming social relationships. Another common manifestation is the presence of self-stimulatory behaviors such as rocking the body or repetitive manipulation of objects. Persons may exhibit a wide variety of inappropriate behaviors ranging from tactile defensiveness, a reluctance to engage in exploration, to hyperactivity and, possibly, self-injury. In addition to noncommunicative behaviors with others, many persons with autism engage in abnormal behaviors with respect to objects. Many times these behaviors seem to relate to fixations.

Individuals with autism often seem to benefit from a sense of "sameness" in their physical environment. For example, some autistic children may refuse to enter a room unless the arrangement of furniture is maintained. This type of increased structure and reduced stimulation along with traditional forms of behavior management form one of the most commonly adopted formats for educational efforts. It is important to note that as many as 50% of persons with autism are not considered likely to develop functional communication skills (Smith, 1998).

Classroom Accommodations

- Provide an area and opportunity for quiet.
- Establish a walking area to allow physical release in a quiet and safe place.
- Provide consistent structure and organization.
- Label areas for specific activities and consider color coding as a means of categorization.
- Establish a seating arrangement in cooperation with the student; maintain consistency.
- Provide digital rather than face clocks whenever possible.
- Provide a physical outlet such as a "squeeze ball" to enable a longer seating period for the student.
- Establish consistent and clear routines.
- Work with guardians to establish consistency between school and home.
- Think ahead about fire drills, tornado drills, etc. Plan a consistent routine for the student and a peer helper.
- Alert substitute teachers in advance; whenever possible, another adult familiar with the child should be in the classroom to help.
- Establish consistency and some form of advanced organizer to help the student become attentive to transitions, e.g., cues, signal, music, lights.
- Use multimodality instructional processes whenever possible: physical movement, role-playing, manipulatives, art, puppetry, pictures, tactiles, etc.

Deaf/Blind Disability

Individuals who simultaneously fall under the legal descriptions to determine both deafness and blindness are under a separate IDEA category and are referred to as persons with the condition of deaf-blindness. The number of deaf-blind individuals is approximately 25/100,000. This small number of cases puts deaf-blindness in the very-low-incidence category of disabilities recognized by the IDEA. Though it might seem reasonable that students with deaf-blindness could be served by the techniques developed to adapt instruction for blind and deaf students, in reality the concomitant presence of the two disabilities is so problematic that most professionals agree that children with deaf-blindness require instruction tailored specifically to them.

Causes of deaf-blindness include the effects of rubella and a hereditary condition known as Usher's syndrome which causes congenital deafness and progressive blindness in addition to mental retardation (Smith, 1998). Other causes that have been identified include injuries incurred during birth, the effects of diseases such as encephalitis and meningitis, and the results of physical abuse (Cartwright et al., 1995).

The education of persons with deaf-blindness is very challenging, since two means of communicating information, visual and auditory, are compromised or absent. As a result, most agree that the expertise of specially trained special educators, and even teams of such persons, is required for students with deaf-blindness. Though students with deaf-blindness are sometimes afflicted with other disabilities, for instance mental retardation, and it is difficult to assess their cognitive ability, students with deaf-blindness are known to work at all levels of mental ability (Vaughn et al., 1997).

Classroom Accommodations

- Investigate all possibilities for using adaptive computing.
- Use assistive responding devices as needed.
- Review work areas for appropriate height and accessibility of supplies and equipment.
- Examine trafficking needs of the student.
- Review the classroom environment to ensure that the student has appropriate access to peers for socialization and cooperative learning groups.
- Provide accessible means of reviewing drawings, charts, graphs, and/or models.
- Provide models, raised-line drawings, or thermo forms.
- Use proper scale and accuracy on models and drawings.
- Provide braille text.
- Allow for response with a computer or tape recorder.
- Review directions with the student.
- Use tactile signals.
- Clearly label items or equipment with braille.
- Get feedback from the student.
- Allow more time.

Traumatic Brain Injury Disabilities

Traumatic brain injury (TBI) was added to the list of very-low-incidence disability categories recognized by the government in the 1990 IDEA. The classification applies to any injury that results from external force and that causes a decreased function in either physical or psychological ability. This category does not include injuries sustained at birth, congenital injuries, or degenerative neural disorders (Cartwright et al., 1995).

TBI is the leading cause of death and disability in children and adolescents in the United States. The most frequent causes of TBI are related to motor vehicle crashes, falls, sports, and abuse/assault. More than 1 million children sustain head injuries annually; approximately 165,000 require hospitalization. However, many students with mild brain injury may never see a health care professional at the time of the accident. Researchers disagree considerably about the permanence of the effects of a mild brain injury. Some say that less than 1% of head injured individuals suffer permanent effects, while others believe more than 30% are permanently affected.

Vaughn et al. (1997) presented statistics on the types of accidents involved in producing traumatic brain injuries. They reported that over 50% of brain-injured children were hurt as the result of automobile accidents and over 20% from the result of falls. Sports and recreational accidents are the next leading cause, followed by violence. These authors also pointed out that over 75% of children less than 3 years old with traumatic brain injuries received the damage as the result of physical abuse. The Brain Injury Association (formerly the National Head Injury Foundation) calls TBI "the silent epidemic" because many children have no visible impairments after a head injury. Symptoms can vary greatly depending upon the extent and location of the brain injury. However, impairments in one or more areas are common (such as cognitive functioning, physical abilities, communication, or social/behavioral disruption). These impairments may be either temporary or permanent and may cause partial or total functional disability as well as psychosocial maladjustment. In summary these impairments include the following:

- Physical impairments: speech, vision, hearing, and other sensory impairments; headaches; lack of fine motor coordination; spasticity of muscles; paresis or paralysis of one or both sides; seizure disorders, balance, and other gait impairments.
- Cognitive impairments: short- and long-term memory deficits; impaired concentration; slowness of thinking; limited attention span; and impairments of perception, communication, reading and writing skills, planning, sequencing, and judgment.
- Psychosocial, behavioral, or emotional impairments: fatigue, mood swings, denial, self-centeredness, anxiety, depression, lowered self-esteem, sexual dysfunction, restlessness, lack of motivation, inability to self-monitor, difficulty with emotional control, inability to cope, agitation, excessive laughing or crying, and difficulty relating to others.

Any or all of these impairments may occur to different degrees. The nature of the injury and its attendant problems can range from mild to severe, and the course of recovery is very difficult to predict for any given student. It is important to note that with early and ongoing therapeutic intervention the severity of these symptoms may decrease, but in varying degrees.

While the majority of children with TBI return to school, their educational and emotional needs are likely to be very different from before the injury. Although children with TBI may seem to function much like children born with other handicapping conditions, it is important to recognize that the sudden onset of a severe disability resulting from trauma is very different. Children with brain injuries can often remember how they were before the trauma, which can result in a constellation of emotional and psychosocial problems not usually present in children with congenital disabilities. Further, the trauma impacts family, friends, and professionals, who recall what the child was like before the injury and who have difficulty shifting and adjusting goals and expectations.

Therefore, careful planning for school re-entry (including connecting the trauma center/rehabilitation hospital with the school's special education team) is extremely important in meeting the child's needs. It will be important to determine whether the child needs to relearn material previously known. Supervision may be needed (e.g., between the classroom and restroom) as the child may have orientation problems. Teachers should also be aware that because the child's short-term memory may be impaired, what appears to have been learned may be forgotten later in the day.

Classroom Accommodations

- Eliminate distractions.
- Review medications and the effect on the student.
- Be aware of limitations due to increased stress and fatigue.
- Consider a student's frustrations when planning the testing schedule.
- Be straightforward.
- Provide repetition and consistency.
- Allow for time-out if a student needs it.
- Review directions in advance.

- Give undivided attention to the student.
- Allow for signaled response.
- Don't pretend to understand if you do not.
- Focus on what is said, not how well it is said.
- Listen patiently.
- Allow more time.
- Reinforce lengthening periods of attention to appropriate tasks.
- Review lighting and background for appropriateness.
- Eliminate background noises.
- Maximize availability of visual media and/or models.
- Clearly label items or equipment.
- Allow for direct manipulation of material when appropriate.
- Get feedback from the student.
- Provide a reader when appropriate.
- Teach compensatory strategies for increasing memory.
- For students with perceptual problems, avoid computer answer sheets.
- Allow alternative response modes (e.g., circles or dictation) for students with perceptual problems

Teachers should also consider pacing the class work in a variety of ways, including the following:

- Present information in small units.
- Allow longer time for processing information.
- Provide shortened assignments.
- Allow extra time to complete tests.
- Use active learning situations whenever possible.
- Present information in multiple modalities.
- Provide printed directions for steps involved in an activity.
- Collaborate with specialists and seek out support from aides.
- Establish priorities and keep awareness of important functional skills.
- Be positive and supportive every day when the student enters the classroom.
- Communicate to the student that he/she is important and appreciated.
- Remain calm and redirect inappropriate behavior.
- Avoid situations known to cause frustration.
- Intervene quickly--don't ignore the first violations of the management policies.
- Help the student with self-monitoring.

Suggestions for Common Academic Skill Deficits

Students with traumatic brain injuries may have some specific classroom needs for success and improvement.

Deficit: The student does not demonstrate responsibility in organization and planning, including recognizing due dates, completing assignments, getting to class on time, and bringing materials to class.

Strategies:

- Develop a planning system to include checklists, planning guides, daily log and schedule, labels, and timers. Set up an organizational file. Post a schedule of activities and monitor frequently.
- Work with guardians, specialists, and aides to help monitor and direct the individual. Have the student write assignments in a daily log. If necessary, use behavior modification and tangible rewards.

- Allow time for success and work toward self-monitoring. Use consistency of routines and expectations in your own teaching. Include activities that involve planning.
- Have the student repeat directions or expectations after you have given them. Help the student maintain a portfolio of assignments.

Deficit: The student demonstrates a limited ability to store and retrieve information and an inability to keep abreast of sequence or specific details in lessons.

Strategies:

- Share written expectations and written directions whenever possible.
- Use visual and auditory cues to draw attention to important details.
- Underline and highlight key ideas for taking notes (partial outlines, tape recording, lists of key concepts and key words, etc.) or recording information from experiments.
- Teach study skills and mnemonic strategies to help recall information. Provide opportunities for repetition and practice.
- Use special education resources and materials to teach specific skills.
- Keep your expectations reasonable for the individual.

Deficit: Limited ability to carry over prior learning to new situations.

Strategies:

- Point out similarities to previous work, chunk information, help the student with associations, and review prior learning in the new context.
- Guide the student through reasoning sequences with activities (grouping, sorting, categorizing, games, challenge lessons).
- Direct responses through guided questioning.
- Work with the student privately to develop reasoning and explanations, and subsequently conduct a similar activity with the entire class.
- Present ability-appropriate deductive and inductive reasoning exercises. Practice the skills you wish students to use through simulations and multimodality activities.
- Provide time for creative work in the visual, practical, and expressive arts. Use constructions, art projects, music, creative dramatics, and literature to broaden student understanding of the integrated nature of learning.

Deficit: The student's work is of substandard quality, with a lack of ownership other than completion of the assignment.

Strategies:

- Check for understanding by asking the student to provide clarification with an extended response.
- Do not allow the student to skip steps or details.
- Work with clarification and refinement through repeated submissions.
- Allow the student to work cooperatively with others or with an aide to find and correct errors. Teach more by teaching less with quality.
- Retain high expectations, but provide opportunities to complete and/or repeat laboratory exercises outside of class time. Provide adaptive materials and equipment to allow full participation by the student. Use a buddy system or aides to help the student with manipulations that are too difficult to do alone.

- Monitor for inconsistent performance. Point out similarities to previous work of good quality. Don't argue. Be supportive, clarify expectations of quality, and direct the student back to the task.

Suggestions for Common Behavioral Deficits

Deficit: The student demonstrates low tolerance for frustration.

Strategies:

- Do not expect traditional behavior management approaches to be effective. In many cases, the student's response may be due to physiological origins and is currently beyond the individual's control.
- Learn to detect behaviors leading up to the outburst and intervene prior to it happening.
- Preplan and allow the student to get away from the activity in a quiet area.
- Provide an understanding person who will listen to feelings and frustrations.
- Establish a place in the school where the individual can get needed rest or emotional release without interfering with the educational program of the school.
- Remain calm and model appropriate behaviors.

Deficit: The student's behavior is rude, immature for his or her age, silly, and/or does not comply with expectations.

Strategies:

- Give the student feedback on social behaviors.
- Indicate you care about the individual as a person. Take time to increase insight by discussing the situations with the individual privately.
- Videotape situations and study them together.
- Discuss alternative and appropriate options that will not interfere with learning and instruction.
- Provide opportunities to role-play and discuss case studies with students.
- Remember that feelings and emotions play a large role in teaching effectiveness.
- Use conflict resolution strategies to handle differences without anger or violence.
- Encourage independence and initiation. Be supportive and caring. In noting limitations, focus on behaviors not the individual.
- Continue on a daily basis to help with student socialization in the class. Seek out opportunities for acceptance of students who are isolated or slighted in group activities.

Other Health-Impaired Disabilities

The description of a disability involving other health impairments requires that an individual have a medical condition that restricts and limits his/her activities (Best, 1992). Smith (1998) identified a number of causes, which include hereditary diseases (sickle cell anemia and cystic fibrosis) and infectious diseases (rubella, hepatitis, and HIV/AIDS). The IDEA additionally includes maladies such as heart conditions, diabetes, asthma, and many others.

The most serious medical conditions, such as AIDS and various cancers, clearly carry with them the possibility that students with these conditions, their families, other students, and their instructors may have to cope with death and the issues that surround dying. Vaughn et al. (1997) provided some guidelines for approaching this issue. The authors stress that dealing openly with the issue of death is extremely important, but also caution educators that they must use appropriate official communications with parents, counselors, and medical professionals under such circumstances.

In less serious cases, educators should remember the limitations that the health considerations place on students regarding what they cannot do and what they can accomplish on their own. Clearly, modifications to reduce stress and exertion are indicated for these students.

Classroom Accommodations

- Become familiar with the impairment. If it is degenerative, learn the symptoms and progression.
- Communicate with the student, guardians, and other professionals.
- Provide encouragement.
- Always keep in mind opportunities for socialization and interaction with others.
- Use peer helpers in appropriate ways.
- Plan in advance.
- Review learning priorities in the case of extended absence, and organize appropriate makeup lessons during the regular period of instruction.
- Don't make assumptions about when and where the student needs help; offer assistance but don't insist.
- Be aware of side effects of medication and understand fluctuations. (During exacerbations, the student may appear as if intoxicated--slurred speech, staggering, and unfocused eyes.)
- Plan a "take-home" packet with each unit to allow the student to work in a non-school setting.
- Consider assignments in electronic formats.
- Use electronic communication -- e-mail and the Internet.
- Plan for flexible attendance and alternative testing arrangements.
- In cases of uncertainty, don't hesitate to discuss issues tactfully with the student.

Multicategorical Disabilities

Multicategorical disabilities are defined under the IDEA as situations wherein a person is affected by two or more separate disabilities. The term is not applied to the condition of deaf-blindness, unless additional disabilities occur. Deaf-blindness is afforded its own category under the Act (Cartwright et al., 1995). Often, mental retardation is the additional disability that qualifies an individual for recognition under this category. An example is an individual who has cerebral palsy, a neuromotor disability, and is also mentally retarded (Vaughn, et al., 1997).

Students with multicategorical classification are often severely or profoundly disabled and require substantial and prolonged care from specialized professionals. The number of students with multicategorical disabilities is difficult to ascertain because the stated criteria for qualifications are variable and many persons with a disability might indeed have a concomitant condition, such as a vision problem, but have not been diagnosed.

Classroom Accommodations

- Determine specific impairments and means of communication accessible to the student.
- Remain in communication with the student, guardians, and other professionals.
- Determine the degree of accommodation and assistance required.
- Provide encouragement.
- Always keep in mind opportunities for socialization and interaction with others.
- Use peer helpers in appropriate ways.
- Plan in advance.

- Refer to other IDEA sections relating to specific impairments that may be present. Be aware of the compounding complexity of necessary accommodations with multiple disabilities.

Summary

All learners have unique educational needs. Many science teaching strategies used to instruct students without disabilities are effective and appropriate for students with disabilities as well. However it is important that the regular classroom teacher is attentive to special accommodations that will assist in the learning process for individual students. The teacher must also be tolerant when conditions exist where the teacher perceives that a student with disabilities is receiving instruction outside of the scope of his/her abilities. Much learning can take place outside of the context of teacher directed learning. Students learn from observing and the participating in activities.

Learning is constructed largely through actions and experiences by the learner. Real experience in science is critical if students are to develop cognitive constructs that will lead to improved understanding and comprehension. Student orientation is important, the concepts must be taught and practiced, appropriately adapted student work stations are essential. Safety, both real and perceived, is important. The environment must not only be safe, students must feel safe and comfortable in moving around on their own. Mobility specialists are important resource people in the process for students with sensory or orthopedic impairments.

Developing a communication foundation for learning is essential. Teachers must be concerned about building and developing interactions that expand the frequency and functions of communication. Patience is also important. Communication is often one of the greatest challenges students with disabilities face. The risks of not communicating are compounded with both educational and social consequences.

A key principle in instructional congruence is learning with the students rather than teaching to the students. Often the achievement gap is a consequence of disengagement by students who do not see a cultural or language connection between their lives and the science they are being taught. Student discourse is often a critical factor. Students must be allowed to converse and share their own questions as they collect data and work collaboratively in science investigations. They should be allowed (not required) to share experiences from their own cultures, such as experiences with disease or disability and how it has affected their lives or lives of family members. Time should be taken to conduct additional research utilizing resources from all subject areas to help develop connections and associations. The key to high quality science learning is "construction" in the minds of the learners where they can apply their understanding across many settings.

What is unique about students with disabilities is that there are sensory or learning impairments that limit their access to information shared in the classroom. It is critical that the necessary accommodations be made to allow all students access to the resources of the educational context. So often it is the caring, engaged teacher who makes a difference by taking time to seek out resources and work with an individual student who has unique learning needs. The difference evolves not only in the classroom but in all future decisions and life choices the individual makes. The specifics shared in this chapter are just intended as a springboard. Once a teacher decides to learn more about various disabilities, resources such as the internet are literally at our fingertips.

Chapter 5
Mastery Teaching: Investigating Bones

Overview

The instructional sequence on Investigating Bones is an adaptation of the instructional strategy suggested in Mastery Teaching. An initial focus activity occurs in Lesson 1 -- Investigating Mystery Bones. Following the focus lesson students are exposed to the science standards and objectives of the lesson sequence. The 15 lessons that follow are flexible in the order and manner they are delivered. In Mastery Teaching the arrows go both ways, with instructional input, modeling, guided practice, and independent practice lessons selected at the discretion of the teacher as a result of observations and interactions with the students. Each lesson lists the science standard(s) addressed, the materials needs, and the role of the teacher reflecting different steps in the model. Following the sequence are suggestions for adapting the lessons for students in different disability categories and enrichment suggestions using different categories of multiple intelligence theory.

Anticipatory Set or Focus: The purpose of the anticipatory set or focus is to engage students' interest in the topic of the lesson, activate prior knowledge, and prepare students for the instructional sequence to follow.

Objectives and Purpose: In specific behavioral terms, the objectives note the learning outcomes expected from the students. Sharing the objectives with the students following the anticipatory set is often very helpful in focusing students on the lesson purpose. This communication of purpose gives the students and the teacher a target to aim for in their learning and teaching.

Instructional Input and Modeling: Learning efficiency can be improved if the teacher makes a proactive effort to determine the most effective way to present the information or skills the students need to be successful in performing the learning tasks as noted in the objectives. Input should be organized, stated clearly, and a model of the information or procedure should be provided, when appropriate. As a general rule, an effort should be made to include as many modalities as possible to accommodate differences in learning style and maximize sensory stimulation.

Monitor and Adjust: It is important to periodically obtain feedback from the students to ensure they have grasped the essential information noted in the learning objectives. This checking for understanding can occur at any time throughout the lesson. Some suggestions for effective monitoring are: have students signal the answer to a posed question, use choral responses, and sample individual written or oral responses.

Guided Practice: Guided practice is an opportunity for students to perform activities that provide additional reinforcement and enrichment of the lesson information with teacher support.

Independent Practice: Once the students have a clear understanding of the material to be learned, many will need additional practice to ensure fluency and imprinting of the information.

Science Standards

The student provides evidence that demonstrates an understanding of the following:

- Characteristics of organisms, such as survival and environmental support; the relationship between structure and function; and variation in behavior (National Center on the Economy and

Education, Elementary Performance Standards, 1997)

- Structure and function in living systems, such as the complementary nature of structure and function in cells, organs, tissues, organ systems, whole organisms, and ecosystems (National Center on the Economy and Education, Middle School Performance Standards, 1997)

Objectives

After satisfactory completion of this lesson sequence, the student will be able to do the following:

1. Infer and/or predict the size of an animal from an unidentified bone.
2. Describe similarities and differences between the skeletons of different animals.
3. State the name of 20 bones using formal nomenclature (taxonomic names) with 90% accuracy.
4. Match the names of 20 bones with the appropriate component of a human skeleton with 90% accuracy.
5. Compare and contrast different joint types (ball and socket, hinge, gliding, etc.), function of ligaments and tendons, and different types of bones (e.g., birds vs. mammals).
6. Assemble a skeleton using dry bones and a skeletal illustration.
7. Draw and label a human skeleton "inside" a tracing made around the body of student volunteers.

Lesson 1
Investigating Mystery Bones

Science Standard

The student provides evidence that demonstrates an understanding of the following:

- Characteristics of organisms, such as survival and environmental support; the relationship between structure and function; and variation in behavior (National Center on the Economy and Education, Elementary School Performance Standards, 1997)

Materials

- **an assortment of bones**. A bone collection can be started with cleaned chicken and turkey bones. Bones can be obtained from supply houses (e.g., Carolina Biological Supply), found in forested or rural areas, sometimes loaned from students (these should be cleaned, disinfected with bleach, and sprayed with a clear-coat finish), or loaned from other professionals. Secondary schools and universities are possible sources of bones for short-term loan. Common animal bones can often be loaned for a short period from a naturalist center in the area. Naturalists often volunteer to talk to students if asked. In addition, they can be a good source of information to help you build background knowledge.

- **a collection of resources.** Acquire a collection of resource books on bones, with pictures whenever possible, that can be kept in the classroom during the instructional sequence. Three older books that are excellent resources are the *Bones Teachers Guide* (Elementary Science Study, 1967), *Elementary Science Study Bones Picture Book* (Elementary Science Study, 1967), and *How to Make a Chicken Skeleton* (Elementary Science Study, 1967). These are available from Delta Education (www.delta-education.com).

Anticipatory Set or Focus

- **Share a set of mystery bones**. Allow students to explore the bones in small groups (3-5) and share inferences as to the animal each bone came from, the size of the animal, and which part of the body it fits. Discuss and compare different types of joints and body movement patterns associated with each joint. Compare and contrast skeletal drawings of different animals. Discuss types of joints—ball & socket (shoulder), hinge (knee), pivot (neck), gliding (wrist), immovable (skull)—and how they affect movement and flexibility.

Lesson 2
Bone Identification

Science Standard

The student provides evidence that demonstrates an understanding of the following:

- Characteristics of organisms, such as survival and environmental support; the relationship between structure and function; and variation in behavior (National Center on the Economy and Education, Elementary School Performance Standards, 1997)

Materials

- Skeleton Transparency Master (see Appendix C)

Instructional Input and Modeling

Ask each student to stand, allowing sufficient space for free body movement. The teacher then models by touching and orally identifying various skeletal parts (e.g., skull). If possible, have a visual on the overhead with a labeled skeletal drawing (see Appendix C). The more senses involved, the greater likelihood the students will learn the bones with fewer stimulations. The students are asked to model and repeat orally each step in the sequence pattern. After going through a sequence of five to eight skeletal parts two or three times (e.g., skull, mandible, clavicle, scapula, sternum, ribs, pelvis, or ilium), students are prompted to be the first to touch the body part announced orally. The teacher then follows through two or three practice sets doing this form of stimulated response, touching the different skeletal parts as students respond orally while touching their corresponding skeletal parts. Different variations can be used, with the teacher touching and remaining silent, or the teacher naming without touching. The steps are then repeated for other bones in the body such as the arm bones and/or leg bones.

Lesson 3
Identifying Human Bones

Science Standards

The student provides evidence that demonstrates an understanding of the following:

- Characteristics of organisms, such as survival and environmental support; the relationship between structure and function; and variation in behavior (National Center on the Economy and Education, Elementary Performance Standards, 1997)

- Structure and function in living systems, such as the complementary nature of structure and function in cells, organs, tissues, organ systems, whole organisms, and ecosystems (National Center on the Economy and Education, Middle School Performance Standards, 1997)

Materials

- a professional human skeletal poster or poster book

Instructional Input

Use a response mode similar to the steps in Lesson 2 but explain various aspects of the skeleton. Challenge students by asking about the number of specific bones: (e.g., carpals (8), tarsals (7), phalanges (56), vertebra (24), etc. Discuss function, form, and comparisons of various skeletal parts in the human body.

Review student understanding through:

a. Obtaining signaled response from each small group member by stating skeletal parts and asking the students to touch the identified part of the skeletal system.

b. Then, ask for a choral response in which the teacher touches various skeletal parts and all students respond orally.

c. Individual responses can be obtained by going around the group in a pattern with the teacher touching various skeletal parts followed by an oral student response. This is less desirable because it singles out the responding student.

Lesson 4
Bone Identification Card Game

Science Standards

The student provides evidence that demonstrates an understanding of:

- Characteristics of organisms, such as survival and environmental support; the relationship between structure and function; and variation in behavior. (National Center on the Economy and Education, Elementary Performance Standards, 1997)

- Structure and Function in living systems, such as the complementary nature of structure and function in cells, organs, tissues, organ systems, whole organisms, and ecosystems. (National Center on the Economy and Education, Middle Level performance Standards, 1997)

Materials

- a deck of cards with each skeletal part printed on a card (i.e. clavicle, scapula, ribs, vertebral column, ilium, carpal, metacarpal, phalanges, tibia, fibula, skull, mandible, sternum, humerus, radius, ulna, femur, patella, tarsals, metatarsals). Heavy paper printed on a desktop computer and cut to playing card size works well.

Guided Practice

Arrange students into groups of 3 or 4, and give each group one deck of cards. The cards are placed face down on a table and one student draws a card. If he or she can touch the appropriate skeletal part, he/she keeps the card, and the person to the left draws the next card. If the student cannot touch the body part or if he or she is incorrect, the card is passed to the next person to the left, who then must touch the correct skeletal part. The game continues through the deck, and the individual with the most cards is the winner.

Lesson 5
Bone Identification - Active Demonstration

Science Standards

The student provides evidence that demonstrates an understanding of the following:

- Characteristics of organisms, such as survival and environmental support; the relationship between structure and function; and variation in behavior (National Center on the Economy and Education, Elementary Performance Standards, 1997)

- Structure and function in living systems, such as the complementary nature of structure and function in cells, organs, tissues, organ systems, whole organisms, and ecosystems (National Center on the Economy and Education, Middle School Performance Standards, 1997)

Materials

- a deck of cards with each skeletal part printed on a card (i.e. clavicle, scapula, ribs, vertebral column, ilium, carpal, metacarpal, phalanges, tibia, fibula, skull, mandible, sternum, humerus, radius, ulna, femur, patella, tarsals, metatarsal). Heavy paper printed on a desktop computer and cut to playing-card size works well.

Guided Practice

1. Ask each group of 3 or 4 students to pass the deck of cards to the person in their group who knows the bones the best. They then form a semicircle facing the student with the deck of cards. The game involves showing the members of the group each card and not progressing to the next card until each member of the group has touched the appropriate bone. It can be made a challenge activity between groups as students hold hands and squat when their team is finished.

2. Arrange students in work groups of 3 or 4. Select one student to go through the cards in a fashion similar to flash cards, touching the appropriate skeletal parts. Repeat until all students in the group have had a chance to "deal" the cards. A challenge activity is to see which group can go through the deck the fastest.

Lesson 6
Constructing a Skeletal Poster

Science Standards

The student provides evidence that demonstrates an understanding of the following:

- Characteristics of organisms, such as survival and environmental support; the relationship between structure and function; and variation in behavior (National Center on the Economy and Education, Elementary Performance Standards, 1997)

- Structure and function in living systems, such as the complementary nature of structure and function in cells, organs, tissues, organ systems, whole organisms, and ecosystems (National Center on the Economy and Education, Middle School Performance Standards, 1997)

Materials

- crayons or markers
- pencils
- large paper (newspaper end rolls work well and are inexpensive)
- skeletal picture (see Appendix C)

Guided Practice

Arrange students in groups of 3 or 4. Using large paper, have one student lie down on the paper. Trace the body of that student in pencil, holding the pencil straight up and down. The subject being traced should turn one foot out, then stand and trace around the other foot. Draw a light line from the top of the head through the torso as a guide to assist with bilateral symmetry. You may wish to mark the spots for major joints. Now draw in the bones and label each part of the skeletal system. An option is to draw in the skeleton and rather than write in the bones, use the cards made for activity 4 to label the bones. It is often useful to do the activity twice--the first time with a picture as a guide and the second time with the students completing the task without assistance.

Lesson 7
Planning and Active Learning

Science Standards

The student provides evidence that demonstrates an understanding of the following:

- Characteristics of organisms, such as survival and environmental support; the relationship between structure and function; and variation in behavior (National Center on the Economy and Education, Elementary Performance Standards, 1997)

- Structure and function in living systems, such as the complementary nature of structure and function in cells, organs, tissues, organ systems, whole organisms, and ecosystems (National Center on the Economy and Education, Middle School Performance Standards, 1997).

Materials

- portable chalkboard or poster board. The activity should be conducted outdoors or in an area with ample space for student movement.

Guided Practice

Arrange students in groups of 6 to 8. Present them with the names of a series of bones written on chalkboard or poster board. Each student must touch his or her skeletal part to another skeletal part of each of the other group members. About four touch parts work well. For example:

1. Tibula to fibula
2. Humerus to femur
3. Patella to carpals
4. Tarsals to ulna

The students are given 3 to 5 minutes to plan as a group how they intend to complete the activity. The teacher then says "go," and the students must complete all of the tasks, hold hands, and sit down. The first group to sit down wins.

Lesson 8
Assembling Bones

Science Standards

The student provides evidence that demonstrates an understanding of the following:

- Characteristics of organisms, such as survival and environmental support; the relationship between structure and function; and variation in behavior (National Center on the Economy and Education, Elementary Performance Standards, 1997)

- Structure and function in living systems, such as the complementary nature of structure and function in cells, organs, tissues, organ systems, whole organisms, and ecosystems (National Center on the Economy and Education, Middle School Performance Standards, 1997)

Materials

- small animal skeletons from a biology department or biological supply house (e.g., www.carolina.com)

Independent Practice

1. Encourage students to assemble the bones using the knowledge of their own bones. Follow this with a more complete assembly exercise, using photographs of the assembled skeleton. These are normally provided with skeleton kits obtained from supply houses.

2. Compare skeletons of different animals. Obtain books on skeletons from a library and make comparisons between different animals. Another possibility is to utilize a resource person (e.g., fish and game manager, biology teacher, wildlife conservationist, museum curator).

Lesson 9
Making a Chicken Skeleton

Science Standards

The student provides evidence that demonstrates an understanding of the following:

- Characteristics of organisms, such as survival and environmental support; the relationship between structure and function; and variation in behavior (National Center on the Economy and Education, Elementary Performance Standards, 1997)

- Structure and function in living systems, such as the complementary nature of structure and function in cells, organs, tissues, organ systems, whole organisms, and ecosystems (National Center on the Economy and Education, Middle School Performance Standards, 1997)

Materials

- a dressed chicken with head and feet. Put the chicken into a pot. Fill pot with water to cover chicken. Let it boil slowly for 1 ½ to 2 hours. Add water if necessary. You may wish to remove some parts such as the skull after about ½ hour or when the meat comes off easily. Wash the removed parts thoroughly with cold water and use an old toothbrush to clean off all the meat. If meat is still attached, boil the bones a little longer. There are approximately 120 bones in a chicken, and if you get over 100 bones, you have done well. Lay out the bones, and let them dry overnight.

Independent Practice

1. Assemble the bones by gluing the skeleton together with a quick drying cement. Oil-based modeling clay and waxed paper are helpful in holding the parts together while the glue dries. The Elementary Science Study Guide titled How to Make a Chicken Skeleton (1967) is an excellent resource (available from www.delta-education.com).

2. Compare your skeleton with a complete picture and draw in the missing parts.

Lesson 10
Inquisitive Sketch Investigation

Science Standard

The student provides evidence that demonstrates an understanding of the following:

- Impact of science, such as historical and contemporary contributions; and interactions between science and society (National Center on the Economy and Education, Middle School Performance Standards, 1997)

Materials

- Inquisitive Sketch(es) and Inquisitive Sketch Assessment sheet (Appendices D, E, F). A classroom library containing resource books related to American Indians, particularly books related to the life of those living on the plains, is very valuable not only to help students solve the problem at hand but also to enrich their learning and provide ideas for further extensions. You need an Inquisitive Sketch for each student.

Independent Practice

A practical application of the information learned in this unit is to engage in a problem-solving activity in which bones provide some clues to what happened at an archeological site and what it may have looked like in days past. Create the proper conditions: Students will need background in the process of inferring, a knowledge of using resources to obtain information, and a certain amount of background information in order to work effectively.

1. Present the Inquisitive Sketch to each student.

2. Fact finding: In small groups, students are encouraged to search through the Inquisitive Sketch and collect and categorize as much data as possible.

3. Formulation of inferences: Students go through the data collected during fact finding and try to infer uses and explanations for the materials that are found in the Inquisitive Sketches. This generally involves an extensive use of resources. The teacher should serve as an active facilitator of how and where to find information.

4. Evaluation of inferences: Students now go through their various inferences and rate them from excellent to poor, depending upon how well they have been able to substantiate their viewpoints.

5. Solution Finding: Students are encouraged to incorporate their inferences into a synthesis of the how, why, when, and where of the Inquisitive Sketch. This is then prepared in a written or taped narrative description.

6. Acceptance finding: During the final sessions, students from all groups present and discuss their hypotheses. An attempt is made to develop a narrative description that represents a class consensus.

Lesson 11
Inquisitive Sketch Investigation with Topographic Lines

Science Standard

The student provides evidence that demonstrates an understanding of the following:

- Impact of science, such as historical and contemporary contributions; and interactions between science and society (National Center on the Economy and Education, Middle School Performance Standards, 1997).

Materials

- Inquisitive Sketch(es) and Inquisitive Sketch Assessment sheet (Appendices D, E, F). A classroom library containing resource books related to American Indians, particularly books related to the life of those living on the plains, is very valuable not only to help students solve the problem at hand but also to enrich their learning and provide ideas for further extensions. Review information on topographic lines. You will need an Inquisitive Sketch for each student.

Independent Practice

A practical application of the information learned in this unit is to engage in a problem-solving activity in which bones provide some clues to what happened at the site and what it may have looked like in days past. Create the proper conditions: Students will need background in the process of inferring, a knowledge of using resources to obtain information, and a certain amount of background information in order to work effectively.

1. Present the Inquisitive Sketch to each student.

2. Fact finding: In small groups, students are encouraged to search through the Inquisitive Sketch and collect and categorize as much data as possible.

3. Formulation of inferences: Students go through the data collected during fact finding and try to infer uses and explanations for the materials that are found in the Inquisitive Sketches. This generally involves an extensive use of resources. The teacher should serve as an active facilitator of how and where to find information.

4. Evaluation of inferences: Students now go through their various inferences and rate them from excellent to poor, depending upon how well they have been able to substantiate their viewpoints.

5. Solution finding: Students are encouraged to incorporate their inferences into a synthesis of the how, why, when, and where of the Inquisitive Sketch. This is then prepared in a written or taped narrative description.

6. Acceptance finding: During the final sessions, students from all groups present and discuss their hypotheses. An attempt is made to develop a narrative description that represents a class consensus.

Lesson 12
Shake, Rattle and Roll

Science Standards

The student provides evidence that demonstrates an understanding of the following:

- Characteristics of organisms, such as survival and environmental support; the relationship between structure and function; and variation in behavior (National Center on the Economy and Education, Elementary Performance Standards, 1997)

Materials

- dice
- crayons or markers
- activity sheet (see Appendix G)

Guided Practice

Arrange the students in pairs. Provide each student with a marker and activity sheet, and one die for every two students. Tell them they must alternate in shaking of the die and they should continue until all of the bones indicated on the drawing are colored in.

1. A student must first throw the number 1 in order to color in the skull.

2. After that, the student can throw any number. But all of the parts in capital letters must be filled in before players can start on the parts written in lower-case letters.

3. Players cross out the name of the bones they have colored in as they go.

4. Before completing the game, the individual will need to have thrown 4-ones, 2-twos, 4-threes, 4-fours, 2-fives, and 3-sixes.

5. The students may time themselves to determine how long it takes them to complete the game. They may also play in pairs to see who finishes first.

The sheet does not contain the words “mandible” or “scapula”. If students mark either or both of them, they cannot win.

Lesson 13
Interactive Skeleton Compact Disk

Science Standards

The student provides evidence that demonstrates an understanding of the following:

- Characteristics of organisms, such as survival and environmental support; the relationship between structure and function; and variation in behavior (National Center on the Economy and Education, Elementary Performance Standards, 1997)

- Structure and function in living systems, such as the complementary nature of structure and function in cells, organs, tissues, organ systems, whole organisms, and ecosystems (National Center on the Economy and Education, Middle School Performance Standards, 1997)

Materials

- compact disk: The *Interactive Skeleton* is a complete, accurate 3-D human skeleton that shows detail, muscle attachment, and landmark. It is designed as an educational resource in medicine, anatomy, surgery, and allied health fields. It provides outstanding enrichment for children at all levels. Price: approx. $100. Available from:

  http://www.primal pictures.com
  Primal Pictures Ltd.
  Ramillies House
  Ramillies Street
  London W1V 1DF, UK
  Telephone: USA 1-800-821-8312

Independent Practice

1. The classroom teacher or technology specialist should become familiar with the software. The information contained on the disk can provide all students with opportunities to become more familiar with the human skeleton. At the high end, the material on the disk can challenge the most able student. It has been used by first-year medical school students.

2. Students should be allowed to explore and become familiar with the options contained in the program. If more structure is needed, a teacher can construct a series of questions or provide students with a series of challenges.

Lesson 14

Assessment - Concentration Style

Science Standards

The student provides evidence that demonstrates an understanding of the following:

- Characteristics of organisms, such as survival and environmental support; the relationship between structure and function; and variation in behavior (National Center on the Economy and Education, Elementary Performance Standards, 1997)

- Structure and function in living systems, such as the complementary nature of structure and function in cells, organs, tissues, organ systems, whole organisms, and ecosystems (National Center on the Economy and Education, Middle School Performance Standards, 1997)

Materials

- 2 decks of cards, one containing the questions in one color and the other containing the answers in a different color. Heavy paper printed on a desktop computer and cut to playing-card size works well.

Guided or Independent Practice

1. Instruct students to match the questions with the answers.

2. The game can be played independently or in small groups.

3. The activity can be made into a competitive game challenging the student groups to see who can finish first.

QUESTIONS:	**ANSWERS:**
Joint type at the wrists, ankles, and part of the spine. Bones slide against each other.	Gliding
The smallest bone in the body, inside the ear.	Stirrup
The smallest bones in the body are the malleus and incus, and stapes. What are their common names?	Hammer, anvil, stirrup
Joint type in knees, fingers, and toes.	Hinge
The largest bone in the body, from thigh to knee.	Femur
A break in a bone.	Fracture
Joint type at the hips and shoulders, which can move in almost any direction.	Ball-and-socket
Joint type in the neck, which allows the head to turn and nod.	Pivot
Animals with four limbs.	Vertebrates
The number of bones in the adult human skeleton.	206
Strong inelastic fibers that hold bones together at joints.	Ligaments
The bowl-like form of several bones that supports the body and protects the digestive organs.	Pelvis
The hardest material in the body.	Enamel
The substance in the middle of bones where blood cells are made.	Marrow
Another name for breastbone.	Sternum
Another name for the skull.	Cranium
Tough, strong cords that attach bones to muscle.	Tendons
A collection of 33 bones commonly called spine, or backbone.	Vertebrae
Animals that do not have a backbone.	Invertebrates
The knee joint works much like a simple machine. Which one ?	Lever
The largest joint in the body.	Knee

Lesson 15

Assessment - Multiple Intelligence

Science Standards

The student provides evidence that demonstrates an understanding of the following:

- Characteristics of organisms, such as survival and environmental support; the relationship between structure and function; and variation in behavior (National Center on the Economy and Education, Elementary Performance Standards, 1997)

- Structure and Function in living systems, such as the complementary nature of structure and function in cells, organs, tissues, organ systems, whole organisms, and ecosystems. (National Center on the Economy and Education, Middle School Performance Standards, 1997)

Materials

- professional skeleton model, poster, or book (for students doing logical/mathematical assessment)

Guided Activity

Arrange students into groups of four, and allow them to select the form of assessment that they prefer. Let them work together to accomplish their task from those listed below. Have each group share how it addressed the challenge presented in the strategy.

Linguistic — Share a story about a skeletal accident you had or saw. Use proper nomenclature when possible.

Logical/Mathematical — Determine the number of bones in the human body, and name the number of each type of bone.

Measure the length of two bones for all of your classmates and show the relationship on a scattergram; indicate the correlation coefficient.

Spatial — Draw a body outline, draw in the bones, and label as many as possible.

Kinesthetic — Develop an active learning game that helps teach skeletal nomenclature to students.

Musical — Create a tune that helps teach skeletal nomenclature to students.

Interpersonal — Plan a strategy in groups of 4 to 6 students. Each student in your group must touch the first bone with the second bone of all of the other students.

Continue with the remaining three bone pairs then sit down and hold hands. The goal is to be the first group finished.

Tibia-fibula
Patella-vertebrae
Humerus-femur
Phalanges-tarsals

Naturalist

Describe what typically happens to bones after an animal dies.
List advantages and disadvantages of an endoskeleton compared to an exoskeleton.

Specific Accommodations by Disability Category

Motor/Orthopedic

- Examine accessibility to materials and movement needs of the student.
- Provide a supportive peer assistant of the same gender to work together on signaled response and card game activities.
- Provide accessible means for student to participate in the group construction of a skeletal poster. If this is not possible, consider a smaller drawing on a work surface of appropriate size or a computer sketch (Lesson 6)
- If student has limited motor control, consider tools or supports to serve as aids; have students work in groups in skeleton assembly.
- Allow extra time for student and peers to continue with activities of choice outside of regular school day or at home.
- Provide an aide or peer assistant to handle the bones and assist the student in getting a thorough tactile experience with all of the materials and/or models.
- Allow students to experience and manipulate bone prior to group lesson (Lesson 1)
- If a student is in a wheel chair, allow the student to touch a model. (Lesson 1)
- If a student has limited limb movement or control, pair that student with a same gender peer who can touch the appropriate bones. (Lesson 2)
- Allow student groups to be "competitive" or "non-competitive" which can provide a more relaxed atmosphere for those who desire it. (Lesson 5 & 7)
- Acquire bones of a larger animal (i.e., dog) to allow for easier manipulation. (Lesson 8 & 9)

Visually Impaired

- Provide a pre-teaching experience before class activity; allow the visually impaired student to explore bones and review vocabulary. (Lesson 1)
- Magnify handouts and get thermo forms constructed with braille notation. For low-vision students provide enlarged handouts on:
  1. Scientific names of bones
  2. Shake, rattle and roll (Lesson 12)
  3. Inquisitive Sketches (Lesson 10, 11)
  4. Card games (Lesson 4, 14)
- Provide a supportive peer assistant of the same gender to work together on signaled response and card game activities.
- Allow extra time for student and peers to continue with activities of choice outside of school day or at home.
- Look for software and talking books relating to bones, skeletal systems, American Indians, and archeology.
- Acquire bones of a larger animal (i.e., dog) to allow for easier manipulation. (Lesson 8 & 9)
- Pair the student with a same gender peer who can guide their hands until they have mastered the facts. (Lesson 2)

Hearing Impaired

- Locate student for direct eye and lip visibility; be sure background has sufficient contrast.
- Print cards in large type so student can easily read the cards from a distance for activities.
- Pre-teach vocabulary and allow student to explore and handle bones prior to lesson sequence.
- Provide a supportive peer assistant to help during games and construction activities.

- Allow extra time for student and peers to engage in activities of choice outside of school day and at home.
- Prepare print directions and allow the student to review them in advance.
- Provide materials to the interpreter in advance.
- Slow the pace of instruction to allow student-interpreter's interactive communication.
- Pre-plan and provide group assistance to insure the deaf student is included in the group during the skeletal poster activity. Alert students to establish lip-eye contact before speaking. (Lesson 6)

Learning Disabled

- Pre-teach vocabulary and allow student to explore bones prior to lesson sequence.
- Seek out resources for visual media and models on bones, the human skeleton, American Indians, and Archeology. (Lessons 10 & 11)
- Provide a reader when appropriate.
- Allow for noncompetitive participation.
- Provide a teacher associate when appropriate.
- Prepare a "take home" kit where students can practice with an adult or supportive peer.
- Allow students to self-select opportunities to practice during non-classroom instructional time (i.e., before or after school).

Attention Deficit/Hyperactivity Disorder

- Pre-teach vocabulary and allow student to explore bones prior to lesson sequence.
- Position student so there is good visibility and opportunity for proximity control.
- Seek out resources for visual media and models.
- Slow down pace of activities and allow adequate time for student participation.
- Provide a non-obtrusive teaching associate when appropriate.
- Preview activity sequence in advance and, when appropriate, write a contract with the student specifying what behavior is expected.
- Pair the student with a supportive peer during group activities and games.

Developmentally Delayed

- Provide pre-instruction on vocabulary; select vocabulary appropriate for the student's learning.
- Allow student to explore bones in advance and provide advanced instruction whenever possible.
- Provide a supportive peer or teacher associate to assist with card game and drawing activities.
- Allow for a signaled response in a non-threatening environment.
- Allow extra time for student and when appropriate provide a teacher associate. Encourage the student to engage in activities of choice outside of the school day or at home.
- Prepare a "take-home" set of games that the student can practice with a supportive adult.
- Provide examples of prior work that student can review in advance with a supportive adult.
- Acquire models that may have fewer sections to assemble. (Lesson 8 & 9)
- Prepare print instructions and expose student to them in advance of group lessons.

Behavior Disordered

- Review directions in advance of activities and clarify expectations.
- When appropriate, write a contract in advance specifying what behavior is expected and where a student can go if the he or she begins to experience frustration.
- On group-response activities, seat student in location to minimize distraction and provide close teacher proximity.

- Be patient and supportive.
- Provide student with supportive noncompetitive peers.
- Allow for noncompetitive participation during game and challenge activities.
- Establish a predetermined signal or utilize an unobtrusive teacher associate to intervene when the student begins to demonstrate impulsive behavior.
- Make sure you continually state and clarify expectations prior to each activity.
- Use proximity and observation during group activities, be prepared to intervene when appropriate.
- In cases of a high risk of inappropriate activity, consider dropping the activity from the sequence. (Lesson 7)

Speech/Language

- Pre-teach vocabulary; allow student to explore bones prior to instructional sequence.
- Allow for signaled responses.
- Allow for computer or written responses.
- Allow student an opportunity to volunteer; listen and be patient; support efforts of communication in class; allow the student an opportunity to communicate what he or she has learned in private.
- Provide a supportive peer assistant.
- Present a multi-modality output so student can reach information visually or tactilely.
- Provide a "take-home" set of materials so the student can practice with a supportive adult.

Autism

- Provide pre-teaching experiences on vocabulary and exploring with bones; practice the activities in the sequence prior to the lesson in class.
- Provide a supportive peer assistant of the same gender to work together on the activities.
- Slow the pace of activities to allow for student's participation.
- If necessary, allow a teacher associate to assist with and/or conduct activities with the student.
- Review the routines ahead of time and provide a consistent structure and organization.
- Seat the student in close proximity to the teacher.
- Allow for noncompetitive participation.
- Present multi-modality lessons so the student can receive the information visually or tactilely.
- Allow extra time outside of the school day to allow the student to practice in a quiet, non-distracting environment.

Deaf/Blind

- Examine trafficking needs of the student.
- Provide a pre-teaching experience prior to classroom activities; allow the student to explain the lessons and review the vocabulary.
- Provide a supportive peer assistant of the same gender to work together with the student.
- Prepare all of the materials in braille and thermo form in advance.
- Use tactile signals.
- Allow additional time.
- Prepare a "take-home" set of materials to allow the student to gain additional experience with a supportive adult.
- Pre-plan material displays and word stations.
- Provide examples of prior work that the student can review in advance with a supportive adult.
- Use proper scale and accuracy when making drawings or models.

Traumatic Brain Injury

- Provide pre-teaching experience using the actual bones; practice the activities in the sequence.
- If appropriate, write a contract with the student specifying what behavior is expected.
- If appropriate, provide a supportive peer assistant of the same gender determine if student has a sensitive touch response and plan appropriately.
- Provide student with good visibility; use unobtrusive proximity control.
- Slow down and use appropriate pacing.
- Search out resources for visual media and models on bones, the human skeleton system, American Indians, and archeology.
- Be aware of any potential "sensitive touch response" and consider dropping activity from the sequence. (Lesson 7) In some cases, after communication with the student, allow student to be an observer.
- Maintain consistency. Be sure to state and clarify expectations prior to the end of the lesson.

Other Health-Impaired

- Talk with the student and determine activities that are appropriate and desirable for the student.
- Communicate with guardians and other health professionals to determine any dangers of overly strenuous participation.
- Provide a supportive peer of the same gender.
- Prepare a “take-home” set of materials to allow the student to review at home or engage in the activities in a better context with a supportive adult.
- Allow for noncompetitive participation.
- Review your pacing.
- Be aware of the student and watch for any fluctuations that indicate discomfort or evidence side effects of medication.
- In cases of uncertainty, don’t hesitate to discuss issues tactfully with the student, in private, whenever possible.

Multicategorical

- Determine specific impairment and establish learning priorities.
- Pre-teach; allow the student to explore materials and learn appropriate vocabulary in advance.
- Use peer helper of same gender in appropriate ways.
- Prepare a “take-home” set of materials with which the student can practice with a supportive adult.
- Control pacing and provide encouragement.

Other

- Communicate with student, guardians, and other professionals in advance.
- Determine degree of accommodation and assistance needed.
- Use peer helpers in appropriate ways.
- Plan in advance, consider routines, accessibility, trafficking of the student and materials.
- Always keep in mind opportunities for positive socialization.
- Be patient and supportive.

Multiple Intelligence Activities

Verbal/Linguistic

Acrostic Poems. To accommodate verbal/linguistic learners, have them choose different bones and write an acrostic poem describing each bone's characteristics. An example for the femur bone is given below.

F-Found in the thigh
E-Elastic hamstring is behind
M-Moves back and forth and side to side
U-Under hip joint
R-Right above the knee

This could be done in partners or on the computer. Have students take turns sharing their bone acrostics.

"Day in the Life" story. Another verbal/linguistic activity is to write or tell a story about a "day in the life" of a specific bone. Students could choose a bone and describe how their movements and activities of the day impact that specific bone.

Logical/Mathematical

Feature analysis chart. There are many ways to incorporate math and logic in the study of bones. One activity is to make a feature analysis chart, and compare and contrast the characteristics of the skeletons of different animals. This could be done as a class by having small groups rotate to the different animal skeletons to fill out their charts.

Statistic gathering. Another activity is to gather statistics about the human skeleton, such as the number of bones in the hand compared to the number of bones in the foot, the number of ribs, and the average length of an arm in the class. This activity could also include calculating proportions of one bone to another, such as femur to tibia. Another extension would be to calculate the percentage of the elements in the composition of bone and bone marrow. Students could be assigned to certain statistics to gather and share them with the class through a poster or as a trivia game question.

Visual/Spatial Activities

Skeleton model museum display. Students can make a model human or animal skeleton from modeling clay or papier-mâché. They should include a paragraph that describes the animal exhibited and explains the distinct features of the skeleton they've chosen to represent. When all the models are displayed in the classroom, students can share them with other classes and parents.

X-ray examination. An x-ray technician or other expert could bring x-rays to class for the students to see and demonstrate how x-ray technology works, how x-rays are interpreted, and how bones fracture. Another option is to visit a hospital x-ray department.

Bodily/Kinesthetic

Movement analysis. Have students choose a favorite action, such as shooting a basket or riding a bike. Then have them practice the motion to observe which bones might be involved. Next, have them describe how each involved bone moves to complete the action. Another twist would be to imagine trying to perform this motion without the support and strength of involved bones. This could be done in small groups or with volunteers in front of the class.

Bone examination. Examine actual animal bones. Try to predict where each bone would fit in a human body, and predict the animal it might belong to. Students may want to feel the shape of their own bones for hints. A human skeleton model can be a helpful resource.

Musical-Rhythmic Activities

Create song or rap. To remember specific bones and their functions, students could make up a song or a rap to a familiar tune or rhythm that describes the bones and their functions. This could be done individually, in small groups, or as a class.

Instruments. Students could make or examine instruments made from animal bones. They could experiment with sounds and identify changes in pitch or tone according to size and shape of bones.

Song analysis. Create a collection of songs written about bones and analyze the lyric descriptions for realistic reliability. "Translate" the lyrics into technical bone terminology.

Interpersonal

Structured controversy. In partners or small groups, have students develop the pro and con sides of the following problem: Should museums keep and display bones of Native Americans or Egyptian mummies? Have each group share its ideas and findings from research.

Cooperative game. Have each group of students create a cooperative game to review bones in the human body. They should include a written list of rules and instructions for play, along with creating any materials necessary. Once all games are completely created, groups can rotate to each game and play for review.

Intrapersonal

Reflection journal. Have students keep a daily reflection journal throughout the bone unit. They can write an entry each day on either a given topic (how it feels to break a bone, or how to strengthen growing bones) or on a topic the students choose that they've learned or questions they have.

Self-directed bone project. Allow students to choose a project or product to create that demonstrates their understanding of bones and the skeletal system.

Naturalist

Animal adaptations research. Have students research and examine the skeleton of a particular animal. Have them describe how the distinct features of the animal's bones aid in survival in the animal's natural habitat and its daily living activities. The students should examine the bones to determine how the animal has adapted to its surroundings.

Classification. Students could categorize animals according to their skeletal systems

Chapter 6
Direct Instruction: An Investigation of the Suffocating Candle

Overview

Gaining Learner's Attention: The purpose of gaining attention is to introduce students to stimulus change. Prerequisite knowledge should be assessed through informal discussion of a topic that is familiar to the students.

Objectives: The teacher provides the students with a description and example of subordinate concepts and rules. The objectives should be stated in behavioral terms with observable student outcomes.

Prerequisite Learning: The teacher stimulates recall of subordinate concepts and rules. The requisite vocabulary for the upcoming instructional sequence is reviewed, and new vocabulary is introduced and discussed.

Stimulus Material: The teacher presents illustrative examples of new concepts or rules. Student thinking is stimulated through teacher-directed instructional input. Demonstrations may be used to guide student thinking and provide a clear direction of expectations and clarity of procedures.

Guidance Cues: The teacher provides verbal cues to properly guide assimilation of prior and new knowledge at the beginning of the instructional sequence. Students are observed during the initial activities so the teacher can assist them in conducting sound investigations that have good scientific merit and accurate data collection.

Eliciting Performance: The students apply rules or concepts to new examples.

Feedback: The teacher confirms the correctness of rule or concept application. The student reports are presented and discussed. Students are asked to share their data and discuss their results; learning is extended through probing questions.

Performance Assessment: The students demonstrate the application of a concept in a group assessment, followed by an individual assessment, if necessary.

Enhancing Retention and Transfer: The students are provided with spaced reviews, including a variety of examples.

Lesson Sequence Overview

The sequence presented here is an adaptation of Model 53: The Suffocating Candle contained in Science: A Process Approach II, 1968 (available from Delta Education). Many of the textual elements have been extracted from the guide.

Gaining Attention

Begin with a discussion of fire and burning. Ask questions relating to things that will burn and things that won't burn. If desired, make a list. Ask students why things that can burn are not burning now. Ask: How can you start something burning? What can be done to make a fire burn faster? What can be done to make a fire burn slower? Discuss some of the advantages of fire and some of the dangers of fire.

Share with students the value of quantitative measurement in the scientific study of any phenomenon, and indicate that mathematics is one of scientists' most valuable tools. Share with them the need to describe an experiment in a way that others can duplicate your procedures and the importance of replication and verification in scientific study. Tell them that an important part of the evaluation of their effectiveness as a student is the scientific disposition they display while conducting their experiments.

Discuss safety concerns related to handling glassware, caution and safety near an open flame, safety regarding pupil movement and the handling of materials, and courtesy and sharing within and between work groups.

Science Standards

- Understands transfer of energy, such as transformation of energy as heat, light, mechanical motion, and sound; and the nature of a chemical reaction (National Center on the Economy and Education, Middle School Performance Standards, 1997)

- Frames questions to distinguish cause and effect; and identifies or controls variables in experimental or non-experimental research settings (National Center on the Economy and Education, Middle School Performance Standards, 1997)

- Works individually and in teams to collect and share information and ideas (National Center on the Economy and Education, Middle School Performance Standards, 1997)

Objectives

At the end of this lesson sequence the student will be able to do the following:

1. Identify three conditions necessary for sustained burning.
2. Construct predictions based on a series of observations that reveal a pattern.
3. Apply the observation skills of volume measurement and burning time.
4. Construct a graph from data collected during investigations with two related variables.
5. Draw a line of best fit through a series of data points.
6. Employ skills of *interpolation* and *extrapolation* in making predictions.
7. Formulate an inference between volume of air in a container and burning time of a candle.
8. Describe how the process skill of predicting can be used as a tool to help focus a scientific investigation.

Prerequisite Learning

Suggestions are shared along the margins of these pages to provide additional teacher guidance related to accommodating students with disabilities, with particular attention to those students with learning disabilities, attention deficit disorder/hyperactivity disorder, and/or developmental delay. While reviewing the vocabulary, whenever possible, display the actual objects. For example (holding up a meter stick): "How long is this stick? What is the distance between each of the numbers on the stick? What is the distance between each mark within each number? This tool employs what system of measurement? What number base is the metric system built on?"

The same questioning sequence can be used with a 1000 ml. graduated cylinder. Units of time can be discussed as well, if necessary.

Student pages are numbered to help maintain order. (Pages are triple punched when they are to be included in a 3-ring binder.)

Review Prior to Instructional Sequence

Vocabulary

Prediction - act of foretelling

Observation - receiving information from our senses (hearing, sight, smell, tactile, taste)

Inference - guess based on information from observation

Measurement - act of determining the dimensions, capacity, or amount of something

Metric - system of measurement built on base 10

Meter - base unit of length in the metric system

Centimeter - 1/100 of a meter

Millimeter - 1/1000 of a meter

Liter - base unit of volume in the metric system

Milliliter - 1/1000 of a liter

Gram - base unit of mass in the metric system

Kilogram - 1000 grams

Time - element of measurement based on duration and lacking specific dimensions

Day - duration of 1 full rotation of the Earth

Hour - 1/24 of a day

Minute - 1/60 of an hour

Vocabulary words are reviewed prior to beginning an activity.

Second - 1/60 of a minute

After vocabulary review, display a transparency of the graph titled: "Prerequisite Competency Check-Graph of Growing Plant." Question students concerning the data shown on the graph and introduce the prediction skills of interpolation and extrapolation.

Discuss interpolation as making predictions between known data points and extrapolation as making predictions beyond known data points. Demonstrate to them the line of best fit and how it can be used to help make predications from an infinite number of data points.

The graph shown here is a record of a growing plant:

Prerequisite graphing skills are reviewed prior to beginning of the activity.

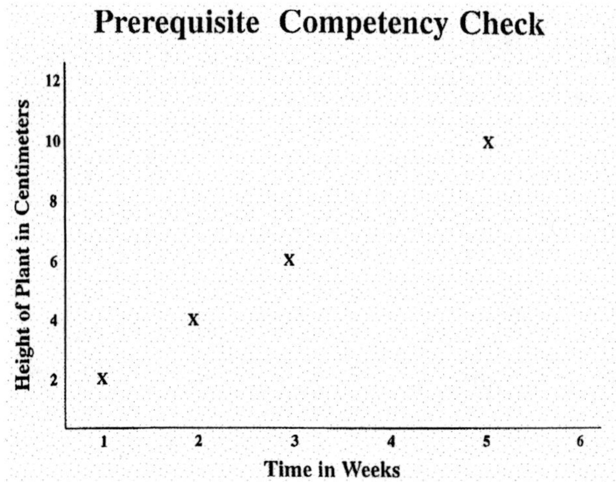

Questions are simple, direct, and sequential when possible.

1. What information is shared on the x-axis?

2. What information is shared on the y-axis?

3. Label the Origin

4. What are the values of x and y at the Origin?

5. How tall was the plant after 1 week?

6. How tall was the plant after 2 weeks?

7. How tall was the plant after 3 weeks?

8. How tall was the plant after 5 weeks?

9. How much did the plant grow between week 3 and week 5?

10. Draw a line of best fit through the data

11. How tall would you predict the plant to be at the end of 4 weeks?

12. Explain why you made that prediction

Vocabulary Review

Volume
Graduated Cylinder
Milliliter
Liter
Variable
Prediction
Inference
Average (mean)
Line Graph
Line of Best Fit

Vocabulary is listed as reminder.

Interpolation
Extrapolation

New vocabulary is clarified.

Lesson 1
The Suffocating Candle-Teacher Demonstration

Science Standards

- Understands transfer of energy, such as transformation of energy as heat, light, mechanical motion, and sound; and the nature of a chemical reaction, (National Center on the Economy and Education, Middle Level Performance Standards, 1997).

- Frames questions to distinguish cause and effect; identifies or controls variables in experimental or non-experimental research settings (National Center on the Economy and Education, Middle Level Performance Standards, 1997).

Materials

- aluminum pie tin
- sand
- candle
- glass jar

Stimulus Material

Distribute the student record sheet to all students before the demonstration. Set up a demonstration using an aluminum pie tin with a layer of sand, a candle, and a jar larger than the candle with a large enough opening to place over the candle. Light the candle on a desk or table so all the students can see. Ask, "What conditions do you need to have a fire?" Try to elicit the responses of fuel, oxygen, and sufficient heat (kindling point) to get the fuel burning. Then discuss, "How can you put out a fire?" Again, elicit from the students the removal of one or more of the conditions needed for a fire.

Demonstrate blowing out the candle and ask why the candle has gone out. Students will usually say that the oxygen was taken away. Demonstrate putting out the candle by waving a book or paper in front of it. Through conversation you can usually bring out that the temperature is cooled below the kindling point of the fuel.

Then ask the students, "What do you think will happen if I put this jar over the candle?" Ask them to write their predictions about how long the candle will continue to burn. Repeat the experiment several times, sometimes stimulating an air exchange and sometimes not. Discuss the need for the control of variables and the need to create the same conditions for each experiment in order to get good data. Discuss the use of multiple trials and taking an average to come up with a best number to plot on the graph.

The Suffocating Candle - Student Record Sheet

Objectives

At the end of this lesson sequence the student will:

1. Identify three conditions necessary for sustained burning.
2. Describe three conditions that can be changed, any of which will put out a fire.
3. Apply the observation skills of volume measurement and burning time.
4. Construct a graph from data collected during investigations of two related variables.

The objectives are stated and shared with the student.

Materials

Materials needed are provided. _____ 1 pencil

Student Record

Guide is provided to help student keep a record of important information stored during demonstration.

Three conditions needed for sustained burning:

____

____

____

Three ways to put out a fire:

____

____

____

Lesson 2
The Suffocating Candle

Science Standards

- Understands transfer of energy, such as transformation of energy as heat, light, mechanical motion, and sound; and the nature of a chemical reaction, (National Center on the Economy and Education, Middle Level Performance Standards, 1997).

- Frames questions to distinguish cause and effect; and identifies or controls variables in experimental or non-experimental research settings, (National Center on the Economy and Education, Middle Level Performance Standards, 1997).

Guidance Cues

Divide the class into groups. Be sure each child in each group has a specific task. Some suggestions are as follows:

1. One child could be the safety officer who holds the matches, lights the candle when necessary, puts the match out by dipping it in a jar of water, and watches to see that others do not carelessly get too close to the lighted candle. (Of course, if regulations do not permit a child to light the candle, you will have to do this.)
2. Another child could be responsible for putting the jar over the lighted candle and ventilating the jar before each trial. A simple way to ventilate a jar is to alternately stuff a cloth into the jar and remove it, repeating the procedure a few times. Unless the air in the jar is renewed between trials, the burning times may vary considerably. The jar should be placed over the candle quickly, and it should not be held inverted above the flame for any length of time.
3. A third child could observe the candle, call "Start" and "Stop" at the agreed on signals.
4. The timer could watch the clocks second hand and read the time at the "Start" and "Stop" signals.
5. The recorder could write down the times that the timer called and calculate the interval.

Have the groups first make two or more measurements of burning time for each jar and record their observations in tabular form. Observe students as they conduct their investigations. Watch to insure that they make predictions prior to conducting the experiments. Check their graphs to be sure the information relating to the data and the units of measure are displayed on each axis. Look at the origin and consistency of unit graduations on each axis. Observe as they draw in their lines of best fit and use their graphs to interpolate and extrapolate predictions.

Members of Our Cooperative Work Group

Leader

____

Materials Manager

____

Technician

____

Reporter/Recorder

____

Objectives

At the end of this lesson sequence the student will:

1. Construct predictions based on a series of observations that reveal a pattern.
2. Apply the observation skills of volume measurement and burning time.
3. Construct a graph from data collected during investigations of two related variables.
4. Draw a line of best fit through a series of data points.

Materials

- pencil
- book of matches
- aluminum pie tin
- Jars A, B, D
- 500 grams of sand

Materials list offers numbers and picture clues to help students who may have reading difficulties.

A	B	D
___	___	___
Smallest Jar	Slightly Larger Jar	Large Jar

___ 1 small container of water to dip match in after burning.

___ 1 small container to put in used matches

___ 1 candle

___ 1 sheet of material to put candle on

List is inclusive if it includes writing items and paper needs.

___ 1 50 milliliter graduated cylinder

___ 1 1000 milliliter graduated cylinder

___ 1 sheet of graph paper

___ water

___ paper towels

Clean up supplies are included.

Rules of Classroom Safety

Use unbreakable materials and materials without points or sharp edges when possible.

1. Form a line when picking up materials.
2. Use caution when handling glass.
3. Be respectful and careful anytime there is the use of fire.
4. Be cooperative and supportive of others in your work group.

Directions

Directions are short, simple, and sequential.

___ 1. Form a line and walk slowly to pick up the materials needed for your experiments.

___ 2. Determine the burning time of the candle under the three jars (A, B, D); conduct three trials for each jar.

___ 3. Determine the average burning time for each jar.

___ 4. Determine the volume of the three jars (A, B, D).

___ 5. Construct a graph using the data you have collected.

___ 6. Draw a line of best fit.

Record of Data Collection

Guides are provided for recording data.

Jar A

Burning Time 1 __________

Burning Time 2 __________

Burning Time 3 __________

Average Burning Time - Jar A __________

Volume of Jar A __________

Each student should have his/her own copy of handout sheets.

Jar B

Burning Time 1 __________

Burning Time 2 __________

Burning Time 3 __________

Average Burning Time - Jar B __________

Volume of Jar B __________

Jar D

Burning Time 1 __________

Burning Time 2 __________

Burning Time 3 __________

Average Burning Time - Jar D __________

Volume of Jar D __________

Format of Graph - (If necessary refer to graph titled Prerequisite Competency Check)

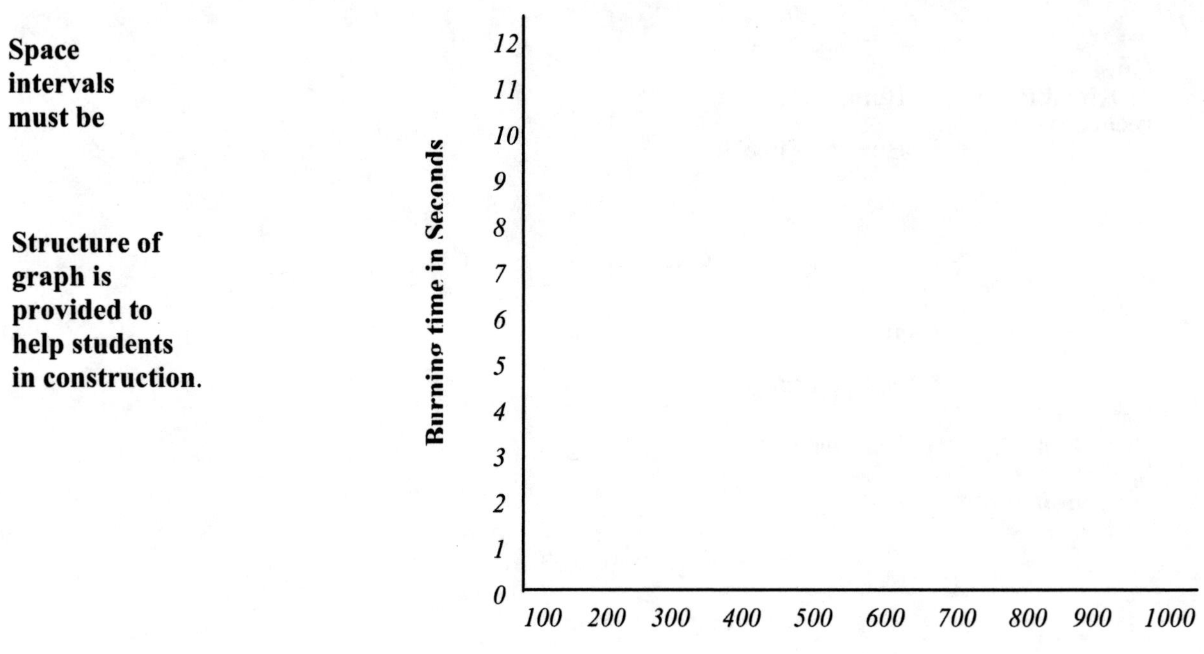

Volume in Milliliters

Lesson 3
Student Record Sheet Interpolation

Members of Our Cooperative Work Group

Leader

____

Material Manager

____

Technician

____

Reporter/Recorder

____

Objectives

At the end of this lesson sequence the student will be able to do the following:

1. Construct predictions based on a series of observations that reveal a pattern.
2. Apply the observation skills of volume measurement and burning time.
3. Construct a graph from data collected during investigations of two related variables.
4. Draw a line of best fit through a series of data points.
5. Employ skills of interpolation in making predictions.

Materials

- pencil
- book of matches
- aluminum pie tin
- Jar C
- 500 grams of sand
- completed graph from Activity 2

Materials list offers numbers and picture clues to help students who may have reading difficulties.

Checklist blanks are provided to help students keep a record of items gathered for the experiment.

___	___	___	___
A	B	C	D
Smallest Jar	Slightly Larger Jar	Medium Jar	Large Jar

List is inclusive if it includes writing items and paper needs.

___ 1 small container of water to dip match in after burning.

___ 1 small container to put in used matches

___ 1 candle

___ 1 sheet of material to put candle on

___ 1 50 milliliter graduated cylinder

___ 1 1000 milliliter graduated cylinder

___ 1 sheet of graph paper

Clean up supplies are included.

___ water

___ paper towels

___ Jar C (to be picked up after construction of your graph including a line of best fit)

Jar C

Burning Time 1 __________
Burning Time 2 __________
Burning Time 3 __________

Average Burning Time - Jar C __________

Predicted volume of Jar C (using the graph you have constructed)

____

The skill used in making the prediction (predicting between known points of data)

____

Measured volume of Jar C ____

Difference between the predicted volume of Jar C and the actual volume of jar C __________

Checklist (continued from Lesson 2)

Checklist is provided for students to check off each completed step.

___ 1. Pick up jar C

___ 2. Determine the burning time of jar C

___ 3. Use your graph to predict (infer) the volume of jar C

___ 4. Measure the volume of jar C

___ 5. Compare your prediction with the measured volume.

Lesson 4
Student Record Sheet-Extrapolation

Members of Our Cooperative Work Group

Leader

____

Material Manager

____

Technician

____

Reporter/Recorder

____

Objectives

At the end of this lesson sequence the student will:

1. Construct predictions based on a series of observations that reveal a pattern.
2. Apply the observation skills of volume measurement and burning time.
3. Construct a graph from data collected during investigations of two related variables.
4. Draw a line of best fit through a series of data points.
5. Employ skills of extrapolation in making predictions.

Materials

___ 1 pencil

___ 1 book of matches

___ Jar E (to be picked up after construction of your graph including a line of best fit)

A	B	C	D	E
Smallest Jar	Slightly Larger Jar	Medium Jar	Large Jar	Jumbo Jar

___ 1 small container of water to dip match in after burning.

___ 1 small container to put in used matches

___ 1 candle

___ 1 sheet of material to put candle on

___ 1 1000 milliliter graduated cylinder

___ 1 graph constructed during Lesson 2

___ 3 sheets of graph paper

___ water

___ paper towels

Rules of Classroom Safety

1. Form a line when picking up materials.
2. Use caution when handling glass.
3. Be respectful and careful anytime there is the use of fire.
4. Be cooperative and supportive of others in your work group.

Directions

1. Form a line and walk slowly to pick up the materials needed for your experiments.
2. Determine the burning time of the candle under Jar E; conduct three trials.
3. Determine the average burning time.
4. Extend the graph made in Lesson 2 adding the data you have collected.
5. Draw a line of best fit.
6. Use your graph to predict (infer) the volume of jar E.
7. Measure the volume of jar E.
8. Compare your prediction with the measured volume.

Record of Data Collection

Jar E

Burning Time 1____________________

Burning Time 2 ____________________

Burning Time 3 ____________________

Average Burning Time - Jar E ____________________

Extension of Your Graph

Burning Time in Seconds

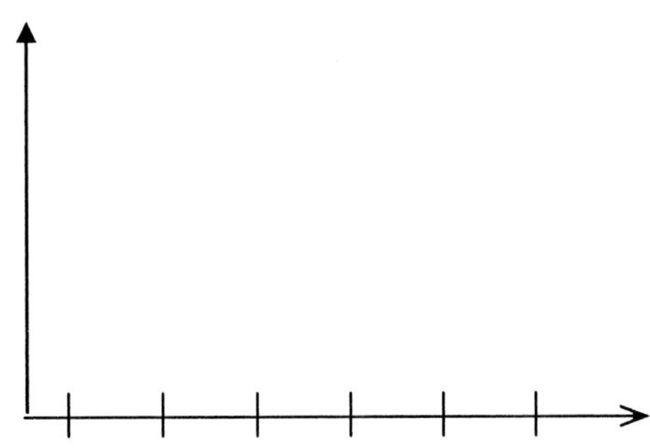

Volume of Container in Milliliters

Some structure is provided but less information than prior experiment.

Eliciting Performance

Predicted volume of Jar E (using the graph you have constructed, and extending the boundaries)

____

The skill used in making the prediction (predicting beyond known points of data)

____

Measured volume of Jar E ____

Formulate an inference between the volume of air in a container and burning time: __________

Feedback

Ask the students in each group to share their graphs and the process skills used (interpolation and extrapolation) in making their predictions. Ask: "Which prediction process was more accurate- interpolation or extrapolation ? Why ?" Discuss two common extrapolations -- weather prediction and the stock market. Ask about predications close to known data points and those farther away. Discuss the degree to which they trust the weatherman for predictions about the weather the next day? the next week? the next month?

Reinforce the work of students where the graphs are done well. Discuss how to present the data in ways that others can have a clear understanding of what you did. Discuss the importance of affirmation in science and perhaps bring out the problems when scientists get too eager, as in the case of the scientists who claimed they had a process for "cold temperature fusion" which was discredited by other scientists who replicated their research. If the students are mature enough, you may wish to describe "lines of best fit" which are not straight lines.

Performance Assessment

A group competency check can be conducted as a group activity in which students collect their own data rather than the bounce height data shared in parentheses on the graph. The same questions are appropriate. However, if the answer bank is used, modifications will be needed.

Group Competency Check

Data Collected from a Bouncing Ball Investigation

	Drop height of Ball in Centimeters	Bounce Height of Ball Centimeters
Data is simplified so student can focus on skill in demonstration.	100	(50)
	80	(40)
	60	(30)
	40	(20)

Questions are direct and sequenced.

Instructions

1. Construct a graph from the data collected from a Bouncing Ball Investigation shown above.
2. Draw a line of best fit.
3. Predict how high the ball will bounce if dropped from 90 centimeters _________
4. The skill you used to make this prediction is __________________
5. Predict how high the ball will bounce if dropped from 200 centimeters _________
6. The skill you used to make this prediction is __________________
7. Predict how high the ball was dropped from if it bounced to a height of 25 centimeters

   ____
8. The skill you used to make this prediction is ___________________
9. Predict how high the ball was dropped from if it bounded to a height of 75 centimeters.
10. The skill you used to make this prediction is ___________________
11. (not in answer bank) Formulate an inference that describes a relationship between the drop height and bounce height of a ball:

Answer Bank

	45	100	50	150
Word bank is provided for students who have difficulty with vocabulary and spelling.	Interpolation	Extrapolation		

Individual Competency Check

Materials Needed

- spring, or rubber band, with two large paper clips
- meter stick
- 5 metal washers of the same size

Ask the student, or student group, to hang the spring (or rubber band with paper clips) on the meter stick, place one washer at the other end and record the amount of stretch of the spring. Repeat for two and four washers. Ask the student(s) to make a graph of their data. Now, ask the student(s) to predict how much the spring will stretch with three washers and describe what prediction skill they used (interpolation), and how much the spring will stretch for five washers and the prediction skill they used (extrapolation). Allow them to test their predictions. Follow with a discussion of what they did and relate the discussion to the instructional objectives.

Enhancing Retention and Transfer

1. Gather an assortment of bouncing balls. Conduct investigations collecting data and predicting the height of the first bounce using activities similar to those presented in this sequence.

2. Compare different bouncing balls making inferences between the height of the first bounce and the number of bounces.

3. Make inferences about the composition of the balls, the height of the first bounce and the number of bounces.

4. Graph data from one ball recording the bounce height of multiple bounces. (i.e. if the first bounce height from 100 cm. is 60 cm., drop the ball from 60 cm. and record the bounce height, etc.). Discuss the shape of the graph and use the data to make interpolations and extrapolations for other drop heights.

5. Set up stations where you can put inclined planes end to end so that a marble released on one plane will roll up the other. (Foam insulation tubes for pipes cut in half work very well.) Roll the marbles from different release points and record the high point of the marble on the other plane. Again, draw lines of best fit and make predictions using the skills of interpolation and extrapolation.

Suffocating Candle

Specific Accommodations by Disability Category

Motor/Orthopedic

- Preview activity sequence with the student and discuss areas of comfort and discomfort relating to the experiments.
- Establish cooperative work groups.
- Examine accessibility and good visibility for the student if he/she elects to not light the candle or place jars over the candle.
- Purchase measuring instruments with adaptations which allow the student to be an active participant (i.e. graduated cylinders with handles).
- Provide a computer with software for recording data and making graphs.
- Purchase a device such as an "extended arm" to allow the student to place the jar on the candle or move objects.
- Allow extra time for student and peers to continue with activities outside of regular class time.
- Review work area for height, accessibility of supplies and equipment, and safety.
- Be especially careful if student does not have good tactile sensory receptors. They can easily get a severe burn from candles.

Visually Impaired

- Review the workspace and brainstorm about accommodations that might allow the student greater participation in the experiments.
- Preview the activity sequence. Have an associate work with the student in lighting the candle and placing the jar over the candle.
- Set up cooperative work groups.
- Acquire an alternative sensing device that gives an auditory signal when the candle goes out. (Lesson 2, 3, 4)
- Have measurement devices available with adaptations for students with visual impairments.
- Provide a computer with software for recording data and making graphs.
- Provide tactile measuring devices, graduated cylinders, and meter sticks.
- Provide a series of raised tactile drawings of the teacher demonstration sequence. Provide oral description of what is being done throughout the demonstration (Lesson 1).
- Plan responsibility in advance relating to communication during group activities.
- The activities involve using glassware and candles. Consider accessibility and safety in handling the materials.

Hearing Impaired

- Prepare printed directions in advance and laminate a copy so the direction sheets are not affected by spilled water.
- Set up cooperative work groups.
- Allow for additional time to work on experiments outside of regular class time.
- Provide visuals that accommodate using step-by-step directions.
- Present lessons silently.
- Repeat responses of other students, or delay student response until the deaf student has good eye contact with the speaker (Lesson 1).
- Prepare students for communication during cooperative group work. Place deaf student with supportive peers.

Learning Disabilities

- Provide reading assistance using a teaching associate if needed
- Provide prior exposure to the print materials and vocabulary in advance, include supportive peers.
- Establish cooperative work groups.
- Provide assistance in graphing and interpretation, as appropriate.
- If necessary review specific responsibilities for working in the cooperative group prior to the start of each experiment.

Attention Deficit/Hyperactivity Disorder

- Position the student so there is good visibility.
- If necessary review specific responsibilities for working in the cooperative group prior to the start of each experiment.
- Provide prior exposure to print materials and vocabulary
- Establish cooperative work groups in advance; include supportive peers.
- Provide assistance in graphing and interpretation, as appropriate.
- Select a work station location that minimizes distractions.
- Provide additional opportunities to do investigations outside of regular class time.

Developmentally Delayed

- Work with the student on lighting the candle, predicting burning time, placing a jar over the candle, and discussing predictions a few times before the whole class experiment.
- Discuss participation options with the student; determine appropriate involvement during class time.
- Provide pre-instruction on vocabulary; select vocabulary appropriate for the student's ability.
- Share instructional packet with special education teacher in advance
- Allow opportunities for the student to conduct experiments with a supportive adult outside of class time.
- Establish cooperative work groups.
- Provide a partial graph to the student as appropriate.
- Provide reading assistants; utilize a teaching associate when possible.
- Use either peer assistants or associates to assist in graph construction.
- Provide additional opportunities to make predictions after graph is completed.

Behavior Disordered

- Consider appropriateness of the activity sequence for the student. There are safety considerations of others and you will be working with fire and glassware.
- Consider having the student conduct the experiments individually in a private setting.
- When appropriate, write a contract in advance specifying what behavior is expected and where the student can go if he/she begins to experience frustration.
- Consider trafficking of materials. Have materials organized and available when possible.
- Use proximity control and/or, when appropriate, a teacher associate.
- Select a work station location that minimizes distractions
- Be clear about duties and responsibilities of each member of the cooperative work group.

Speech/Language

- Prepare printed directions in advance and laminate a copy so the direction sheets are not affected by spilling water.
- Establish cooperative work groups in advance.
- Allow students to use a note pad and/or alternative communication devices.
- Discuss the learning outcomes and activities with the student in private.
- Practice patience in listening and model patience for the students in the class.
- Conduct the entire learning sequence without oral expression.

Autism

- Work with the student on lighting the candle, predicting burning time, placing a jar over the candle, and discussing predictions a few times before the whole class experiment.
- Discuss participation options with the student; determine appropriate involvement during class time.
- Control pacing and slow the pace of activities to allow for participation by the student; utilize a teacher associate to provide assistance.
- Provide pre-instruction on vocabulary; select vocabulary appropriate for the student's ability.
- Allow opportunities for the student to conduct experiments with a supportive adult inside/outside of class time.
- Provide a partial graph to the student, if appropriate.

Deaf/Blind

- Review the workspace and preview the activity sequence, brainstorming ways to increase the students involvement. Have an associate work with the student in lighting the candle and placing the jar over the candle.
- Provide tactile graphing materials.
- Conduct the experiments in advance with the adult attendant including the student when additional practice is appropriate. Discuss experimental procedures and desired learning outcomes before the experiments are done in the regular classroom.
- Acquire an alternative sensing device that gives a tactile signal when the candle goes out.
- Have measurement devices available with adaptations for students with visual impairments.
- Provide a computer with software for recording data and making graphs.
- Allow opportunities for additional practice.

Traumatic Brain Injury

- Consider appropriateness of the activity sequence for the student. There are safety considerations of others and you will be working with fire and glassware.
- Consider having the student conduct the experiments individually in a private setting.
- When appropriate, write a contract in advance specifying what behavior is expected and where the student can go if he/she begins to experience frustration.
- Review directions in advance.
- Prepare printed directions in advance and laminate a copy so the direction sheets are not affected by spilled water.
- Consider trafficking of materials.
- Use proximity control and/or, when appropriate, a teacher associate.
- Consider pacing.
- Provide a computer with software for recording data and making graphs.

Other Health Impairments

- Talk with the student and determine activities that are appropriate and desirable.
- Review safety considerations and possible consequences if an accident involving glass breakage occurs.
- Establish cooperative working groups.
- Provide a computer with software for recording data and making graphs.
- If student is taking medication that affects his/her energy level, conduct the experiment at a time when the student is alert.

Multi-Categorical

- Interview the student and/or other professionals providing assistance and establish appropriate learning priorities.
- Practice lessons in advance with a supportive adult; determine learning aids, (i.e., partial graphs) and prepare them in advance.
- Establish cooperative learning groups and include student to maximum extent possible.
- Consider visibility if student will primarily be an observer.
- Determine in advance the degree of accommodation and assistance required.

Suffocating Candle
Multiple Intelligence Modifications

Note: Enrichment through the addition of multiple intelligence activities might conflict with the basic premise of direct instruction because students will pursue different learning outcomes through self-selected approaches.

Verbal/Linguistic

- Select a time for story telling about bones, skeletons, and sharing of personal experiences, however students must use the appropriate scientific terminology in their conversation. This can be done in cooperative groups.
- Allow time for discussion and synthesis after the data collection activities. Encourage students to describe how they could apply what they have learned to new situations.
- Students can examine the lives of people who control fires (firefighters), or make fires (cooks or foundry workers); discuss the materials they use as fuels.

Logical/Mathematical

- The activities in the sequence are based on the application of logical/mathematical skills. Quantitative data collection, computation, and graphing activities are essential elements of the instructional sequence.
- Students can be encouraged to examine ways to share information that is clear, concise, and attractive to the reader. Ways to convey more information through better graphs can be explored.
- Have students graph temperature and weather conditions. Get a local maximum/minimum temperature table. Make comparisons and extrapolate weather forecasts.

Visual/Spatial

- Students can share a summary of their experiments through a sequence of drawings.
- The concept of fire can be explored through pictures and examining fire and its importance in human history.
- The vividness of colors associated with burning can be displayed through artistic expression.

Musical/Rhythmic

- Students can study musical sounds associated with fire and burning.
- Songs of romance and celebration associated with the warmth of winter seasons (i.e. roasting chestnuts by an open fire) can be included.

Interpersonal

- Students will be working in cooperative groups and conducting their investigations using collaboration and dialog.
- Students can plan ways to investigate other aspects of burning (i.e. different fuels) and work together to design experiments to answer their hypotheses.

Intrapersonal

- The activities should challenge the students' higher order thinking skills. A student can investigate using technology for data collection and reporting.
- A student could prepare a report of constructive and destructive factors associated with burning.

Naturalistic

- Students can use the internet to examine sources of energy, supplies of different types of fuel, and social implications involving energy use and disposal of waste products.
- Fossil fuels and the likely implications of fossil fuel use for the future of humankind can be studied.
- Students can study whaling and the importance and value of whale oil to the American colonists.

Chapter 7

Guided Discovery: An Investigation of Energy Sources

Overview

The instructional sequence on energy represents a modification of the Guided Discovery Learning Cycle approach presented in the Science Curriculum Improvement Study modality titled, *Energy Sources* (1970). The concept of the "teachable moment" is integrated into the approach. However, embedded within the overall sequence centered around the conceptual scheme of energy flow are mini-sequences that expose students to more specific concepts related to energy awareness. These minisequences often contain one, two, or all of the elements in the learning cycle. For example, an exploratory activity might close with an explanation. Or students could build on prior learning at the beginning of the lesson with the concept (explanation) and transition into the application (elaboration) phase as the primary learning experience. This approach is found to work effectively in the classroom.

Exploration: The exploration phase of Guided Instruction provides students with experiences to familiarize them with the concept being studied. During exploration activities, the students interact with each other and explore materials and ideas together. The teacher serves as a resource and guide. Questioning is appropriate, telling or explaining the concept is not. The primary goal is to develop a common base of experience through hands-on activities. The model lesson sequence on energy includes several short activities that allow the students to use tactile sensations and materials uncommon to conventional teaching.

Concept (Explanation): The concept phase is more teacher-directed. Students are guided in learning experiences that directly relate to the concept(s) being studied. Appropriate vocabulary is introduced. In this phase, the students should develop an understanding of the concept of energy and the importance of energy transfer as a means of explaining phenomena in our daily lives. During activities, the students construct and share their explanations of the principle or conceptual scheme. The teacher or other students help clarify misconceptions and direct student learning toward the desired learning outcomes.

Application (Elaboration): During these activities, the students form connections with previous learning and apply their knowledge to new situations. The teacher is again a questioner and guide. The role of the teacher is to help students internalize the concept. The teacher observes their ability to accommodate and apply their knowledge to new and unfamiliar experiences. Students use these new experiences to extend their knowledge and skills.

Evaluation: Evaluation should be formative and ongoing throughout the sequence of instructional activities, not summative. Evaluation should be both cognitive and affective, with attention to attitudes and values students exhibit during instruction. The teacher should look at the learning outcomes and ways the students can naturally display their understanding of the concept(s). Much of the evaluation can be conducted through well-guided questions and allowing students to express their learning through pictures, oral explanation, and free writing.

Science Standards

The student produces evidence that demonstrates understanding of the following:

- ➢ Properties of objects and materials, such as similarities and differences in the size, weight, and color of objects; the ability of materials to react with other substances; and different states of matter (National Center on the Economy and Education, Elementary School Performance Standards, 1997).

- Position and motion of objects, such as how the motion of an object can be described by tracing and measuring its position over time; and how sound is produced by vibrating objects (National Center on the Economy and Education, Elementary School Performance Standards, 1997).

- Motions and forces, such as inertia and the net effect of balanced and unbalanced forces (National Center on the Economy and Education, Middle School Performance Standards, 1997).

- Transfer of energy, such as transformation of energy as heat, light, mechanical motion, and sound; and the nature of a chemical reaction (National Center on the Economy and Education, Middle School Performance Standards, 1997).

Lesson 1
Paper Airplane Flight Contest

Science Standard

The student produces evidence that demonstrates understanding of the following:

- Transfer of energy, such as transformation of energy as heat, light, mechanical motion, and sound; and the nature of a chemical reaction (National Center on the Economy and Education, Middle School Performance Standards, 1997)

Exploration

Materials

- 8 1/2 " x 11" sheets of copy paper (preferably used) for each student
- string
- meter sticks or tapes (if possible meter sticks with braille markings to allow students with visual impairments to make measurements)

Advance preparation

- Select a suitable area for testing the airplanes. The playground, a gymnasium, or multipurpose room are preferable to the classroom. Use an indoor area if the day is windy. All sheets of paper should be of the same size and weight. Arrange the students into groups of 4 to 6.

Making the Airplanes

- Show students the paper they will use to construct their airplane. Explain that the contest is to see *whose plane flies the greatest distance.* Instruct them to write their name on their plane.

Explain two rules: (1) Each plane must be made from **one** piece of paper; (2) no other objects may be added to the paper (no tape, glue, or paper clips). If a child has no design ideas for a plane, team the child with another pupil for assistance.

Launching the Airplanes

- Students should launch all planes in the same direction from one starting point. Have the children line up behind the starting point and each take their turn. *Planes need to remain in place where they land so everyone can see the distances of flight in comparison with each other.* After all students have thrown the planes, measure the distance of flight from the launch point and prepare a graph of the data.

Students may modify their designs or build another airplane if they have new ideas they would like to try. Allow time for this work. Hold a second contest to test the changes made.

Concept

On a chalkboard or overhead, write the heading, "Variables that Affected the Distance of Flight". Ask students to identify the variables that affected the flight distance of their airplanes. They might mention the height from which a plane was thrown, the launching speed, the design of the plane, etc. Introduce the definition of the word "variable" as a factor with an impact on the outcome of the experiment. You may also wish to discuss controlled and uncontrolled variables.

Discuss the role of energy in the flight of the airplane. Use the terms “energy source”, “energy receiver”, “energy transfer,” and “energy chain”. For example, the food students eat is an energy source and the muscles in the arm are an energy receiver; the arm is an energy source and the airplane is an energy receiver; the flying airplane is an energy source and the air and object that the airplane strikes is an energy receiver; finally, the energy for conducting the experiment dissipated as heat.

You may discuss the two types of energy: kinetic and potential; and seven forms of energy: chemical, electrical, heat, light, mechanical, nuclear, and sound. You may also wish to discuss the Law of Conservation of Energy that states: Energy cannot be created or destroyed, but only changed in form or type. Invite a self-evaluation of their understanding.

Application

If your pupils are particularly interested in the paper airplanes, schedule a contest in which the objective is a *long flight time* rather than a great flight distance. For this contest, all participants release their planes simultaneously at your signal. The last plane to hit the ground or an obstacle is the winner.

Lesson 2
Ice-Melting Contest

Science Standard

The student produces evidence that demonstrates understanding of the following:

- Properties of objects and materials, such as similarities and differences in the size, weight, and color of objects; the ability of materials to react with other substances; and different states of matter (National Center on the Economy and Education, Elementary School Performance Standards, 1997)

Exploration

Materials

- a plastic baggie for each student (plus a few extras)
- a bag of ice cubes
- graduated cylinders for measuring (if possible graduated cylinders with floats to allow measurement by students with visual impairments)
- paper towels

Advance preparation

Arrange the students into groups of 3 or 4. Each student receives a baggie with 3-4 ice cubes in it. They are asked not to handle the bags until the contest begins. They are informed that they will have a fixed time interval in which to see how much water they can obtain by melting the ice.

Contest Rules

1. Children must remain in their seats and keep the ice cubes in the plastic bag until the end of the contest.

2. Leave the water in the plastic bag until you are instructed to transfer the water from the bag into the graduated cylinder.

3. The teacher will give the start and stop signals.

4. Water that spills or leaks out of the bag will not be measured.

5. If a bag breaks and the student wants a new bag, he or she can receive one, but the team will receive a 5-milliliter penalty for each new bag.

When all students are ready, start the contest, challenging the students to convert as much ice to water as possible. Signal the students to stop at the end of the designated time (2-3 minutes generally works well).

The students are given time to transfer the water from their ice cubes to the graduated cylinder(s). A penalty is assessed if the cylinders contain any ice. You may clean up immediately or after the class discussion.

Concept

After the students have transferred the water into the graduated cylinder, invite them to present their findings. Use a histogram to display and compare the class results. Students can describe the *methods* they used to melt the ice. Ask the children to identify the *energy sources* they employed to melt the ice. Use the students' statements to inquire about the *variables* involved in the contest and invite the students to describe the *effects* each of these might have on the amount of water obtained. Ask what happened in terms of energy source, energy receiver, and energy transfer.

Application

Invite students to preserve an ice cube as long as they can by preventing the *transfer of energy*. Allow them a week to prepare a container that can receive up to six ice cubes and to keep a log of their work. Indicate that the container cannot contain an external power source. Keep all of the containers in the classroom for 24 hours. Then open the containers and determine which student has the most ice. The activity's real value comes when the children compare and evaluate the various successful and unsuccessful procedures. When reading the records of the participating students, you can evaluate their ability to plan, carry out, and describe an experiment independently.

Evaluation

1. Ask each student to write a paper containing answers to the following:
2. How did you attempt to preserve your ice cubes?
3. How effective was your strategy?
4. How would you get the ice cubes to last longer next time?

Lesson 3
Temperature Change as Evidence of Energy Transfer

Science Standard

The student produces evidence that demonstrates understanding of the following:

- Transfer of energy, such as transformation of energy as heat, light, mechanical motion, and sound; and the nature of a chemical reaction (National Center on the Economy and Education, Middle School Performance Standards, 1997)

Exploration

Materials

- thermometer with braille markings (see Appendix H)
- containers for the thermometers (four or more per group)
- a hot water source
- ice water (if possible, computer-interfaced temperature probes that can be used by students with visual impairments collecting data through auditory output)
- graduated cylinders and/or syringes with adaptations for students with visual impairments
- paper towels.
- optional: student blindfolds that can be used to simulate circumstances for students with visual impairments while conducting the investigations

Advance preparation

Prior to the activity, spin the base of the thermometers so each student group has an opportunity to standardize its own thermometer. You can begin with either a bucket of ice water in which the assumed temperature is 0 degrees Celsius or a container of water with a thermometer in it. Students should be arranged in groups of three to four. If you wish to simulate a situation involving visual impairment, designate one student to wear a blindfold and inform the group that the student with the visual impairment should collect all of the data in the experiments.

Concept

Targeted concepts include: Measuring temperature in a system using a thermometer; measuring the amounts of transferred energy as indicated by changes of temperature; and predicting temperatures of mixtures of warm and cold water.

The type of thermometer used in the activities is a bi-metal strip in a coil. Conventional thermometer scales are based on the freezing and boiling temperatures of pure water at sea level. There are two standard scales -- the Fahrenheit scale and the Celsius scale.

Application

1. Place the thermometer into the ice water solution and determine the temperature, then place the thermometer into the hot water solution and determine the temperature.

2. Challenge each group to prepare a mixture that is a specific temperature (i.e. 20 degrees Celsius), by mixing appropriate amounts of hot and cold water. Do not allow them to use the thermometer until after they have completed the trial. They should record the amount of hot and cold water used, and then check the accuracy of their attempt by using the thermometer to determine the actual temperature.

3. Additional challenges can be offered depending upon student interest and abilities.

Lesson 4
A Plane on a String

Science Standards

The student produced evidence that demonstrates understanding of the following:

- Transfer of energy, such as transformation of energy as heat, light, mechanical motion, and sound; and the nature of a chemical reaction (National Center on the Economy, 1997)

Exploration

Materials

- model planes (see below)
- meter sticks and meter sticks with braille markings
- string and fishing line
- blindfolds if desired to simulate data collection for students with visual impairments. The planes can be assembled with the students or in advance.

Model Plane Construction

Materials

- 1 propeller, 1 hook, 1 rubber band # 33 (available from http://www.delta-education.com)
- 1 super jumbo straw (e.g. McDonalds), 1 regular straw, 2 popsicle or paste sticks
- Tools: hole punch, scissors, stapler, piece of sandpaper

Procedure

1. Fold the super jumbo straw in half and cut it in the middle. Punch a hole near the end of each piece. Slide the regular straw through the holes (see Appendix I).

2. Trap the ends of the super jumbo straw halves between the two popsicle sticks. (You may wish to taper 1 side of the sticks in advance with sandpaper to make it easier to slide on the propeller and hook.) Staple through the popsicle sticks at the intersection of the ends of the straws. Be sure to catch each straw end with one edge of the staple (see Appendix I).

3. Slide the propeller on one end of the popsicle stick and the hook onto the other end. Catch 1 end of the rubber band to the hook and the other to the propeller.

Concept

1. The activity is interrupted and each group is asked to prepare an energy chain of at least six links describing the energy source, energy receiver, and evidence of energy transfer for each link: (for example, food you ate this morning to finger (finger can move), finger to propeller (propeller turns), propeller to rubber band (rubber band twists), rubber band to propeller (propeller turns), propeller to air (Newton's Third Law: For every action, there is an equal and opposite reaction) and plane moves forward on string, moving plane to string (change in temperature), and finally, energy dissipated as heat.

2. Introduce the terms "energy source", "energy transfer", "energy receiver" and "energy chain" as a means to present an operational description of the flow of energy in a system.

Application

Ask students to plan an investigation in which the plane goes the maximum distance on the string without touching the other end. Discuss the importance of separation and control of variables in replicating an experiment. Use a contest or challenge to see which team is the closest without touching the other end. Discuss replicability, variables, and degree of confidence in making predictions.

1. Arrange students in groups of 3 or 4. Ask students to tie a string or fish line to a chair or table at about seat height, then thread the plane on the string and tie it to another chair or table approximately two meters away.

2. Allow students to explore how to make the plane travel along the string.

3. Encourage students to explore and discover the plane and how it operates. Each group is challenged to investigate variables that will enable its plane to fly the length of the string without touching the other side.

Lesson 5
Energy Transfer in Chemical Change

Science Standard

The student produces evidence that demonstrates understanding of the following:

- Transfer of energy, such as transformation of energy as heat, light, mechanical motion, and sound; and the nature of a chemical reaction (National Center on the Economy, 1997)

Exploration

Materials

- plastic containers for water
- measuring spoons
- sodium thiosulfate (approximately 500 grams)
- anhydrous magnesium sulfate (approximately 500 grams)
- thermometers, and/or computer interface with temperature probes
- Alternative source of anhydrous magnesium sulfate: Epsom salts is a form of magnesium sulfate that includes water as part of the crystals. Anhydrous magnesium sulfate can be obtained from Epsom salts if the water is baked out in an oven. To enable pupils to compare the interaction of sodium thiosulfate and water with that of still another material, provide the class with Epsom salts. One group should observe the rather small temperature change that accompanies the dissolving of Epsom salts in water, and another group should bake samples of Epsom salts in their home ovens. Bake: One half pound Epsom salts in an aluminum pie tin @ 450° F. for about an hour. Cool. If caked, turn upside down, break into small pieces and bake an additional half hour.

Procedure

Arrange students into groups of 2-4, depending upon the availability of materials. The effects of chemical changes that are exothermic (heat gain) or endothermic (heat loss) are investigated in these activities. Water serves as an energy source as sodium thiosulfate dissolves. Water is an energy receiver, gaining heat while anhydrous magnesium sulfate dissolves.

Heat consumed by dissolving sodium thiosulfate.

Provide each student group with approximately 30 grams of sodium thiosulfate and invite them to investigate some of the variables that affect the temperature of sodium thiosulfate solutions. Ask them to record the water temperature, place approximately one teaspoon of sodium thiosulfate into a water glass, 250 ml. (about 8 ozs.), half full and observe the temperature change as the crystals dissolve. Discuss the temperature drop as evidence that heat was given up by the water and consumed by the process of dissolving sodium thiosulfate.

Heat produced by dissolving magnesium sulfate.

Provide each student group with approximately 30 grams of anhydrous magnesium sulfate and invite them to investigate some of the variables that affect the temperature of anhydrous magnesium sulfate solutions. Ask them to record the water temperature, place approximately one teaspoon of anhydrous magnesium sulfate into about half of a glass of water, and observe the temperature change as the crystals dissolve. Discuss the temperature gain as evidence that heat was transferred to the water and obtained during the process of dissolving anhydrous magnesium sulfate.

With this anhydrous magnesium sulfate, the class can carry out dissolving projects that are similar to those described previously with sodium thiosulfate. The only difference is that heat is produced during the dissolving process, so that the solution temperature rises rather than falls. Children might investigate how the quantities of water and anhydrous magnesium sulfate, the initial temperature of the materials, and variables affect the amount of temperature rise. Each group should prepare an energy chain to describe the energy flow from the beginning to the end of the experiments.

Concept

Discuss the terms "energy source", "energy recess" and "evidence of energy transfer". The teacher may wish to discuss the importance of the understanding of chemical change as a very useful tool in making human life more comfortable.

While students make their observations, challenge them to concentrate on the temperature drop that occurs while the crystals dissolve, rather than on the solution's final temperature. This is a more abstract way to interpret the data because the temperature drop must be calculated from the initial and final liquid temperatures and is not directly observable. The children may find that varying the initial water temperature does not affect the drop in temperature nearly as much as it affects the final solution temperature.

Application

Have students design an experiment in which a specific amount of salt will produce a predictable change in temperature. The students can then replicate conditions and change groups. Have another group carry out the investigation and compare the results with the group that designed the experiment. Each group can present an energy chain to describe the energy flow from the beginning to the end of the experiment.

Lesson 6
Energy Transfer in Chemical Change

Science Standard

The student produces evidence that demonstrates understanding of the following:

- Transfer of energy, such as transformation of energy as heat, light, mechanical motion, and sound; and the nature of a chemical reaction (National Center on the Economy, 1997)

Exploration

Materials

- 1 gallon Ziploc bags
- 500 grams of calcium chloride
- box of baking soda
- phenol red solution (.1 gram of phenol red in 250 ml. of .01N sodium hydroxide)
- clear film canisters
- paper towels

Advance Preparation

- Students should wear safety goggles and engage in appropriate laboratory safety conduct. Arrange students in groups of two to four.

Guiding the Activity

Carefully place the unmixed chemicals in the 1- gallon plastic Ziploc® bag as follows:

- 30 grams of calcium chloride in one bottom corner of the bag
- 15 grams of baking soda in the other bottom corner of the bag
- Half a film canister of phenol red solution in the top half of the bag
- Carefully squeeze as much air out as possible and seal your bag. Without opening the bag, invert the canister of phenol red solution. Feel the chemical interactions in each of the two bottom corners of the bag and then mix all of the materials.

Application

Prepare a report describing as many of the changes as you can. Relate the terms of "energy source", "energy receiver", and "evidence of energy transfer" in describing everything that happened in the experiment.

Plan an investigation using the materials. Describe in advance, what you perceive will happen including evidence of energy transfer. Then conduct your experiment and compare your results with your predictions.

Specific Accommodations by Disability Category

Motor/Orthopedic

- Examine the accessibility and movement needs of the student and modify the environment or setting to allow maximum access. This may require going outdoors or reserving time in the cafeteria, library, multipurpose room, or gymnasium.
- Examine the work area to make sure the height and accessibility of supplies are appropriate.
- Establish cooperative groups and assign student with a disability tasks which allow maximum participation.
- Use data-recording procedures that require minimum writing.
- Allow extra time and/or prepare a set of materials that a student can do at home. (Prepare appropriate safety precautions or stain potentials if spilled, relating to any of the experiments or materials.)
- Use plastic containers for experiments.

Visually Impaired

- Acquire and use adapted materials. Items used in the investigations are adapted graduated cylinders with floats (available from the Lawrence Hall of Science); different-size syringes that can be used as measuring tools (available from the Lawrence Hall of Science and Carolina Biological Supply); flexible braille meter sticks (available from the Lawrence Hall of Science); adapted materials for airplane construction (available from Delta Education); adapted recording tools, both tactile and electronic (available from the Lawrence Hall of Science, Delta Education); and computer interfaces (e.g., Vernier and e-probe).
- Share instructions in large print or braille as appropriate.
- Examine the work area to make sure the height and accessibility of supplies are appropriate. Make sure labels are in large print and/or braille.
- Establish cooperative groups and assign student with a disability tasks that allow maximum participation.
- Allow extra time and/or prepare a set of materials that a student can do at home. (Prepare appropriate safety precautions or stain potentials if spilled, relating to any of the experiments or materials.)
- Provide recording device that can be used during group and class discussions.
- Use tactile and/or auditory signals when appropriate.
- Have a teacher's aide or have the student work cooperatively with other students that who will provide rich oral descriptions about what is being done and what is happening.

Learning Disabled

- Modify activity depending on whether the disability is in reading, writing, etc. Use step-by-step directions, possibly handed out to allow the student to follow visually. Preview directions and vocabulary words used in the activity.
- Number and sequence the steps in the activity.
- Allow extra time and/or prepare a set of materials that a student can do at home. (Prepare appropriate safety precautions or stain potentials if spilled, relating to any of the experiments or materials.)
- Use color coding to highlight important steps or recording responsibilities.

ADD/ADHD

- Preview directions and vocabulary words before the activity. Slow down the pace of the activities and allow adequate time for participation.
- Discuss with student appropriate behaviors expected during the activity. Use private signals to keep the student on task during activity time.
- Carefully select cooperative group members and assign the student to a role that reflects his or her interests and strengths. Make sure every member of the group has a responsibility and each student has an appropriate role in observing and recording.
- Review directions and remain consistent with routines and procedures.

Developmentally Delayed

- Expose the student to many of the activities in advance. Select vocabulary appropriate for the student's learning.
- Preview directions and vocabulary words before the activity. Slow down the pace of the activities and allow adequate time for participation.
- Prepare a set of materials that a student can do at home with a supportive adult. (Prepare appropriate safety precautions or stain potentials if spilled, relating to any of the experiments or materials.)
- Get feedback from the student about understanding and work with special education personnel to review important concepts.
- Review possibilities for easy recording of information and use worksheets that require minimal writing.

Behavior Disordered

- Meet with student in advance and clarify expectations and appropriate behaviors to be exhibited during the activities.
- Select and/or modify the environment or setting to minimize interference during activities. This may require going outdoors or reserving time in the cafeteria, library, multipurpose room or gymnasium.
- Carefully select cooperative group members and assign the student to a role that clearly defines his or her responsibilities. Assign group to work in an area with minimal distractions.
- Use proximity control and seek opportunities to support appropriate behaviors. Plan materials trafficking in advance; use consistent routines.
- Use private signals to allow a student to go to a time-out area during activity time or when something occurs that produces frustration.

Autism

- Provide a preteaching experience with the student. Review directions and vocabulary in advance. Organize materials for easy recording of data and provide assistance if necessary.
- Allow for noncompetitive participation. Carefully select work area to minimize distractions.
- Use an aide when appropriate and slow the pace of instruction.
- Prepare a set of materials that a student can do at home with a supportive adult. (Prepare appropriate safety precautions or stain potentials if spilled, relating to any of the experiments or materials.)

Acquired Brain Injury

- Review rules and expectations in advance privately. Use proximity control and reinforce appropriate behaviors.
- Review all of the materials and supplies for safe use; use plastic materials over glassware whenever possible.
- Slow down and use appropriate pacing with the student during instruction and activities.
- Organize materials for easy recording of data and provide assistance if necessary.
- Allow for noncompetitive participation. Carefully select work area to minimize distractions.
- Prepare a take-home activity packet to provide opportunities for the student to repeat the experiments at home with a supportive adult.

Health Impairments

- Establish communication with the student and family as to what is needed. Be aware of overly strenuous participation that may hurt or exhaust the student.
- Review possible hazards or personal reaction possibilities in advance. Review possible side effects of medication and any possible dangers while doing the activities.
- Prepare a take-home activity packet to provide opportunities for the student to complete the experiments at home with a supportive adult if there are limitations regarding in-class participation.
- If using cooperative groups, assign the student tasks that allow maximum participation with supportive and understanding peers. If necessary, after communicating with the student, inform other group members about health dangers that need to be considered during the activities.
- If student is taking medications, consider the most appropriate time of the day for activities.

Multiple Intelligence Extensions

Linguistic

- Have students discuss their experiment results within and between groups. Organize class for appropriate conduits of conversation between students and student groups.
- Have students compose and write stories about energy and energy flow in natural systems.
- Help the media specialist acquire trade books on energy. Encourage free reading and sharing of information through reports or during class discussions.
- Allow students to work in groups and prepare interview questions for a naturalist concerning energy cycles. Invite the person as a speaker in class.

Logical-Mathematical

- Collect data from each of the experiments and exercises and compare and discuss the results. Use quantitative expression in metric terms whenever possible (e.g., volume of water collected, distance of plane flight, etc.)
- Focus on variables and design experiments relating to how different variables affect the outcomes of the experiments.

Spatial

- Show the results using graphs and charts.
- Have students use pictures and illustrations indicating their experiments and the results.
- Ask them to show the sequence of events in the experiments involving energy transfer and chemical change. Allow them to use color coding to show heating and cooling effects along with the products of the reactions.
- Prepare a web of words relating to energy.

Bodily/Kinesthetic

- Many of the activities allow large muscle movement; these activities are generally enjoyable for kinesthetic learners.
- Have student demonstrate changes in molecular structure and molecular motion in the experiments involving chemical change.
- Follow up the activities with a trip to a power plant or natural area where energy changes and the harnessing of energy can be studied and discussed.

Musical

- Have students insert sound effects into the various experiments and share the sequence in class, using skits and short dramatizations.
- Examine poetry and literature in which energy is an important theme.
- Use media to capture the activities and share the main concepts in a video with appropriate musical background.

Interpersonal

- Assign students to cooperative group roles in which they can share their strengths and divide labor.
- Use discussion groups to collect information that can be integrated into a general conceptual scheme about energy flow. Share concepts and applications within and among discussion groups.
- Allow students to conduct interviews with persons involved in the utilization and transfer of energy as enrichment activity options. Allow them to share the results of their investigations with the class.

Intrapersonal

- Encourage students to keep a reflective journal for each day. Ask them to apply what they learned to everyday life.
- Encourage students to use the Internet and find other instructional activities.
- Utilize the Internet to gather information on energy-related topics.
- Generate questions relating to the topic of energy and allow students to investigate any of the questions and prepare a paper or report.

Naturalist

- Prepare food chains and food web illustrations of plant and animal communities.
- Investigate ways organisms gather and consume food.
- Investigate environmental impacts of energy use.
- Compare renewable and nonrenewable resources.

Chapter 8
Inquiry: An Investigation of the Concept of Density

Overview

The instructional sequence on density consists of a series of educational experiences centered around student-directed problem solving. The Inquiry Teaching approach embodies the essence of constructivism. Each student must be nurtured to gain greater confidence in his or her own thinking, yet must receive sufficient reinforcement to maintain persistence and interest. The role of the teacher should be as a listener to guide student learning and, occasionally, to facilitate and provide direction when the student indicates frustration or exhaustion. The strategy is built around Suchman's description of inquiry shared in the Inquiry Development Program (Hutchins, 1970) which includes "messing around with stuff, getting ideas, messing around with ideas, and messing around with stuff again." The sequence presented here attempts to apply the ideology of inquiry teaching through four stages.

Preparation: Children need time to relax and work with materials until, through experience, they develop a sense of meaning. Student familiarity with the inquiry process is accomplished through the use of footprint puzzles prior to beginning the instructional sequence of discrepant events relating to density. Lessons 2 and 3 draw on student exploration with familiar materials and natural objects to help them gain a sense of sinking and floating that goes beyond the common misconception of "light" and "heavy." Melons are excellent objects because they have sufficient mass to challenge conventional thinking. The activities with larger objects can be conducted in an aquarium, sink, or swimming pool.

Incubation: Much learning takes place during times when the learner is not consciously concentrating on the problem. This sequence is designed to function with interruptions. Creativity is not instantaneous: Learners need to use a period of incubation without having it affect their daily performance. Students need to learn to be puzzled and relaxed, to establish comfort with cognitive conflict and tension, and to sustain a willingness to let go of certainties and consider possibilities.

Illumination: The development of illumination is often called the period of insight. It is characterized by a conscious awareness, enabling the student to intellectually record and draw out the idea or concept. Activities 4-9 apply the principle of mass/volume relationship to solve density-related problems. Some activities can rely on the application of intuitive thinking; however, the introduction of the use of mathematics to quantitatively express density in mathematical terms (e.g., grams/milliliters) can greatly advance student thinking.

Verification: To ascertain a sound understanding of a concept, the students should be challenged to solve problems that require them to apply the principle in an unfamiliar circumstance. Activities 10-12 involve the presentation of questions that require student manipulation of the density principle to solve varied problems. Activity 13 provides a twist to challenge the thinking of the most able learners.

Although the ability to understand density in a mathematical sense does not normally develop in children until the ages of 10-12, experiences with the concept are appropriate for very young children. These early experiences provide cognitive structures that enable students to pick up the mathematical relationships that develop later in a natural and meaningful fashion.

Density is an important concept in many fields of science and engineering. The application of the concept involves the simultaneous application of two variables: mass and volume. Mass and volume are relatively explicit phenomena with which children have an abundance of experiences both in school and at home. From the beginning of life, children have opportunities to observe how things respond when placed in liquids. They discover many fundamental perceptions about how objects behave in liquids in common activities like adding milk to cereal or playing with objects while bathing.

Although children have an abundance of experiences, they may be confused because of a tendency to focus on weight. Discrepant events involving mass-volume relationships allow the teacher to create a challenge that children can generally solve if they discuss the problem in cooperative groups. The amount of support and guidance will vary depending upon the students and the time devoted to the lessons. Children hold many common misconceptions about the concept of density. Inquiry lessons require the students to apply their own reasoning to phenomena they observe or directly experience. The series of lessons offered in this sequence can be used intermittently as independent discrepant events or as an instructional sequence.

Lesson 1
Developing Inquiry Thinking Through Footprint Puzzles

Science Standards

The student produces evidence that demonstrates the following behaviors:

- Understands the impact of science, such as historical and contemporary contributions, and interactions between science and society
- Uses evidence from reliable sources to develop descriptions, explanations, and models
- Proposes, recognizes, analyzes, considers, and critiques alternative explanations; distinguishes between fact and opinions
- Works individually and in teams to collect and share information and ideas (National Center on the Economy and Education, Middle School Performance Standards, 1997)

Materials

- footprint puzzles : Appendices J and K

Guiding the Investigation

The footprint puzzles have been used successfully with students from grades 3 through adulthood. First, display the footprint puzzle as a transparency or distribute a copy to each student. Students are then encouraged to ask questions to which the teacher responds either "yes" or "no." If students feel that they know a part or the entire story the puzzle tells, they can call for a theory and share their thinking. It is important that the teacher does not respond either positively or negatively to theories. Students should be told that if they wish to talk to their peers, they can call for a "recess" at any time. After a request for a recess, allow students 1-2 minutes for interaction and discussion among themselves. During a typical session, there can be several periods of questions and several theories presented, interspersed with several recesses. The process continues until there is a general sense of comfort that the story is an accurate depiction of the information shared in the diagram. Students will generally ask, "Are we right?" You can decide whether to give them an affirmation or to force them to rely on their own thinking with a response such as: "Do you feel good about your answer? If so, feel comfortable with it." "Can a scientist, when he or she explains something like the structure of an atom, ask if it is the right answer? You too, must build confidence on your capacity to reason."

The footprint puzzles provide the teacher with a convenient opportunity to orient student thinking into the Inquiry Teaching process. The "yes" or "no" question format requires that students formulate the thought they want to investigate and frame it as a question. This is analogous to the formulating hypotheses step in the scientific method. During recess sessions they exchange information and develop consensus based on the data they accumulated during the questioning phase. When presenting theories, they provide a plausible explanation of the event. This is analogous to many scientific theories that are constantly undergoing changes and refinement (e.g. atomic models, genetic theories, plate-tectonics, Big Bang) based on additional data through improved technology, better research methods, and better scientific reasoning.

Once students become familiar with the process, they become very proficient in applying the strategy to respond to the discrepant events presented in the density sequence. Some students will pick up the process more quickly than others. Consistency as a teacher is very important. Do not provide information to students. Require that they elicit information through their questions. You will find that some students, even though they employ good reasoning techniques and think well, require teacher affirmation in order to feel comfortable that their thinking is on track. A best approach might be one of "weaning" them from affirmation in selected instances rather than withholding affirmation from the beginning.

The footprint puzzle in Appendix J depicts a boy in the school, after school hours, on detention. Another boy stops by the window and makes faces at the boy inside. This angers the boy inside and he throws a superball that he has in his pocket and breaks the window. By chance, a police car is coming up the street. The boy who was making faces sees the police car and flees into the park. The police officer, seeing the broken window, pursues and catches the boy. They both walk to the police car and the police officer questions the boy about the incident.

The footprint puzzle in Appendix K depicts a scene in which a skunk, while browsing, goes under a cabin and is caught in a trap meant for a squirrel or small predator. A man goes outside, shoots the skunk, drags it toward the trees, buries the skunk and the trap, goes behind the garage, and burns his clothes. His wife brings out new clothes and they both walk back into the cabin.

Lesson 2
Pop Cans

Science Standards

The student produces evidence that demonstrates the following behaviors:

- Understands properties and changes of properties in matter, such as density and boiling point; chemical reactivity; and conservation of matter

- Proposes, recognizes, analyzes, considers, and critiques alternative explanations; distinguishes between fact and opinions

- Works individually and in teams to collect and share information and ideas (National Center on the Economy and Education, Middle School Performance Standards, 1997)

Materials

- aquarium or deep plastic shoe box
- 1 can regular Mountain Dew
- 1 can diet Mountain Dew

Discrepant Event

Depending on the age of the students, you may wish to precede this lesson sequence with Sink and Float Activities in which students have an opportunity to explore, observe, and record sinking and floating behaviors of an assortment of common objects, including items made of wood, metal, and plastic.

An aquarium or plastic shoe box is filled with water so the liquid depth is greater than that of a pop can inserted sideways. Test the box before use to be sure it will not crack and can be filled to a sufficient depth to observe sinking and floating.

A can of regular pop is placed in the water and the can sinks. A second can of diet pop is placed in the aquarium and it floats.

You may have to try several cans because the amount of air at the top does affect the density, and some cans of regular pop will float. Mountain Dew generally works well. Coke products may require that you go through several cans to find a can of regular pop that sinks.

Procedure

1. Arrange students in cooperative learning groups of 3-4.
2. In a large group setting, allow students to ask questions that you answer with only" yes" or "no."
3. Allow students to call for a recess at any time. If a recess is requested, allow 1-2 minutes for discussion.
4. If desired, have each cooperative group prepare an explanation of the phenomenon.

Explanation

The dissolved sugar increases the density of the liquid. If the density of the object (container, air, and pop) is greater than that of the liquid it is placed in (water), it will sink. If the density is less than that of the liquid, it will float.

Lesson 3
Fruits and Vegetables

Science Standards

The student produces evidence that demonstrates the following behaviors:

- Understands properties and changes of properties in matter, such as density and boiling point; chemical reactivity; and conservation of matter

- Proposes, recognizes, analyzes, considers, and critiques alternative explanations; distinguishes between fact and opinions

- Works individually and in teams to collect and share information and ideas (National Center on the Economy and Education, Middle School Performance Standards, 1997)

Materials

- aquarium or swimming pool
- variety of fresh fruits and vegetables

Discrepant Event

An aquarium is most often used for this discrepant event series. Another option is to conduct the experiments in a swimming pool. The fruits and vegetables should be rinsed off and cleaned in advance. The container must be large enough to place the object in the water and deep enough so that it can be determined if the object sinks or floats. Distribute the assortment of objects in front of the students, asking them to make a prediction sheet indicating whether the object will sink or float. You may provide students time to handle the objects before testing the predictions, either as a demonstration or in groups. Melons are ideal because they are fairly heavy and generally float.

Procedure

1. Arrange students in groups of 3-4.
2. Before presenting the discrepant events, allow students to handle the items and make predictions about whether each object will sink or float.
3. Then place the items individually in the aquarium and observe if they sink or float.
4. In large-group settings allow students to ask questions that you answer with only "yes" or "no."
5. Allow students to call for a recess at any time. If a recess is requested, allow 1-2 minutes for discussion.
6. If desired, have each cooperative group prepare an explanation of the phenomenon.

Extension

Prepare a saltwater solution and repeat the experience.

A good affirmation activity is to put a potato in fresh water (it will usually sink) and then in saltwater (it will generally float). Then cut the potato into several pieces and conduct an inquiry session with students about whether the pieces will sink or float. It is common even for older students to abandon their logic system and make an inference that the smaller pieces might behave differently.

Explanation

Those objects with an overall density less than that of the liquid will float and those with a density greater than that of the liquid will sink.

Lesson 4
Introduction to Flinking

Science Standards

The student produces evidence that demonstrates the following behaviors:

- Understands properties and changes of properties in matter, such as density and boiling point; chemical reactivity; and conservation of matter

- Proposes, recognizes, analyzes, considers, and critiques alternative explanations; distinguishes between fact and opinions

- Works individually and in teams to collect and share information and ideas (National Center on the Economy and Education, Middle School Performance Standards, 1997)

Materials

- 8-oz. plastic cups
- white vinegar
- baking soda
- peanuts and peanuts in the shell
- raisins

Discrepant Event

Flinkers are objects that may sink or float depending upon the conditions.

Procedure

1. Arrange students in cooperative learning groups of 3-4.
2. Ask them to predict whether the objects will sink or float. You can start with peanuts in the shell, followed by just the peanuts, and finally peanuts split in half.
3. Allow students to handle the items and make predictions about whether each object will sink or float.
4. Then place the items in the cup of water and observe if they sink or float.
5. In a large-group setting, allow students to ask questions that you answer only with "yes" or "no."
6. Allow students to call for a recess at any time. If a recess is requested, allow 1-2 minutes for discussion.
7. If desired, have each cooperative group prepare an explanation of the phenomenon.
8. Now introduce baking soda. Have each group add a tablespoon of baking soda to the water. Then allow them to carefully add vinegar (be sure they are cautious about the amount of foaming).
9. Have students observe the items as they “dance” in the water.
10. If desired, have each cooperative group prepare an explanation of the phenomenon.

Explanation

Those objects with an overall density less than that of the liquid will float, and those with a density greater than that of the liquid will sink. In most cases a raisin taken from a box will sink. Most peanuts will sink. However, if there is sufficient air between the two cotyledons, in some cases the density will be less than that of water and the peanuts will float. If the cotyledons are separated, the peanut halves will generally sink.

However, when baking soda is placed in the water and vinegar is added, bubbles will collect on the raisins and/or peanuts, making the overall density less than that of the water and the objects will rise. Frequently some of the bubbles will break when the objects return to the surface and the object will become more dense, thereby sinking again. The phenomenon can be called "dancing raisins" or "dancing peanuts." Other nuts and seeds also work well.

Lesson 5
Making Controllable Cartesian Divers

Science Standards

The student produces evidence that demonstrates the following behaviors:

- ➢ Understands properties and changes of properties in matter, such as density and boiling point; chemical reactivity; and conservation of matter

- ➢ Works individually and in teams to collect and share information and ideas (National Center on the Economy and Education, Middle School Performance Standards, 1997)

Materials

- ➢ 2- liter plastic bottles or smaller plastic bottles if desired (one for each student)
- ➢ graduated plastic pipettes
- ➢ small nuts that can sleeve tightly over the pipette at the larger graduations
- ➢ plastic cups
- ➢ food coloring, if desired
- ➢ scissors

Discrepant Event

Flinkers are objects that may sink or float depending upon the conditions. You are to design a flinker in which sinking or floating is under your control.

Sequence

1. Arrange students in cooperative learning groups of 3-4. Allow each student to make his or her own Cartesian diver.
2. Construct the Cartesian divers:
    - ➢ Sleeve a nut over the graduated plastic pipette until it is snug. Depending upon the brand of plastic pipette you select, you may need to also add a washer.
    - ➢ Snip off the extra pipette "tail" with a scissors.
    - ➢ Put water in the pipette and test it until it barely floats.
3. Place the diver in a 2–liter plastic bottle almost completely filled with water. Put the cap on tightly, squeeze the bottle, and observe what happens.
4. In a large-group setting allow students to ask questions that you answer only with "yes" or "no."
5. Allow students to call for a recess at any time. If a recess is requested, allow 1-2 minutes for discussion.
6. If desired, have each cooperative group prepare an explanation of the phenomenon.

Extension

Place food coloring in water and allow students to add colored water to their Cartesian divers. Ask them to explain why the color fades as the Cartesian diver is used. It is also interesting to just allow the colored Cartesian divers to stay overnight and discuss why the color fades even when the Cartesian divers are not used.

Explanation

One can vary the density of the Cartesian diver by increasing or decreasing the air pressure within the container. When the container is squeezed, water goes into the Cartesian diver as the air pressure within the Cartesian diver is equalized with the pressure in the outer container. When the pressure is lowered, the air pressure is again equalized and water is ejected from the Cartesian diver. When making the original diver, adjust the density so it is just slightly less dense than the liquid before putting it into the container.

Lesson 6
Investigating Colored Solutions

Science Standards

The student produces evidence that demonstrates the following behaviors:

- Understands properties and changes of properties in matter, such as density and boiling point; chemical reactivity; and conservation of matter

- Works individually and in teams to collect and share information and ideas (National Center on the Economy and Education, Middle School Performance Standards, 1997)

Materials

- 2 kilograms of kosher or pickling salt (about 5 lbs.)
- 4000 ml. glass containers (about 1 gallon)
- food coloring – 4 colors
- different sized measuring devices for cup and tablespoon from 10 to 300 ml
- eyedropper – at least one for each student
- 20 plastic cups – 250 ml. (about 8 ozs.)
- stirring sticks
- drinking straws
- 200 "pill cups" (about 25 ml)
- paper towels
- potatoes

Advance Preparation

Mix solutions of 1/3 cup of salt to 2000 ml (about 1 gallon) of water. Add one color of food coloring (e.g., red). Repeat for 2/3 cup, 1 cup, and 1 1/3 cups of salt, coloring each solution differently. Shortly before class, cut raw potatoes into slices approximately 3 cm. thick.

Discrepant Event

Your challenge is to make a liquid solution of two or more colors.

Sequence

1. Arrange the students in cooperative learning groups of 3-4. Give each student a drinking straw and a plastic pill cup. Have a 250 ml. (about 8 ozs.) cup available at each table as a "disposal."

2. Have each group get about 2/3 of a pill cup of the four mixed-colored solutions. Demonstrate how to stick a straw into the potato, add a few drops of solution, and observe what happens.

3. After making observations, demonstrate how the students can put their finger on the straw, remove the straw from the potato, and dispose of the solution into the 8-ounce cup.

4. Challenge students to explore with the solutions and record how the solutions mix or stay separate. Challenge them to make a solution consisting of layers of each of the four colors.

5. Caution students not to mix the colors in the main containers.

Explanation

The different concentrations of saltwater have different densities. If the solutions are arranged from lower to higher density, they will remain separate for a period of time.

Lesson 7
Density of Regular Objects

Science Standards

The student produces evidence that demonstrates the following behaviors:

- Understands properties and changes of properties in matter, such as density and boiling point; chemical reactivity; and conservation of matter

- Works individually and in teams to collect and share information and ideas (National Center on the Economy and Education, Middle School Performance Standards, 1997)

Materials

- a variety of rectangular solids made of different materials (e.g., wood, metals, or plastic)
- rectangular solids of regular shapes cut from vegetables (e.g., potatoes, turnips, and carrots). Rectangular objects should be large enough to measure length, width, and height with good accuracy.
- spheres (marbles, plastic spheres, and steel ball bearings). These objects require students to use computational skills from formulas using exponents.
- cylinders (weighted film canisters work well)
- an accurate measuring device for determining length (e.g., rulers with small graduations) and, if available, a Vernier caliper
- a fairly accurate balance or scale to determine mass

Discrepant Event

Your challenge is to determine the density of different objects and use that knowledge to identify objects that will sink and objects that will float in a liquid of known density.

Sequence

Introduce the formula for determining density ($d = m/v$) and challenge students to determine the density of the various objects you have made available while working in cooperative learning groups.

Ask them to share and discuss their results in a large-group setting.

Extension

Have the students compute the density of liquids through the use of a film canister. Use the formula for the volume of a cylinder to determine the volume. Be sure to use the inside measurements for diameter and height. In determining the mass, carefully weigh an empty film canister, then add the liquid and determine the mass of the liquid using the difference between the two masses. Good liquid solutions are different concentrations of saltwater, different concentrations of sugar water, and other liquids such as alcohol.

Explanation

Although experiences with sinking and floating provide students with general conceptual frameworks relating to density, it is important to familiarize students with the value of quantitative investigation. The use of mathematics in developing process skills is a valuable concept.

These activities are generally best suited for students over the age of 12; however, judgments should be based on the abilities and background of an individual student or cooperative learning group. Students must be able to handle the simultaneous relationship between the two variables of mass and volume. The formula for computing density is easy to work with, in that the algebraic relationship is simple and straightforward. It is also a good opportunity to apply formulas for the computation of the volume of rectangular solids and other common shapes (e.g., spheres and cylinders).

Lesson 8

Determining Density of Irregular Objects

Science Standards

The student produces evidence that demonstrates the following behaviors:

- Understands properties and changes of properties in matter, such as density and boiling point; chemical reactivity; and conservation of matter

- Works individually and in teams to collect and share information and ideas (National Center on the Economy and Education, Middle School Performance Standards, 1997)

Materials

- graduated cylinders and overflow cans
- an accurate balance or scale for determining mass
- a variety of objects that can be submerged in water (e.g., pencils, keys, paper clips, erasers, rocks, foods) in which the volume can be determined by displacement, and the mass determined using a fairly accurate balance scale

Discrepant Event

Your challenge is to determine the density of different objects and use that knowledge to identify objects that will sink and objects that will float in a liquid of known density.

Sequence

1. Introduce the formula for determining density ($d = m/v$), arrange the students in groups of 3-4, and challenge students to determine the density of the various objects you have made available.

2. The volume of objects that can fit into a graduated cylinder can be determined directly by carefully reading the volume before inserting the object and determining the change in volume after the object has been submerged in the liquid. For objects less dense than water, a pencil can be used to force submersion. (However, care must be taken to either minimize or determine the displacement of the pencil). If you are using glass graduated cylinders, take care to prevent breakage due to the dropping of dense objects into the cylinder (e.g., metal spheres or strips.)
3. Overflow cans could be used to determine displacement by filling the can to capacity and measuring the overflow after the object is inserted.

Ask students in cooperative learning groups to share their data and explain their results in a large-group setting.

Explanation

If you have good containers for measuring displacement and overflow, determining the density of irregular objects is less advanced than determining that of regular objects.

These activities are generally best suited for students over the age of 12; however, judgments should be based on the abilities and background of an individual student or cooperative learning group. Students must be able to handle the simultaneous relationship between the two variables of mass and volume. The formula for computing density is easy to work with because the algebraic relationship is simple and straightforward.

Lesson 9
Constructing Boats and Determining Carrying Capacity

Science Standards

The student produces evidence that demonstrates the following behaviors:

- Understands properties and changes of properties in matter, such as density and boiling point; chemical reactivity; and conservation of matter

- Works individually and in teams to collect and share information and ideas (National Center on the Economy and Education, Middle School Performance Standards, 1997)

Materials

- aquarium or plastic shoe boxes filled to about 2/3 capacity of water; one container for each cooperative learning group
- plasticine clay, aluminum foil (if desired, wooden rafts)
- items such as balls and rectangular solids that can be used to help mold specific shapes
- washers or other objects that can be placed in containers to determine carrying capacity
- an accurate balance or scale for determining mass
- a fairly accurate measuring device for determining length (e.g., rulers with small graduations) and, if available, a Vernier caliper
- graduated cylinders

Discrepant Event

Your challenge is to construct a boat with the greatest carrying capacity and present an explanation for the approach you used.

Sequence

1. Give each cooperative learning group the same size piece of Plasticine clay (e.g., ½ stick), followed by a challenge to build a clay boat that can hold the greatest number of washers.

2. Follow the activity with a session in which students share and describe what they did.

3. Distribute equal-size sheets of aluminum foil to each cooperative learning group (e.g.,

4. 12" x 12") and present a challenge to build an aluminum foil boat that will hold the greatest number of washers.

5. Follow the activity with a session in which students share and describe what they did.

6. The substantive challenge now becomes to build a boat that will contain the greatest number of washers without sinking. Students should construct a boat, determine its mass, and use a technique to determine its carrying volume before it will take on water. The volume can be determined by using a mathematical formula to determine the volume of a rectangular solid or

hemisphere, or by filling the container with water and determining inside space.

Explanation

Although the experience is common to students, many do not understand how ships made of steel are affected by the same density relationships as other objects. Experiments with clay boats and aluminum foil boats can be used to help students gain an understanding of mass transport over water.

Students can begin by exploring with "boats" and carrying capacity. If students have the skills, the concept of density can be applied to determine capacity using the same processes as in the earlier exercises.

Students can then determine the amount of mass that can be added in building a container with a density of less than one (i.e., mass volume x density). Contests can be used to determine the group that builds a boat that will hold the greatest number of washers.

Lesson 10
Layering Liquids

Science Standards

The student produces evidence that demonstrates the following behaviors:

- Understands properties and changes of properties in matter, such as density and boiling point; chemical reactivity; and conservation of matter

- Works individually and in teams to collect and share information and ideas (National Center on the Economy and Education, Middle School Performance Standards, 1997)

Materials

- a collection of liquids including vegetable oil, glycerin, ethyl alcohol, isopropyl alcohol, milk, soda pop, and kosher salt for making different concentrations of saltwater, and other nontoxic liquids of interest to the teacher or students
- kosher or pickling salt (about 5 lbs.)
- glycerin
- ethyl alcohol
- vegetable oil
- water
- food coloring – 4 colors
- different measuring devices for cup and tablespoon from 10 to 300 ml
- eyedroppers – at least one for each student
- 100 plastic cups –8 oz
- stirring sticks
- drinking straws
- 200 "pill cups" (about 25 ml)
- paper towels
- potatoes

Discrepant Event

Your challenge is to make a liquid construction with the greatest number of layers.

Sequence

1. After allowing students to engage in free exploration, have a contest among the cooperative learning groups.
2. Follow up with a class discussion of the procedures that the students used and those that were most successful.
3. Ask students to explain why they think the liquids layered the way they did and to compare and contrast successful and unsuccessful trials.

Explanation

The different liquids have different densities. If the liquids are arranged from lower to higher density, they will remain separate for a period of time.

Lesson 11
Alcohol and Water

Science Standards

The student produces evidence that demonstrates the following behaviors:

- Understands properties and changes of properties in matter, such as density and boiling point; chemical reactivity; and conservation of matter

- Proposes, recognizes, analyzes, considers, and critiques alternative explanations; and distinguishes between fact and opinions (National Center on the Economy and Education, Middle School Performance Standards, 1997)

Materials

- 100 ml. of 95% ethanol
- 1 ice cube
- a 250 – 300 milliliter beaker or similar clear container
- 100 ml of water

Shortly before the beginning of class, pour the 100 ml. of water into the beaker and, while tilting the glass, very carefully pour in the 100 ml. of alcohol (it will basically stay on top of the water).

Discrepant Event

1. Ask the students to observe closely.
2. Carefully place the ice cube in the liquid. (It should float in about the middle.) After about two minutes, stir the liquid and observe the ice cube. (It will usually float.)
3. Allow students to ask questions to which you respond either "yes" or "no" or to present theories or explanations of the phenomenon. An alternative is to have the students prepare an explanation in their cooperative learning groups.

Explanation

Ice is denser than alcohol and less dense than water. When the alcohol solution is carefully placed over the water solution, they do not mix. Therefore, the ice cube "floats" between the two layers. When mixed, the solution becomes denser than ice and the ice cube floats. This discrepant event provides an excellent opportunity to determine if students can apply the concept of density to explain a phenomenon that challenges their normal intuition.

Lesson 12
A Loaf of Raisin Bread

Science Standards

The student produces evidence that demonstrates the following behaviors:

- Understands impact of science, such as historical and contemporary contributions, and interactions between science and society

- Uses evidence from reliable sources to develop descriptions, explanations and models

- Proposes, recognizes, analyzes, considers, and critiques alternative explanations; and distinguishes between fact and opinions

- Works individually and in teams to collect and share information and ideas (National Center on the Economy and Education, Middle School Performance Standards, 1997)

Materials

- 2 loaves of sliced raisin bread
- balances –accurate to .1 gram
- meter sticks and/or 30—cm rulers
- toaster
- graduated cylinders

Discrepant Event

Design an investigation to answer each of the following questions, carry out the investigation, and prepare a summary of your results and your conclusions:

1. What is the volume of a loaf of raisin bread?
2. How many loaves can you put in a bakery van with one cubic meter of storage space?
3. What percentage of raisin bread is just air?
4. How dense are raisins?
5. How much space will a kilogram of raisins occupy?
6. What is the specific gravity of bread without the raisins?
7. How many raisins are there in one loaf of raisin bread?
8. How many loaves of raisin bread can you make from one kilogram of raisins?
9. Prepare one additional question, and conduct an investigation to answer it.

Sequence

1. Divide students into groups of 3-4, and allow each group to select and work on three of the questions. In the assignment process ensure that all of the questions are selected (e.g., draw numbers and let the groups pick one of the questions in order until they are all selected); assign groups to select a second question to address in an inverse order; and allow them to select a third question of their choice. The major role of the teacher is to assist students in obtaining the materials they need to gather the information they need.
2. If students finish with the initial three questions, challenge them to continue and answer as many

as they can.

3. At the close of the activity, ask the students to share their results and compare the different methodologies used to answer the questions (adapted from Cox, 1971).

Explanation

In this exercise, students must demonstrate flexibility in thinking through the application of the very basic density formula (d=m/v) and to present answers to a variety of common questions. It will take an average group of middle-level students a week to come up with responses to all of the questions.

Lesson 13
Rubber Glove and Alka-Seltzer

Science Standards

The student produces evidence that demonstrates the following behaviors:

- Understands impact of science, such as historical and contemporary contributions, and interactions between science and society

- Uses evidence from reliable sources to develop descriptions, explanations, and models

- Proposes, recognizes, analyzes, considers, and critiques alternative explanations; distinguishes between fact and opinions

- Works individually and in teams to collect and share information and ideas (National Center on the Economy and Education, Middle School Performance Standards, 1997)

Materials

- 2 somewhat transparent low-cost rubber gloves
- 2 Alka-Seltzer tablets

Discrepant Event

1. Put one Alka-Seltzer tablet in the thumb of each glove, and fill the fingers of each glove with water, being careful that the water does not come in contact with the Alka-Seltzer tablet. Suspend each glove on opposite sides of a meter stick balanced on a fulcrum.

2. Ask the students to describe what they think will happen if the Alka-Seltzer tablet in the right glove is dumped out into the water contained in the fingers. Then conduct the experiment and conduct an inquiry session in which students ask questions to which you answer "yes" or "no" and encourage them to present theories to explain what happened.

Explanation

When the Alka-Seltzer comes in contact with the water, it will produce carbon dioxide gas and the glove will expand like a balloon. Although the mass remains the same, the increased volume will cause the side in which the reaction took place to be more buoyant in the surrounding air and it will rise. The demonstration is a discrepant event that will often challenge the most advanced students and introduce the property of air as a buoyant fluid.

Summary

Students are often asked to master a relatively complex science concept with just a few opportunities to engage in experimentation and little opportunity to use their own thinking to solve an assortment of problems relating to a single concept.

The lessons presented in this sequence provide repeated opportunities for students to apply their understanding of the concept of density in a variety of contexts. You will find it interesting as you observe students build on their prior experiences and gain confidence and trust in their own ability to reason.

Students can be challenged to explain how the concept of density is utilized in everyday life, such as in the operation of submarines and weather balloons or at a more complex level how density relates to weather and climate. A GEMS Unit titled *Discovering Density* contains a number of literary connections and puzzling scenarios relating to the concept of density. It is available from Great Explorations in Math and Science (GEMS), Lawrence Hall of Science, University of California, Berkeley, CA 94720. Telephone: (510) 642-7771 or on the web at http://www.lhsgems.org.

Specific Accommodations by Disability Category

Motor/Orthopedic

- Consider larger or smaller containers to accommodate active student participation.
- Provide a nonslippery surface to work on.
- If student has difficulty grasping, use tongs or other tools. Adapt handles and probes as needed to allow for greater active participation.
- Provide a supportive peer assistant. When appropriate, prepare a peer assistant in advance.
- Arrange tables and supplies to allow for comfortable trafficking and access to materials and supplies.
- Prepare for spills. If one occurs, handle it in a courteous way.

Visually Impaired

- Allow the student to experience buoyancy with larger objects in an aquarium or swimming pool. Larger objects can help students acquire a sense of buoyancy and resistance to immersion of floating objects.
- Allow the visually impaired student to touch and become familiar with the objects in advance.
- Provide a supportive peer assistant. When appropriate, prepare a peer assistant in advance to help student skim the surface for objects with a density near that of water.
- For low vision students, consider colors that work more effectively.
- Use a sounding device in the flinker investigations.

Hearing Impaired

- Provide written instructions.
- Position student with a clear vision of the speaker in discussions or cooperative group work.
- Consider the background and setting when conducting demonstrations.
- Allow students to signal answers with written signs.
- Provide a supportive peer assistant. When appropriate, prepare a peer assistant in advance.

Learning Disabled

- Provide prior experiences in private when it is perceived as beneficial.
- Focus on quality of responses and depth of reflection rather than quickness of their response. Make additional time available for repeating or conducting investigations.
- Break up the activity sequence to make accommodations concerning student ability to maintain concentration or focus on the learning activities.

Attention Deficit/Hyperactivity Disorder

- Organize materials and plan traffic patterns in advance and, if appropriate, review them with the student in advance.
- If appropriate, review directions with the student in advance.
- Organize classroom and students to minimize distractions.
- Allow for variety and repetition.
- Use proximity control.

Developmentally Delayed

- Conduct the activity with the student in advance. Work in cooperation with the special education teacher(s).
- Allow student to work with a supportive peer assistant or attendant.
- Prepare a "take home kit" with which a student can get additional practice using parent and/or adult assistance.
- Provide a supportive work environment.
- Allow for signaled responses. For example, prepare signs so a student can signal "sink" or "float."

Behavior Disordered

- Organize materials and plan traffic patterns in advance and, if appropriate, review them with the student in advance.
- Provide printed instructions. If appropriate, review directions with the student in advance.
- Seat student near supportive peers, or in a location to minimize interference with other student learning.
- Use proximity control.
- Have a predetermined signal and location for time-out.
- Be observant and supportive when possible.

Speech/Language

- Allow for signaled response. For example, prepare signs so a student can signal "sink" or "float."
- Allow student to use alternative output device or provide a written response.
- Be patient if a child chooses to ask a question or respond to a question.
- Select supportive cooperative groups.

Autism

- Conduct the activity with the student in advance. Work in cooperation with the special education teacher(s).
- Organize materials and plan traffic patterns in advance and, if appropriate, review them with the student in advance.

- Provide printed instructions. If appropriate, review directions with the student in advance.
- Minimize distractions and place student in a comfortable location.
- Guide the student to work with others through the careful selection of cooperative peers.
- Work with an aide or teacher associate in advance of hands-on investigations.
- Keep pace slow and noncompetitive.

Traumatic Brain Injury

- Provide prior learning experiences.
- Minimize distractions; place student in a comfortable location.
- Allow time for additional exploration.
- Work with an aide or teacher associate in advance of hands-on investigations.
- Keep pace slow and noncompetitive.
- Use proximity control.

- Be supportive.

Deaf and Blind

- Allow students to explore materials in advance.
- Allow the student to experience buoyancy with larger objects in an aquarium or swimming pool. Larger objects can help students acquire a sense of buoyancy and resistance to immersion of floating objects.
- Provide directions in braille; go over the directions with the student in advance.
- Allow additional time for exploration.
- Be patient and supportive.

Other Health Impaired

- Become familiar with heath situation in advance, and have immediate access to contacts with parents and important health professionals.
- Make special efforts to keep in communication with knowledgeable adults.
- Examine materials and traffic patterns in advance, and make the appropriate accommodations relative to the student's condition.

Multiple Intelligence Extensions

Verbal/Linguistic

Students can apply oral language as they engage in the investigation and problem solving. Extensions could include journal writing, written responses, or writing down questions they still have. Students can prepare a report that includes justifications to support the logic of their conclusions.

Logical/Mathematical

The lesson sequence provides many experiences relating to the concept of density, which is usually studied using logical/mathematical reasoning. Students can use classification and grouping strategies to predict objects that will sink or float. The formula for density, [d=m/v], can be used to calculate the actual density of various objects. The concept could be extended to the study of open containers and predictions relating to how much cargo they can hold.

Visual/Spatial

The use of imagery and imagination can be enriched through literature that includes the concept of floating, as often presented in fiction books. The logic of the tenets in the stories can be analyzed and discussed. Drawings can be used as a way for students to show what they learned as their explanations of the discrepant events.

Bodily/Kinesthetic

A swimming pool provides an excellent medium to act out floating and sinking in water and to experience properties of other objects in water. Students could act out demonstrations of sinking and floating in creative dramatics or charades.

Musical/Rhythmic

An abundance of music relates to water transport and the actions of water. Music and sound effects depicting ocean scenes, tropical islands, and human recreation can be studied.

Interpersonal

Most of the lessons involve students working in groups and interacting with each other to discuss and propose explanations for the discrepant events. Explanations could be shared between groups, and surveys could be conducted to compare predictions before conducting the experiments.

Intrapersonal

Journal writings and reflections can be used to study the intellectual development and problem-solving abilities of the students as they experience more sophisticated discrepant events. Students can seek out additional resources that relate to the principle of sinking and floating, or buoyancy. The concept is popular in various types of brain-teaser publications.

Naturalistic

Students can investigate fish and how they regulate their depth with air bladders. Other fresh water and sea organisms can be studied. A scavenger hunt can be conducted in a local recreation area, challenging students to collect objects and determine their density.

Chapter 9
Exploratory Learning: Puzzling Powders and Exploring Electricity

Overview

Exploratory learning is based on the fundamental elements of constructivism--each individual student constructing his or her understanding of things. This instructional approach also asserts that adult intervention interrupts children's natural tendencies in developing understanding through their experiences. For this reason, the teacher's role is as a facilitator and guide. The classroom should become a place for exploration. A classroom designed for exploratory learning is one in which students interact with each other, which provides them with skills in social development and cooperation. It gives them freedom to develop their own ideas and vocabulary.

The activities in Puzzling Powders deal with the properties of ordinary white powders and the use of indicators to identify them and detect their presence in mixtures. This activity is adapted from the unit *Mystery Powders* (1967) in the Elementary Science Study Programs (available from Delta Education). Many of the textual elements have been extracted from the guide. As a beginning, the students explore five unnamed white powders (sugar, salt, baking soda, starch, and plaster of Paris), and try to identify them by tasting, smelling, feeling, and comparing them with known substances. Next, the children share information about the powders and how they are alike and different from each other. Additional tests are then made with heat, iodine, and vinegar, which cause specific reactions with several of the powders. To conclude, the children attempt to determine the presence of individual powders when two or more are mixed together.

While Puzzling Powders is not a sequence in formal chemistry, the study introduces children to the detailed examination of some chemical and physical properties of familiar substances, to the use of indicators, and to other analytic techniques. It has been particularly useful for introducing both teachers and children to investigator science: science in which students obtain answers to their questions directly from the real world. The sequence requires no previous science experience, and the materials are inexpensive and readily available in most communities. The activities can be completed within five to eight lessons of about 45 minutes each.

The second activity sequence involves investigating the concept of electricity. The lessons are a composite of ideas extracted from several sources but adhere to the philosophy of exploratory learning. The first lessons allow for a high level of student participation and discovery in a realm that is very immediate in today's world. One of the very important outcomes is that the knowledge gained is so applicable to our daily lives. Getting things to work that involve electricity is almost a daily concern and most often involves some form of interrupted circuit. Trouble shooting is a wonderful way for children and adults to apply higher order reasoning skills. The topic also provides an excellent opportunity to discuss safety and the hazards of electricity. It provides an avenue to discuss energy use and personal responsibility if we are to preserve our quality of life and environment. True to the nature of exploratory learning electricity allows a teacher to capitalize on divergent student interests in a framework of sound scientific reasoning as a core value.

The fundamental principle of exploratory learning is to allow students to investigate freely without adult intervention and the threat of evaluation. The primary role of the teacher is to support student inquiry and nurture student interest in science. Evaluation should be based on the behaviors you wish to encourage (attentiveness, cooperation with peers, persistence), not on students' knowledge and understanding of science concepts. Under the concept of exploratory instruction, a student with a significant developmental delay should be able to receive an "A" grade in science.

Puzzling Powders

Lesson Sequence

Science Standard

The student produces evidence that demonstrates an understanding of the following:

- Properties of objects and materials, such as similarities and differences in the size, weight, and color of objects; the ability of materials to react with other substances; and different states of matter (National Center on the Economy and Education, Elementary School Performance Standards, 1997)

Materials

Materials for a class of 30 (for all of the lessons):

From a supermarket:

- 450 g. (about 1 lb.) granulated sugar
- 1 box table salt
- 450 g. (about 1 lb.) baking soda
- 450 g. (about 1 lb.) powdered cornstarch
- 1 quart white vinegar
- 200 square feet of aluminum foil
- 100 small paper cups or 100 pill cups
- 1 package coffee filters

A large number of small containers are needed to make the various tests in school. Paper baking cups are least expensive, but pill cups are smaller and more rigid. It is possible to place small piles of powder on wax paper, thereby avoiding the need for so many cups. Baby food jars brought in from home can also be used.

- 1 small roll aluminum foil-for the heat test
- 1 dozen plastic spoons-for measuring powders
- 1 box flat toothpicks-for stirring

From a drugstore:

- 30 ml. (about 1 oz.) tincture of iodine (For the iodine test, dilute the iodine by mixing it with about 2 quarts of water; iodine is poisonous.)
- 4 dozen 30 ml. (about 1 oz.) glass or plastic bottles with plastic dropper
- 15 eyedroppers (to save money, you can use eyedroppers and baby food jars)

Fill 16 of these containers with vinegar, 16 with the diluted iodine, and 16 with water.

From a hardware store:

- 2 kilograms (about 5 lbs.) plaster of Paris
- 4 small cans Sterno (for heat)
- 20 wooden clothespins for holding powders over heat

From home or school supplies:

- Hand lenses and/or microscopes (optional)

Lesson 1
Observing the Puzzling Powders

Science Standard

The student produces evidence that demonstrates an understanding of the following:

- Properties of objects and materials, such as similarities and differences in the size, weight, and color of objects; the ability of materials to react with other substances; and different states of matter (National Center on the Economy and Education, Elementary School Performance Standards, 1997)

Materials

- granulated sugar
- table salt
- baking soda
- powdered cornstarch
- plaster of Paris
- aluminum foil
- flat toothpicks or paste sticks
- plastic spoons

Guiding the Activity

The Puzzling Powders are common white powders. They are safe for the children to taste and are easily obtained. The beginning classes are devoted to identifying the powders and devising ways of distinguishing them from one another. Place 1 teaspoon of each of the five powders onto a sheet of aluminum foil after students have marked the foil A (top left), B (top right), C (center), D (lower left), and E (lower right). Allow the students to explore the unknown powders and let them speculate about what they might be. Each student or small group should be allowed to experiment independently; no discussion of possible techniques for the identification of the powders should precede the work. Warn the children about the dangers of tasting unknown substances. Although in this instance all of the powders are safe, taste-testing is not recommended unless it is done in a separate investigation with emphasis on the sense of taste.

You may want the children to keep notebooks to help them remember what they find out. At first, you can help them design charts on which to record the results of their experiments. A series of sample charts is provided in Appendices L-R. When doing undirected work, your young experimenters may appear to be accomplishing nothing. It is easy to forget that learning is a very slow process; there must be time to "fool around," time to make mistakes, time to try something over and over again, and time just to think. In the process of "messing around," children cannot help learning something about such characteristics as texture, odor, and appearance. Children are quite perceptive about small variations in the texture and appearance of the powders. They find, for instance, that the "white" powders are actually many shades of white. They may refer to the plaster of Paris as "grayish-white" and to the cornstarch as "yellowish-white."

Differences in textures are also discernible. Some powders make more dust than others, some are harsh to the touch, and others feel smooth and silky. The size and shape of individual powder particles can be seen using a hand-held magnifier. Using each of the senses, except taste, ask students to generate words to describe one of the powders.

Once the students have become familiar with the powders, they are ready for more sophisticated tests using water, heat, iodine, and vinegar. Each of the following tests causes a striking reaction with ***one*** of the powders: Heat makes sugar melt, bubble, and turn black; iodine turns starch black; vinegar causes baking soda to fizz; and plaster of Paris warms and hardens with water. In addition, the tests produce smaller changes in other powders. For example, while iodine does turn starch black, it also stains baking soda orange and plaster of Paris yellow. For this reason, children do not usually conclude that the iodine test is a specific test for the presence of starch. When Puzzling Powder mixtures are analyzed later, you may want to point out the usefulness of iodine for starch detection by demonstrating how the same color occurs when only trace amounts of starch are present.

Lesson 2
Mixing with Water

Science Standard

The student produces evidence that demonstrates an understanding of the following:

- Properties of objects and materials, such as similarities and differences in the size, weight, and color of objects; the ability of materials to react with other substances; and different states of matter (National Center on the Economy and Education, Elementary School Performance Standards, 1997)

Materials

- granulated sugar
- table salt
- baking soda
- powdered corn starch
- plaster of Paris
- aluminum foil
- flat toothpicks or paste sticks
- plastic spoons
- eyedroppers

Guiding the Activity

Mix each powder with water. A sample record-keeping chart is included in Appendix M. Some reactions that children describe are these: bubbling, dissolving, and becoming soupy, sticky, or hard. When making a paste with plaster of Paris, the children will find that after about 15 minutes, it hardens and "gets like a rock." Some children may discover that quite a bit of heat is generated in this setting process. Plaster of Paris can only become hard once. Have someone try grinding up a little plaster of Paris to see how hard it gets when remixed with water.

Those children who mix just a little powder with a lot of water may find differences in how the powders "go into water." It is not necessary to use such words as "dissolve" and "insoluble." When children say that sugar "just goes into water and disappears," they are describing solubility with words they understand. They may say about plaster of Paris or starch, "It just stays there," or "It makes the water cloudy," or "You mix it and you mix it and it goes to the bottom."

Lesson 3
Heat Test

Science Standard

The student produces evidence that demonstrates an understanding of the following:

- Properties of objects and materials, such as similarities and differences in the size, weight, and color of objects; the ability of materials to react with other substances; and different states of matter (National Center on the Economy and Education, Elementary School Performance Standards, 1997)

Materials

- granulated sugar
- table salt
- baking soda
- powdered cornstarch
- plaster of Paris
- aluminum foil
- sterno (preferred), candles, or hot plate
- matches

Guiding the Activity

A sample record-keeping chart is included in Appendix N. The heat test can be carried out in school if you use a hot plate, candles, or cans of Sterno. Set these in an aluminum pie tin containing sand. A small sample of a powder can be heated in a little cup made from aluminum foil and held over the heat source with a wooden spring clothespin. The powders should be heated for 1-2 minutes.

When heated, baking soda and plaster of Paris seem to remain unchanged, while salt snaps and crackles. Starch turns brown and might smell like burnt toast. Sugar melts, bubbles, smokes, smells like caramel, turns brown, turns black, and finally hardens. (You can demonstrate how caramel is made by melting a batch of sugar in a pan.) The heat test, then, is a good way to detect sugar, since sugar is the only one of the Puzzling Powders to melt and turn shiny black when heated.

Lesson 4
Filter Test
(as an alternative or in addition to the Heat Test)

Science Standard

The student produced evidence that demonstrates an understanding of:

- Properties of objects and materials, such as similarities and differences in the size, weight, and color of objects; the ability of materials to react with other substances; and different states of matter (National Center on the Economy and Education, Elementary School Performance Standards, 1997)

Materials

- granulated sugar
- table salt
- baking soda
- powdered cornstarch
- plaster of Paris
- coffee filters
- funnels (if available)
- pill cups
- flat toothpicks or paste sticks

Guiding the Activity

A sample record-keeping chart is presented in Appendix O. There may be instances when a teacher is particularly cautious about the heat test or there are school regulations concerning the use of fire. In these instances, an alternative is to substitute a filter test. The filter test may be included as an additional test if desired. Pill cups are filled two-thirds full with water (about 25 milliliters), and ½ teaspoon of each powder is added to the water and stirred. The solutions are poured through a filter (small coffee filters work well) and allowed to dry. The filter paper with the sugar solution will retain a sticky property.

Lesson 5
Iodine Test

Science Standard

The student produces evidence that demonstrates an understanding of the following:

- Properties of objects and materials, such as similarities and differences in the size, weight, and color of objects; the ability of materials to react with other substances; and different states of matter (National Center on the Economy and Education, Elementary School Performance Standards, 1997)

Materials

- granulated sugar
- table salt
- baking soda
- powdered cornstarch
- plaster of Paris
- aluminum foil
- flat toothpicks or paste sticks
- iodine solution
- eyedroppers

Guiding the Activity

A sample record-keeping chart is presented in Appendix P. For the iodine test, have the students take a portion of each powder, some diluted iodine in dropper bottles, and toothpicks for mixing. Cover desks with newspaper for easier cleanup. Dropping the iodine on the powder being tested carries out the iodine test. As the children perform the tests on the Puzzling Powders, they can record the reactions on a chart so that they may refer to them when they test mixtures.

There may be some disagreement about which powders change to blue-black with iodine, for example, "My baking soda gets black, but Alan’s doesn’t." Since only a small amount of starch is necessary to give the characteristic black color, some contaminations may result from mixing up the mixing sticks. Do not warn the children of this beforehand, however. Let them make the tests again to try to discover the reasons for inconsistent results.

Some of the reactions attributed to the iodine, such as hardening and dissolving, are really caused by the water in which the iodine is dissolved. You can tell the children how the iodine solution is made, and remind them of what they observed when they mixed water with the powders.

Just as iodine can be used to detect starch, starch serves as an indicator of iodine. See if the students can discover this by asking them to pick out an iodine solution from others that look the same. Food coloring, ink, cider vinegar, or watercolor paints can be used to tint water to the color of a weak iodine solution. If you have difficulty imitating the color of iodine, you can mask the iodine’s true color with ink or some other dye.

Lesson 6
Vinegar Test

Science Standard

The student produces evidence that demonstrates an understanding of the following:

- Properties of objects and materials, such as similarities and differences in the size, weight, and color of objects; the ability of materials to react with other substances; and different states of matter (National Center on the Economy and Education, Elementary School Performance Standards, 1997)

Materials

- granulated sugar
- table salt
- baking soda
- powdered corn starch
- plaster of Paris
- aluminum foil
- white vinegar
- pill cups
- eyedroppers

Guiding the Activity

A sample record-keeping chart is presented in Appendix Q. The powders can be distributed in the little cups and also treated with a few drops of vinegar. The results of the experiments can be recorded on a similar chart titled "What powder can be identified most easily with vinegar?" A discussion of the results may enable the children to answer this question. Vinegar makes baking soda fizz actively while other powders fizz only slightly or not at all.

Enrichment Activity

Other powders can be tested with vinegar. Baking powder fizzes when either vinegar or water is added, and a solution of powdered milk is curdled by vinegar. Powders other than the Puzzling Powders can be tested with heat, iodine, and vinegar. Children can perform these tests on powders they find at home. They may notice, for example, that other powders fizz when vinegar is added, just as baking soda does. Thus, when powders other than the five Puzzling Powders are tested, fizzing does not necessarily indicate baking soda. Yet, if any powder does not fizz with vinegar, they can be reasonably sure that it does not contain baking soda. This process of elimination by using negative test results is often difficult for children to understand.

Lesson 7
Puzzling Powders Mixtures

Science Standard

The student produces evidence that demonstrates understanding of the following:

- Properties of objects and materials, such as similarities and differences in the size, weight, and color of objects; the ability of materials to react with other substances; and different states of matter (National Center on the Economy and Education, Elementary School Performance Standards, 1997)

Materials

- granulated sugar
- table salt
- baking soda
- powdered corn starch
- iodine
- eyedroppers
- plaster of Paris
- coffee filters
- aluminum foil
- white vinegar
- sterno
- pill cups

Guiding the Activity

To find out if the students can use the water, heat, filter, iodine, and vinegar tests, you can have them determine the composition of some Puzzling Powder mixtures. Mixtures can be made by combining two or more powders.

Before class, make up several Puzzling Powder mixtures. The students should be permitted to move freely about the room, gathering the necessary materials and performing the tests. For variety, you can have everyone make up a mixture of his or her own, and exchange it for someone else's.

Allow students to use their own techniques for identifying mixtures. Instead of looking for the individual characteristics of the components of mixtures, students often determine the composition of the mixtures by attempting to make a matching sample. Although this method is not a typical adult technique, it is a valid procedure, and its use should not be discouraged.

A sample record-keeping chart is presented in Appendix R. Give students some explanation of how to complete it. For example, if heat makes the mixture melt and blacken, then the presence of sugar is indicated. If nothing happens with vinegar (a negative test result), there is probably no baking soda. Try not to call your students' answers right or wrong. The identification of the Puzzling Powders should be based upon the results of their tests. If you think there is no starch in a particular mixture but most of the children's results indicated a black color with iodine, the assumption should be that starch is present.

Specific Accommodations by Disability Category

Motor/Orthopedic

- Have powders easily accessible to students (workbench height, adapted spoons, etc.); use plastic containers for the transfer of liquids (possibly, enema bottles if there is limited muscle strength); allow use of an assistive recording device.
- Use a funnel with tripod supports.
- Use plastic containers.
- Use a peer assistant to ensure the student gets maximum sensory exposure to each powder.
- Work in pairs to help with charting what happens in the experiments.
- Allow student to use alternative recording device.

Visually Impaired

- In the heat test, use an electrical device instead of a flame.
- Use a filter test as an alternative to the heat test.
- Make sure labels and worksheets are printed in regular, large print, and braille.
- If need be, have an aide work with a student and use many oral descriptions.
- Work with a peer to ensure that the student gets full sensory exposure while exploring each of the powders.
- Use computer interface for data collection with auditory output.

Deaf or Hard of Hearing

- Seat the student so there is good visual contact with the teacher and other students.
- Have a limited-hearing student seated where the good ear is faced toward the class or their group.
- When expressing ideas to the group, allow a team helper to communicate these to the group.
- When recording test results, a note taker could write for this person.
- Review instructions for clarity and independent use.
- Use a laptop computer as a communication alternative.

Learning Disabled

- Modify activity depending on whether the disability is in reading, writing, etc.
- Use step-by-step directions, possibly handed out to allow the student to follow visually.
- Preview directions and vocabulary words used in the activity.
- Discuss responsibilities and directions with the student before activity.
- When assigning cooperative group roles, assign the student to a role that reflects his or her interests and strengths.

Attention Deficit Disorder/Attention Deficit Hyperactivity Disorder

- Preview directions and vocabulary words before the activity.
- Slow down the pace of the activities and allow adequate time for participation.
- Discuss with the student appropriate behaviors expected during the activity.
- Assign the group to work in an area with minimal distractions.
- Carefully select cooperative group members and assign the student to a role that reflects his or her interests and strengths.

Developmentally Delayed

- Select vocabulary appropriate for the student's learning.
- Expose the student to many of the activities in advance.
- You may want to ask for an aide to help with some of the tests, like the heat test.
- Prepare a take-home chart for the student to review the reactions for each test.

Behavior Disordered

- Review directions and vocabulary in advance and clarify expectations and appropriate behaviors to be exhibited during the activity if working in groups.
- Assign group to work in an area with minimal distractions.
- Carefully select cooperative group members and assign the student to a role that reflects his or her interests and strengths.
- Use proximity control and seek opportunities to support appropriate behaviors.
- Plan materials trafficking in advance; use consistent routines.

Speech/Language

- Provide a take-home sheet of the vocabulary words in advance of the activity.
- Provide a translator or supportive peer assistant.
- Provide the group with a laptop computer or alternative communication device.
- Assign the student to a cooperative group role that maximizes the likelihood the experience will be positive and successful.

Autism

- Practice the tests to be used in the activity before the lesson in class.
- Provide a supportive peer assistant or adult aide to work together on the activity.
- Allow extra time outside of the school day for the student to practice the tests.
- Consider a note-taker or recording device for data collection.
- Provide assistance and reassurance when possible.

Acquired Brain Injury

- Preteach a segment of the lesson.
- Review directions and vocabulary in advance.
- Organize materials for easy recording of data and provide assistance if necessary.
- Review rules and expectations in private and in advance.
- Use proximity control and reinforce appropriate behaviors.
- Prepare a take-home activity packet to provide opportunities for the student to repeat the experiments at home with a supportive adult.

Health Impairments

- Review possible hazards or personal reaction possibilities in advance.
- Review possible side effects of medication and any possible dangers while doing the activities.
- Prepare a take-home activity packet to provide opportunities for the student to complete the experiments at home with a supportive adult if there are limitations regarding in-class participation.
- Consider the student's abilities and limitations when assigning cooperative group assignments.

Multiple Intelligence Extensions

Linguistic

- Keep a journal of the reactions that were present in each test.
- Discuss your results within and between groups.
- Organize class for appropriate conduits of conversation among students and student groups.
- Prepare a formal laboratory result showing the results of your experiments and/or a forensics report in your investigation for unknowns.

Logical/Mathematical

- Conduct tests to determine the amount of different materials needed to maximize the use of materials (e.g., the baking soda and vinegar mixture that does not waste either substance).
- Plan an investigation to determine the minimum concentration of the various materials needed to get a positive test.
- Plan a process for investigating for other materials. Compare cornstarch with cornmeal and other food products made with corn.

Spatial

- Make a graph of the reactions of each powder for each of the tests.
- Allow students to make drawings to show what happens with each test.
- Extend the study of plaster of Paris to include a project involving sculpture.

Bodily/Kinesthetic

- Provide a classroom context where student movement is allowed.
- Let students gather their own materials for their tests.
- Lay out materials and plan consistent policies for student and materials trafficking.
- Conduct activities in a location where there can be a lot of natural movement that will not interfere with the work of other groups.

Musical

- Develop a song or a rap tune to help students remember how powders react in the different tests.
- Review contemporary music for associations with the powders and their properties (e.g., sweet, effervescent).
- Examine celebrations in a variety of cultures associated with corn and the processing of grain.

Interpersonal

- Include cooperative student behaviors as a major component of evaluation.
- Model a supportive and encouraging classroom atmosphere.
- Assign students to cooperative group roles in which they can share their strengths and divide labor.
- Use feedback and sharing in the activity sequence.
- Use student interactions to search out and find additional related investigations.

Intrapersonal

- Allow each student to explore forensics and find out more about how forensics experts investigate crime scenes.
- Prepare a take-home packet that a student could do individually.
- Allow students to search the Internet for additional resources or activity possibilities.

Naturalist

- Investigate the importance of sugar, and study sugar collection by insects to aid in plant reproduction.
- Investigate ways organisms gather and share food. Investigate food processing and nutrition.
- Determine the possible origins of all of the powders used in the investigations.

Lesson Sequence
Exploring Electricity

Science Standards

Content Standard B K-4

Light, heat, electricity and magnetism concepts

- Electricity in circuits can produce light, heat, sound, and magnetic effects. Electrical circuits require a complete loop through which the electrical current can pass.

Content Standard B 5-8

Light, heat, electricity and magnetism concepts

- Electrical circuits provide a means of converting electrical energy into heat, light, sound, chemicals, or other forms of energy

Vocabulary

Ampere: the base SI unit of electrical current, equivalent to one coulomb per second, formally defined to be the constant current which if maintained in two straight parallel conductors of infinite length, of negligible circular cross section, and placed one meter apart in vacuum, would produce between these conductors a force equal to 2×10^{-7} Newton per meter of length.

Circuit: the complete path of an electric current, including the generating apparatus, intervening resistors, or capacitors.

Conductor: a substance, body, or device that readily conducts heat, electricity, sound, etc.

Electric motor: a machine that converts electrical energy into mechanical energy.

Light bulb: electric lamp consisting of a glass bulb containing a wire filament (usually tungsten) that emits light when heated.

Non-conductor: a material that conducts little or no electricity, heat, or sound.

Ohm: the SI unit of electrical resistance, defined to be the electrical resistance between two points of a conductor when a constant potential difference applied between these points produces in this conductor a current of one ampere. The resistance in ohms is numerically equal to the magnitude of the potential difference.

Volt: the SI unit of potential difference and electromotive force, formally defined to be the difference of electric potential between two points of a conductor carrying a constant current of one ampere, when the power dissipated between these points is equal to one watt.

Materials

- One D cell for every two students

- One D cell plastic holder for every two students (this is optional but it does help keep hot wires from touching students fingers)
- 60-90 centimeters of plastic coated electrical wire for every two students
- One small light bulb
- Wire strippers per every four students (optional)
- Paper and pencil for every student
- Hot mitt or mittens for every student (optional—heat is generated by the D cell and can become hot, but not a fire hazard)
- Small toy that activates by human hands touching two terminals and completes circuit (dollar stores often have small plastic farm animals or globes with batteries that play a song or make a noise when the child touches two sides of the object)

Lesson 1
Light It Up

Prior to the activity and to help set the stage for the unit, ask students to form a circle so that their elbows touch one another. Next, ask students to gently grasp the elbow of the person to their left. The teacher then squeezes the elbow he/she is holding, then that student squeezes the person to their left until each elbow has been squeezed and the motion has returned to teacher. Tell students this demonstrates how electricity moves in a circuit, the Latin word for circle. Now ask students to do this again but this time you will time them, making it a race. Once completed you may tell students that electricity must travel in a complete circle without ever breaking the path. Have students try it again but this time designate one student that will not squeeze. Ask what happened.

OPTIONAL: Tell students to now firmly hold hands and insert into the circle a small toy that makes a noise when held by two students. This can make the game interesting, will get students thinking about electricity and circuits, and can help set the stage.

Guiding the Activity

Students are given D cell, wire, and a light bulb. Students are asked to investigate:

Focus Inquiry Question:

_How many ways can you find to light the bulb using these three materials? (at least 4 obvious methods are possible plus a few inventive ones)

Procedure

Students should be reminded to draw every method discovered that lights the bulbs. Students will need ample time to "MESS AROUND" with the materials. Although this may look like play at first, it truly is discovery and by requiring students to draw a picture of their ideas the teacher has accountability and structure in the lesson. Safety concerns may be addressed by requiring students to stay seated when they have their materials.

Many students will discover a means of lighting the bulb without any instruction from the teacher, however a few students may become frustrated and unable to light the bulb. A few students may create a circuit that gets hot and this may frighten the student. The teacher may need to assist by holding items and even providing masking tape or plastic holders with alligator clips. Most of these students will be successful with a little encouragement from teacher and a reminder to keep connection points tight. Keeping the connection points tight is crucial as well as watching for short circuits that may grow hot to the touch. The teacher needs to constantly ask students to show where they think the electricity is moving from and to. It helps if students start to number the contact paths on their drawings, starting with 1 at the D cell and then continue numbering.

Following the mess around investigation, plan a "classroom museum" walk to view other students' drawings and circuits. This may help those who are a little timid about investigating. Ask students to look for others who have drawings that match their own drawings. Also, ask students to copy and draw ideas that they would like to try using their own materials. Following this "classroom museum" walk, allow students to return to their materials and investigate a few more light the bulb possibilities. Engage in a class discussion for fixing pictured circuits that will not work and/or mark circuit pictures that will work effectively.

Lesson 2
Series and Parallel Circuits

Science Standard

Content Standard B K-4

Light, heat, electricity and magnetism concepts

- Electricity in circuits can produce light, heat, sound, and magnetic effects. Electrical circuits require a complete loop through which the electrical current can pass.

Content Standard B 5-8

Light, heat, electricity and magnetism concepts

- Electrical circuits provide a means of converting electrical energy into heat, light, sound, chemical or other forms of energy

Materials

- 100 cm of additional plastic coated wire
- 3-4 light bulbs for every two students
- wire strippers –optional
- light bulb holders-OPTIONAL
- D cell holders –OPTIONAL (but desirable as the D cells can get hot to the touch)

Guiding the Activity-(HINT: do not leave bulb lit for extended periods of time)

Ask students in teams of two to light 2-4 light bulbs with approximately 100 cm of wire, a D cell and two bulbs.

Focus Inquiry Question:

How many ways are there to light two light bulbs?

Procedure

Students will discover that there are several ways to light the bulbs. Ask students to draw the methods they discover. Once every team has found at least one method, ask the students to each demonstrate and orally explain the path that the electricity is traveling. This can be done as a presentation to the entire class and thus will spark other groups to try new methods OR the teacher may question individual teams while they investigate. Upon completion, ask students which were the brightest bulbs? Ask students to find out what happens if they take out one bulb and leave the other bulb connected. Send the students back to their materials with the challenge to find a method for lighting more than one bulb that stays bright and stays lit even when the other bulb is removed. In most cases students will construct a series circuit. Ask them to investigate what happens when additional bulbs are included. Guide students in helping them create a parallel circuit. Once this is done, make comparisons when additional bulbs are added. Also investigate what happens if batteries are arranged in series and parallel. Discuss parallel circuits which are usually the most desirable wiring for household use.

Some of the students will quickly and easily establish a parallel circuit. Other students will struggle to create a parallel circuit and may need to view classmates working models. Also, it may help if the teacher highlights pattern in student drawings, i.e. note the train tracks or the ladder like appearance of the paths.

BLOWING A BULB: it is optional to challenge the students to group cooperate and connect D cells in a row to blow out 1-3 bulbs in any circuitry.

Lesson 3
Making a Switch

Science Standard

<u>Content Standard B K-4</u>

Light, heat, electricity and magnetism concepts

- Electricity in circuits can produce light, heat, sound, and magnetic effects. Electrical circuits require a complete loop through which the electrical current can pass.

<u>Content Standard B 5-8</u>

Light, heat, electricity and magnetism concepts

- Electrical circuits provide a means of converting electrical energy into heat, light, sound, chemical or other forms of energy

Materials

- 100 cm of additional plastic coated wire
- 3-4 light bulbs for every two students
- wire strippers – optional
- light bulb holders- OPTIONAL
- D cell holders – OPTIONAL (but desirable as the D cells can get hot to the touch)
- 6cm by 6 cm of square cardboard
- paper punch
- 2 brass paper fasteners for each student that can be inserted 2 cm apart from each other in a cardboard square
- one large paper clip attached to one of the brass paper fasteners inserted on the cardboard square (the paper clip should be able to easily swing between the two brass paper fasteners)
- 2 washers for each student

Guiding the Lesson

Ask students to wire a series circuit like they created in the last lesson.

Focus Inquiry Question

How can you turn the light bulb on and off?

Procedure

Students may make individual switches while working in cooperative groups of 2-4 students. Challenge the students to find a method for turning the bulb on and off. Provide them with the materials for a simple tap switch (Figures 13-15) in addition to the D cell, lights, wire, and holders. Remind the students of the human circle they made earlier and what happened when the human circuit was broken.

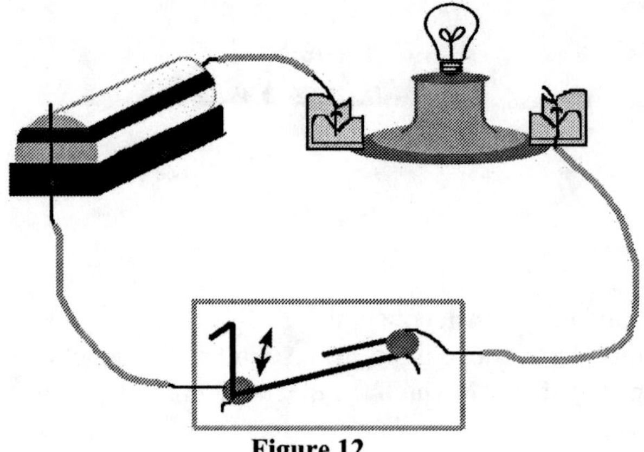
Figure 12

Students will investigate how the switch works. Some students may leave the switch open (paper clip not touching both paper fasteners) while working on their circuit and discover quite by accident that the paper clip can be moved. Others will begin to move the paper clip back and forth easily, but forget to attach the switch to the bulbs AND the D cell. Remind students that electricity must travel in an unbroken circuit to help them discover the correct wiring. Also, asking students to draw the circuit and number the sequential path the electricity is moving with #1 being the D cell will help them discover the mistakes in the wiring sequences.

How to Make a Simple Tap Switch

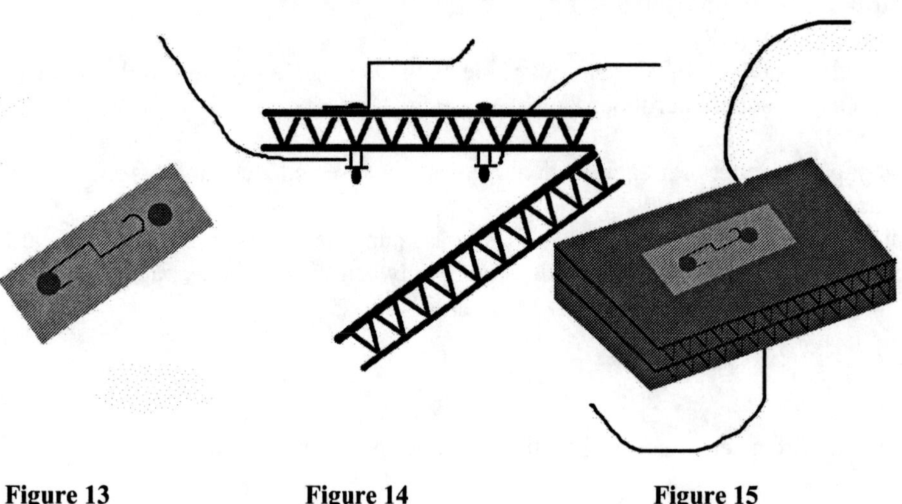
Figure 13 Figure 14 Figure 15

Materials

- piece of corrugated cardboard, approximately 4" x 8"
- 2 paper fasteners

- 2 small washers
- 2 connecting wires, about 20 cm long
- masking tape

Procedure

Bend the paper clip as shown in Figure 12. Make a knife cut halfway through the cardboard so that the cardboard is divided (but still held together) into two 4" x 4" halves.

Take the paper clip and wrap one end tightly around the paper fastener. Then poke the paper fasteners through the cardboard as shown in Figure 13, and wrap one end of a connecting wire around each paper fastener underneath. Add the washers and, pressing them firmly against the wires and cardboard, bend over the ends of the fasteners. Tape the two halves of cardboard together as shown in Figure 14 and the switch is completed.

Lesson 4
Three-Way Circuit

Science Standard

<u>Content Standard B K-4</u>

Light, heat, electricity and magnetism concepts

- Electricity in circuits can produce light, heat, sound, and magnetic effects. Electrical circuits require a complete loop through which the electrical current can pass.

<u>Content Standard B 5-8</u>

Light, heat, electricity and magnetism concepts

- Electrical circuits provide a means of converting electrical energy into heat, light, sound, chemical or other forms of energy

Materials

- battery and battery holder
- light bulb and holder
- wire with alligator connectors
- plain wire
- constructed switches

Procedure

Construct two tap switches as illustrated in Figures 13-15. Set up the circuit as shown in the diagram (Figure 16). Move the "switch" from one position to the other. Describe how the 3-way switch you have made compares to a 3-way switch in a home.

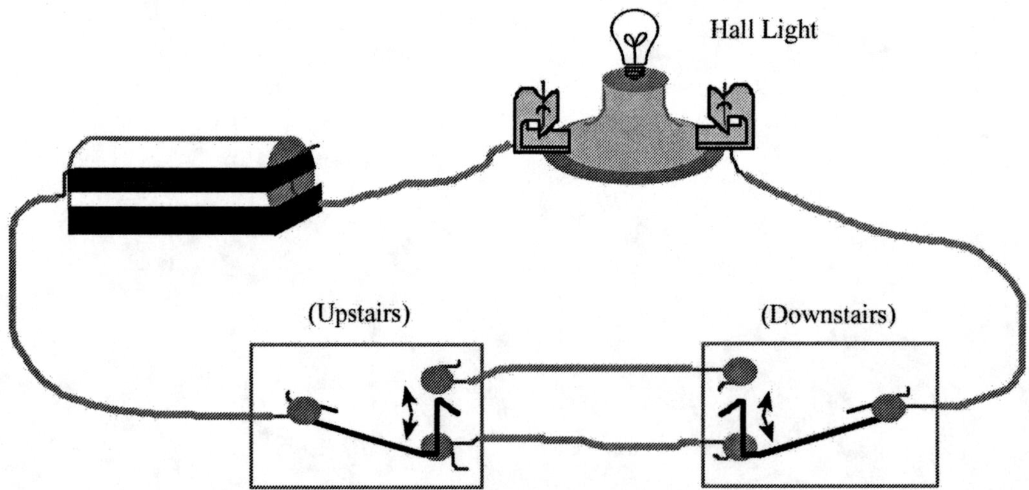

Figure 16

Lesson 5
Conductor vs. Insulator

Science Standard

Content Standard B K-4

Light, heat, electricity and magnetism concepts

- Electricity in circuits can produce light, heat, sound, and magnetic effects. Electrical circuits require a complete loop through which the electrical current can pass.

Content Standard B 5-8

Light, heat, electricity and magnetism concepts

- Electrical circuits provide a means of converting electrical energy into heat, light, sound, chemical or other forms of energy

Materials (for every two students)

- 1 D cell (optional plastic holder)
- 70 –100 cm of plastic coated wire
- 1 ziplock baggie containing small pieces of aluminum (pop lid tab), copper (penny), steel (paper clip), cotton ball, cloth square, small glass or mirror, etc
- 1 bulb

Guiding the Activity

Students will be asked to create a circuit that they created in the previous lesson

Focus Inquiry Question

What items in the baggies will allow the circuit to keep the bulb lit?

Students will begin to insert the metal and cloth items from their bags one at a time. Students may struggle with where to put the items along the circuit; they will need time to investigate placing the items in the circuit. The teacher may need to suggest places that make sense, or ask students to trace the path of electricity. Once students have accomplished this task, students could record on a T chart which items are conductors and which items are insulators.

Lesson 6
Spin Me Around

Science Standard

Content Standard B K-4

Light, heat, electricity and magnetism concepts

- Electricity in circuits can produce light, heat, sound, and magnetic effects. Electrical circuits require a complete loop through which the electrical current can pass.

Content Standard B 5-8

Light, heat, electricity and magnetism concepts

- Electrical circuits provide a means of converting electrical energy into heat, light, sound, chemical or other forms of energy

Materials

- 100 cm of additional plastic coated wire
- 3-4 small electric motors for every two students
- wire strippers –optional
- cardboard Square switches
- D cell holders –OPTIONAL (but desirable as the D cells can get hot to the touch)
- small motors with two wires extending OR small bells

Guiding the Activity (HINT: do not let the motors run for extended time periods)

Students are presented with a small motor and a paper tape flag attached to the top. Tell students the flag can be made to spin when placed in a working circuit.

Focus Inquiry Question

How can you make the flag spin using a D cell and wires and a switch?

Procedure

Students will begin to assemble a working circuit with a switch. Most students will simply insert the motor and attach the wires in the same way they attached the light bulb within the circuit. If some students seem overwhelmed, you may want to simplify the task by just asking students to wire the motor without a switch and then add the switch at a later time. It will also help students to make the correct connections if they make a drawing of the circuit as they have done in prior lessons.

Lesson 7
Building an Electromagnet

Science Standard

Content Standard B K-4

Light, heat, electricity and magnetism concepts

- Electricity in circuits can produce light, heat, sound, and magnetic effects. Electrical circuits require a complete loop through which the electrical current can pass.

Content Standard B 5-8

Light, heat, electricity and magnetism concepts

- Electrical circuits provide a means of converting electrical energy into heat, light, sound, chemical or other forms of energy

Materials (for every 2 students)

- 1 meter of electrical wire
- wire cutters
- 1 10-20 cm long steel nail
- 1 10-20 cm long aluminum nail
- 1 D cell
- 20-50 paper clips
- 1 switch (optional)

Guiding the Activity

Show students a magnet and ask them to observe the magnet when it is passed over a pile of paper clips. Tell students that you would like them to find another way to pick up the paper clips using am electric current.

Focus Inquiry Question

How can a D cell, wire, and a nail be used to create a magnet?
How strong is the magnet? How many paper clips can it attract?

Students will begin to assemble a circuit, however, they may not easily discover the method for introducing the nail into the circuit. The teacher may need to suggest winding wire around the nail and using the flat end of the nail as a magnet. The inference that electricity can induce magnetism should develop in the students. Once students have discovered how to get the current to go through the nail, teacher can suggest that students increase the strength of their magnet by increasing the number of winds of the wire on the nail. Students should record on a graph the number of winds vs. the number of paper clips the electro magnet can attract. Ask students to predict and compare what will happen if the steel nail is replaced with an aluminum nail.

Lesson 8
Making a Light Bulb

Science Standard

Content Standard B K-4

Light, heat, electricity and magnetism concepts

- Electricity in circuits can produce light, heat, sound, and magnetic effects. Electrical circuits require a complete loop through which the electrical current can pass.

Content Standard B 5-8

Light, heat, electricity and magnetism concepts

- Electrical circuits provide a means of converting electrical energy into heat, light, sound, chemical or other forms of energy

Materials

- wire for the filament (separated picture hanger wire or nichrome wire, purchased from a national supplier)
- 2 wires, preferably with alligator clips that can extend from each end of up to ten D-cell batteries in series and attach to the nichrome wire
- approximately 10 D dry cells
- a clear jar or cup (small baby food jar)
- modeling clay
- nail or golf tee for forming the filament

Procedure

Take a piece of unbraided picture-hanging wire or nichrome wire about 15 cm long. (The teacher will need to unbraid the picture-hanging wire in advance.) Wrap the wire around a small nail or golf tee to form a coiled filament. Leave 10 cm of straight wire at each end. It should look like this:

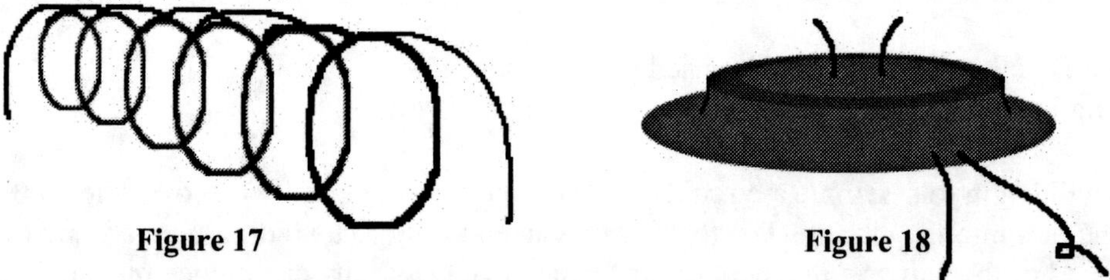

Figure 17 **Figure 18**

Flatten a piece of modeling clay big enough to cover the mouth of a jar. Stick the two bare ends of the connecting wires through the clay. The wires should be just as far apart as the filament is long.

Attach each end of the filament wire to a larger wire, preferably with alligator clips. Put the globe over the filament and press it to the base, as shown in the drawing below. Connect your bulb to a series of 6-10 batteries. If the light does not glow after a count of 10, disconnect and check your connections. It is suggested that you start with 6 batteries and continue to add batteries up to 10.

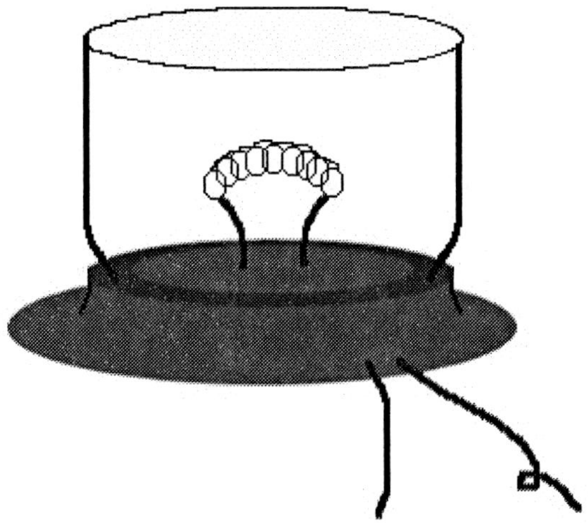

Figure 19

Lesson 9
Electric Question Board

Science Standards

Content Standard B K-4

Light, heat, electricity and magnetism concepts

- Electricity in circuits can produce light, heat, sound, and magnetic effects. Electrical circuits require a complete loop through which the electrical current can pass.

Content Standard B 5-8

Light, heat, electricity and magnetism concepts

- Electrical circuits provide a means of converting electrical energy into heat, light, sound, chemical or other forms of energy

Materials

- 20 brass paper fasteners
- masking tape
- manila folder (one for each child)
- aluminum foil
- scissors
- bulb and bulb holder
- battery with battery holder
- insulated wire
- paper punch

Procedure

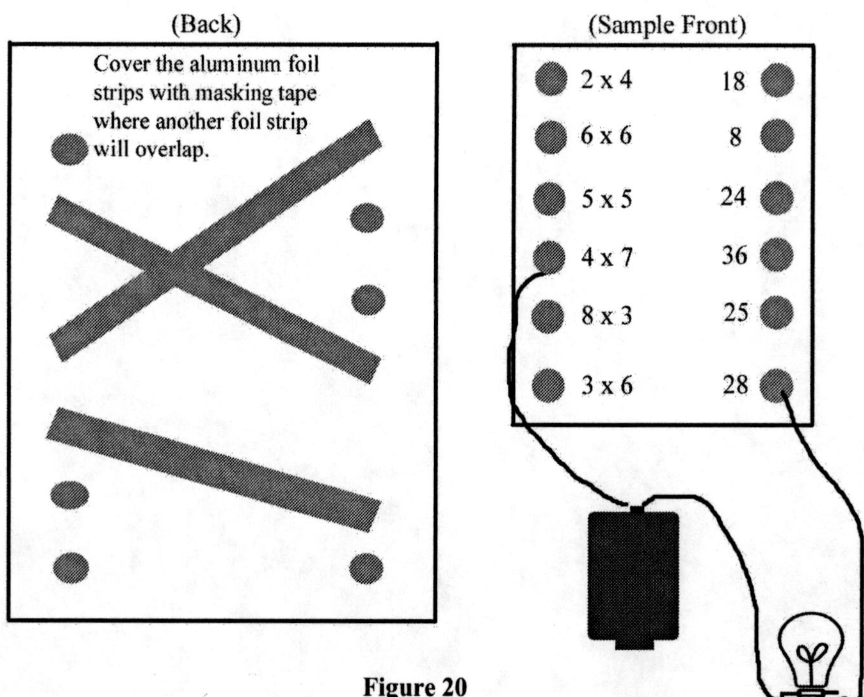

Figure 20

Use a paper punch and punch 10 holes on each side of the manila folder. Prepare strips of folded over aluminum foil that can stretch across to both rows of holes. Run a strip of doubled-over foil from a hole on one side to a hole on the other, and then cover the aluminum foil with masking tape (see Figure 20). Do this with successive holes until all of the holes have a backing of aluminum foil. Each successive strip of aluminum foil should be covered with masking tape. (The aluminum foil is the conductor and the strip of masking tape serves as an insulator.)

Once the circuits have been made, place a question on one side of the folder and the correct answer at the other end of the circuit on the opposite side of the folder. (With a 9" x 12" manila folder, approximately 8-10 questions works well.)

An extension idea: Have each student make an electric circuit worksheet with different questions relating to core knowledge associated with drill and practice in the different subjects of your curriculum. Using their own battery/bulb holders, each student can check out different folders during independent work time to practice skills.

Lesson 10
Lighting a Light Bulb

Science Standard

Content Standard B K-4

Light, heat, electricity and magnetism concepts

- Electricity in circuits can produce light, heat, sound, and magnetic effects. Electrical circuits require a complete loop through which the electrical current can pass.

Content Standard B 5-8

Light, heat, electricity and magnetism concepts

- Electrical circuits provide a means of converting electrical energy into heat, light, sound, chemical or other forms of energy

Materials

- Worksheet

Procedure

Looking at the assortment of pictures presented below, indicate the circumstances in which the bulb will light.

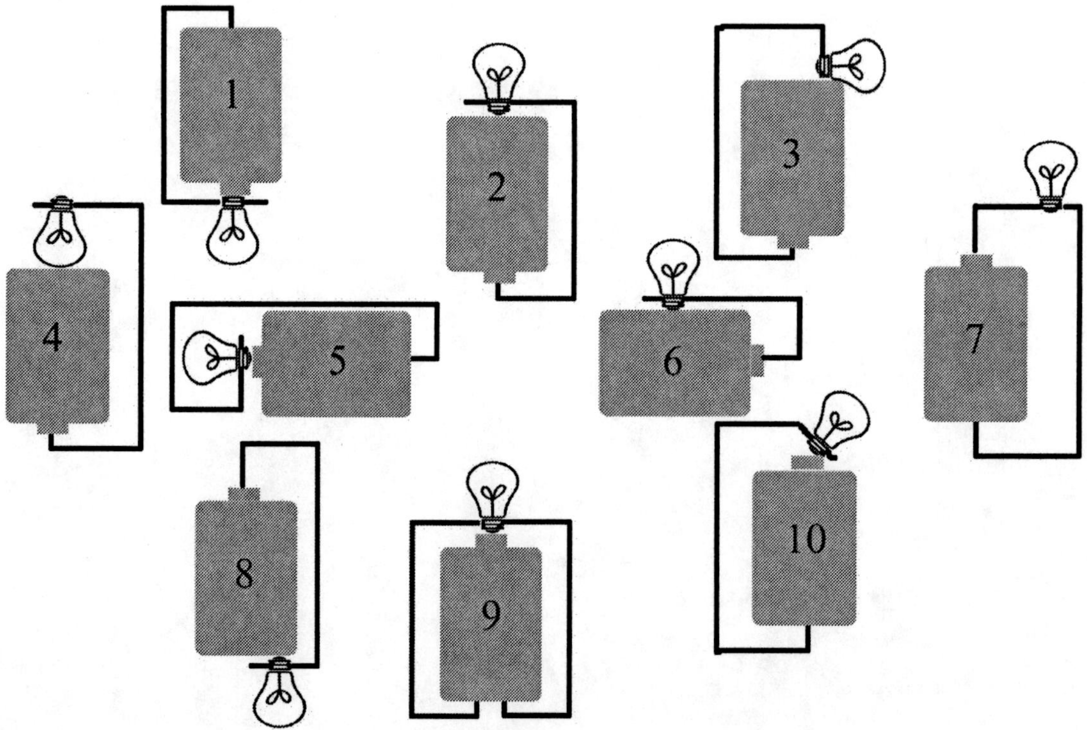

Figure 21

Lesson 11
Investigating Circuits

Science Standard

Content Standard B K-4

Light, heat, electricity and magnetism concepts

- Electricity in circuits can produce light, heat, sound, and magnetic effects. Electrical circuits require a complete loop through which the electrical current can pass.

Content Standard B 5-8

Light, heat, electricity and magnetism concepts

- Electrical circuits provide a means of converting electrical energy into heat, light, sound, chemical or other forms of energy

Materials

- Worksheets

Procedure

1. Light bulbs are arranged in a series circuit as indicated below. How will the bulbs in circuit A compare with circuit B?

A.

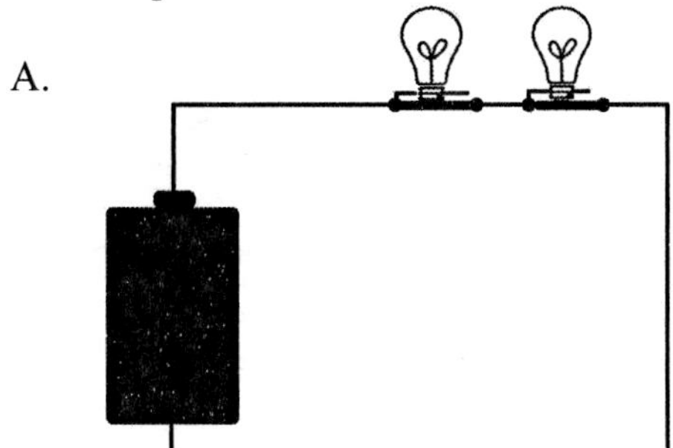

B.

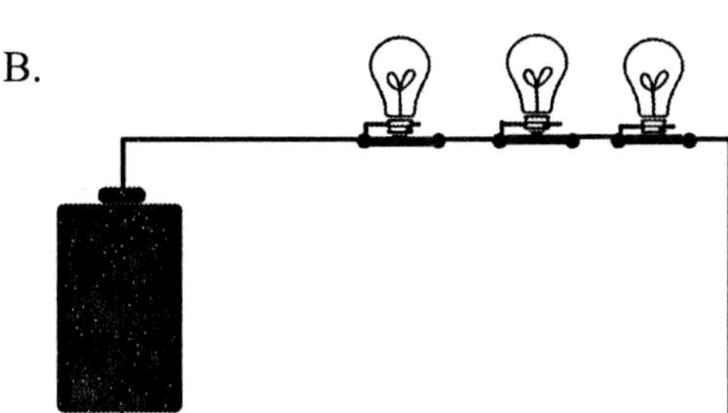

A. The lights will be equally bright in each circuit
B. The lights in circuit A will be brighter
C. The lights in circuit B will be brighter
D. The lights will light in circuit A, but will not light in circuit B

2. Light bulbs are arranged in a parallel circuit as indicated below. How will the bulbs in circuit A compare with circuit B?

A.

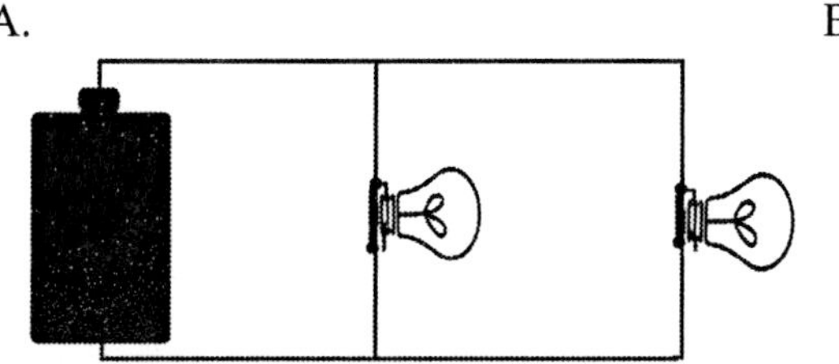

B.

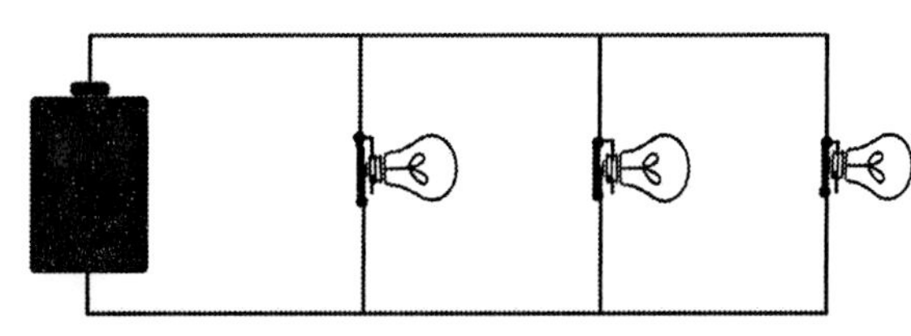

A. The lights will be equally bright in each circuit
B. The lights in circuit A will be brighter
C. The lights in circuit B will be brighter
D. The lights will light in circuit A but will not light in circuit B

3. Three bulbs are arranged in a series circuit as indicated in Figure A and three bulbs are arranged in a parallel circuit as indicated in Figure B.

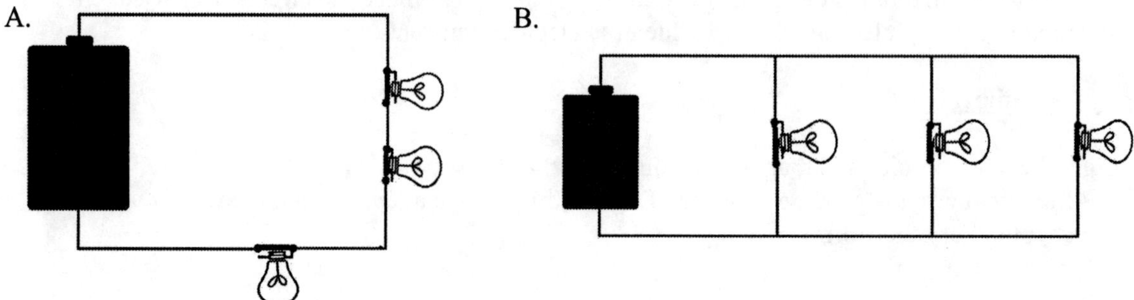

A. The lights will be equally bright in each circuit
B. The lights in circuit A will be brighter
C. The lights in circuit B will be brighter
D. The battery will last an equal period of time in each circuit

4. Consider the following light bulb arrangements:

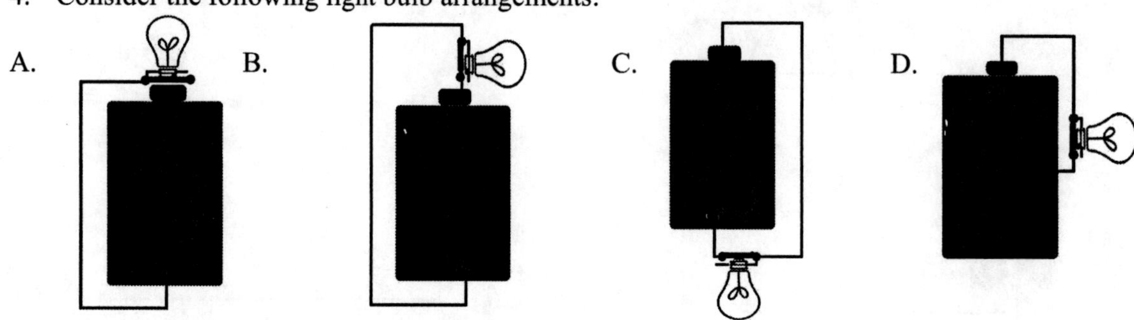

A. A will work. B, C, and D will not work
B. A and B will work, C and D will not work
C. A, B, and C will work. D will not work
D. A, B, C, and D will work

5. Consider the following light bulb arrangements:

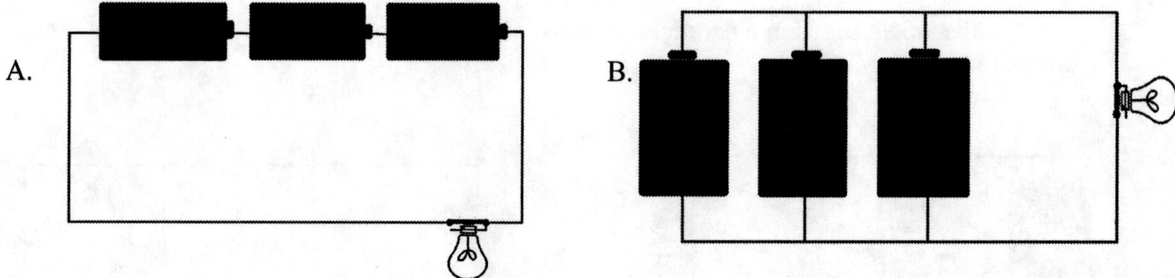

A. Each of the light bulbs will burn equally bright
B. The light in circuit A will burn more brightly
C. The light in circuit B will burn more brightly
D. The lights will light in circuit A but will not light in circuit B

Explanations

The three light bulbs in the series offer more resistance than the two bulbs in series. Ohms Law states that current (measured in amperes) is dependent upon pressure (measured in volts) divided by resistance (measured in ohms). $I = V/R$. In this case, the voltage remains the same and the resistance increases, therefore, there will be less current, and the bulbs in circuit A will burn more brightly.

The three light bulbs in parallel offer less resistance than the two light bulbs. Therefore, the circuit draws more current. In a case where each branch has an identical light bulb, the current is distributed equally among the branches. The light bulbs will burn with approximately the same brightness in both circuits.

The light bulbs in circuit A will burn less brightly because the higher resistance will allow less current to flow through. The battery in circuit A will last longer.

A, B, and C are all drawings of complete circuits. D is not.

The light bulb in A will burn more brightly. Batteries =arranged in a series increase the pressure (voltage), whereas batteries in parallel simply increase the reservoir of available current (amperage) allowing the bulbs to burn longer but at the same brightness.

Lesson 12
Investigating Electrical Units

Procedure

1. Examine the circuit shown below. Each battery is 1.5 volts. A volt meter is placed in the circuit as indicated. What will the volt meter indicate?

   A. 1.5 volts
   B. 1 volt
   C. 3 volts
   D. 6 volts

2. Examine the circuit shown below. Each battery is 1.5 volts. The resistance in each light bulb is 20 ohms. An ammeter is placed in the circuit as indicated. What will be the ammeter reading?

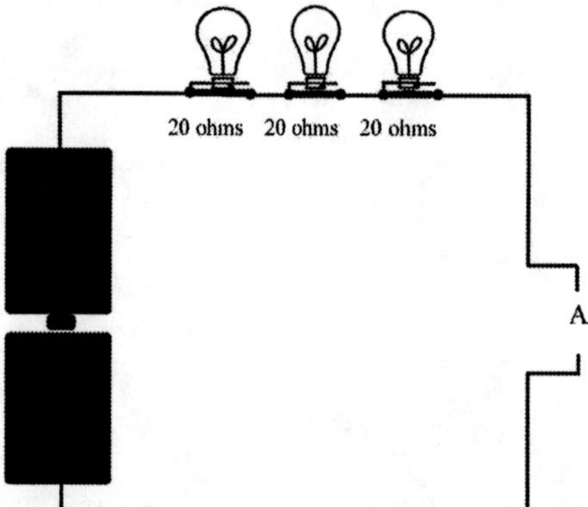

   A. 20 amperes
   B. .2 amperes
   C. .1 amperes
   D. .05 amperes

3. Examine the circuit shown below. A current of six amps flows from the batteries. An ammeter is placed in the circuit as indicated. What will be the ammeter reading?

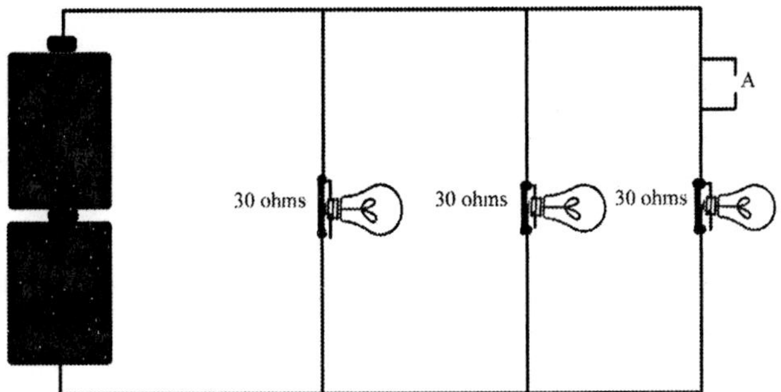

A. 1 ampere
B. 2 amperes
C. 3 amperes
D. 6 amperes

4. Examine the circuit below. Each battery is 1.5 volts. What is the total amount of resistance in the circuit?

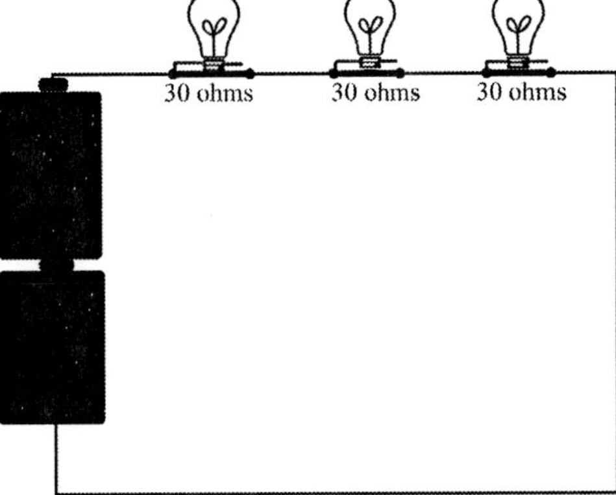

A. 10 ohms
B. 30 ohms
C. 60 ohms
D. 90 ohms

5. Examine the circuit shown below. Each battery is 1.5 volts. What is the total amount of resistance in the circuit?

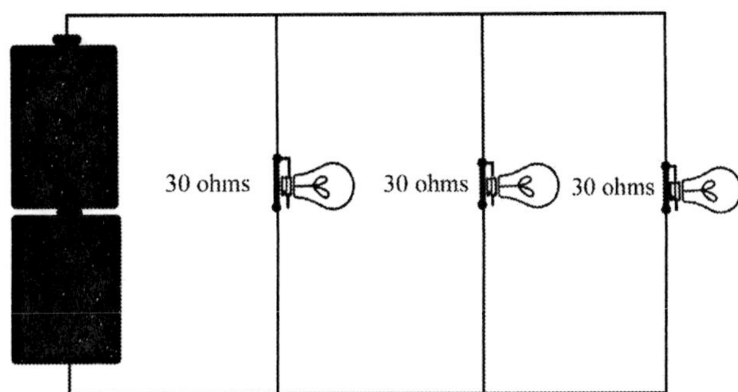

A. 10 ohms
B. 30 ohms
C. 60 ohms

D. 90 ohms

6. Examine the compound circuit shown below. Each battery is 1.5 volts. Each light has 30 ohms of resistance. What is the current measured by the ammeter?

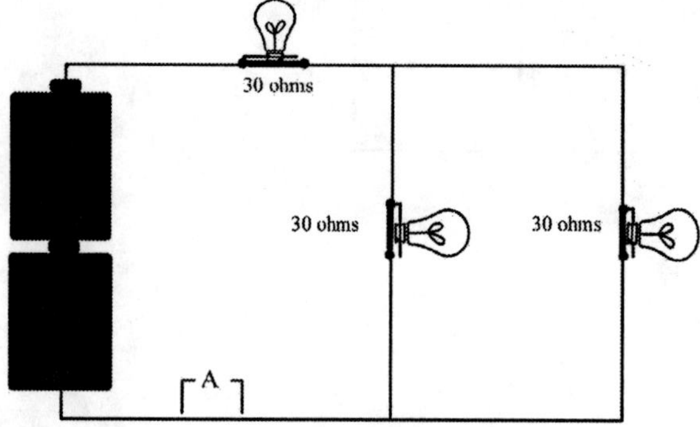

A. .05 amperes
B. .067 amperes
C. .1 amperes
D. .3 amperes

Explanations

The two batteries arranged in series yield a voltage of 3 volts across the circuit. In a series circuit, the sum of the voltage differences is equal to the total voltage. There are three light bulbs, therefore the voltage difference across each light bulb is 1 volt.

The battery voltage is 3 volts. In a series circuit, the total resistance is the sum of each resistor so the total resistance is 60 ohms. Using Ohms Law, $I = \frac{V}{R}$. In this case, 3 volts/60 ohms yields a current of .05 amperes.

You have a current of 6 amperes flowing from the battery in a parallel circuit. The current is distributed equally among the branches, therefore two amperes will flow through the ammeter.

In a series circuit, the total resistance is the sum of each resistor so the total resistance is 90 ohms. In a parallel circuit, the total resistance is calculated using the following formula:

$$\frac{1}{R} = \frac{1}{R1} + \frac{1}{R2} + \frac{1}{R3} \cdots\cdots$$

Each light bulb has a resistance of 30 ohms, therefore the resistance in the overall circuit is

$$\frac{1}{R} = \frac{1}{30} + \frac{1}{30} + \frac{1}{30} = \frac{3}{30} \qquad R = 10 \text{ ohms}$$

To find the current in a compound circuit it is necessary to find the resistance in the branches. The first branch in the series is 30 ohms; the resistance of the second parallel branch is 15 ohms. This yields a total resistance of 45 ohms. Using Ohms Law $I = \frac{V}{R}$, 3 volts/45 ohms yields a current of .067 amperes.

Lesson 13
A Fantasy Trip Around the Circuit

Get in a comfortable position, sit relaxed in your seat. When you are ready, close your eyes.

You are getting smaller and smaller and smaller/ You are approaching the size of atoms and molecules/ Imagine you are an electron/ You are an electron in a copper wire/ The copper wire is mostly empty space/ You see a few hard, dense copper nuclei/ You see other electrons orbiting these nuclei/ There is much space between the electrons and the nuclei/ Suddenly you feel something pushing you/ You are moving very fast in the copper wire/ You zoom by nuclei and electrons/ Some electrons are moving in the same direction with you/ You are moving with lots of energy/ Now the copper changes to nichrome/ You move swiftly into the nichrome wire/ The force is still pushing you ahead/ The nichrome wire appears to be more crowded/ You keep bumping into things/ You bump into other electrons/ The pathway in which you are traveling is getting narrow/ The collisions are getting vicious/ The force is still pushing you through the narrow crowded pathway/ You are getting hot/ You would like to rest/ The force is still pushing you on/ You are getting battered by the collisions/ You are very hot/ There seems to be a red glow in the nichrome pathway/ It is unbearably hot/ Now the nichrome wire ends, and the copper begins again/ There are very few collisions here/ You lost nearly all your energy in the nichrome pathway/ You are very tired/ You feel beat/ Thank goodness the battering has ended/ You can faintly feel the force, pushing you on/ You feel so listless/ You stumble on in the spacious copper pathway/ You are approaching a mysterious box/ You are being pushed into the box/ You move through a refreshing liquid/ It soothes your bruises/ It gives you energy/ You begin to move faster/ You feel rejuvenated/ Your spirit swells/ You come out of the box refreshed/ You're ready for another trip/ You part with your electron spirit/ You get larger and larger/ You are returning to the classroom/ When you are ready, you may open your eyes.

How did you feel when you went through the nichrome wire?
How did you feel when you went through the mysterious box?
What device might the nichrome wire represent?
What device might the box represent?

Science Accommodations by Disability Category
Electricity

(FEMALE students may be less likely to actually do the wiring of circuits, be sure to monitor female student activity levels. Be sure that they are not always doing the recording/drawing while a male student is doing the wiring.)

Motor/Orthopedic

- Use larger sized light bulbs and holders
- Use light bulb holders, i.e. Fahrnstock clips
- Use large wire with large alligator clips attached
- Use D cell plastic holders
- Use non-skid mat work-surface rugs or Velcro attachments on tools
- Work in pairs to help with the drawing of circuitry
- Use a tape recorder for student to describe the connections of working circuit OR how to fix a non-working circuit
- Utilize an easy-hold pointer that can be used for tracing the path of electricity
- Allow student to use alternative recording/drawing device
- Replace hand signal discussion responses with another type of physical response i.e. raise your leg for "yes," or stand up for "yes," or raise your arm
- Consider safety of the student when in contact with warm objects and sharp wires

Visually Impaired

- Use large wire with large alligator clips attached
- Use D cell plastic holders and mark with raised tape the positive end
- Use Braille recording sheets or large print
- Use glue and yarn and foam squares/circles that can attach to paper and record an electrical path that allows the student to feel a raised circuit (recording the wired path is important to the lesson as it allows students to reaffirm circuits must be uninterrupted to work)
- Use larger light bulbs that give heat when lit
- Work in pairs to help identify when a light bulb is lit
- Replace a light bulb with a small buzzer or motor that spins
- Replace hand signal responses with oral responses
- Auditory recordings of the entire class period or just activity directions will allow pace and review to be individualized
- Consider safety of the student when in contact with warm objects and sharp wires

Deaf or Hard of Hearing

- Use hand signal responses for all students when discussing working and non-working circuits, thus making it easy for students to hear/view each others' responses
- Write descriptions of working circuits next to drawings of student-created working circuits during student sharing
- Have students show with equipment the circuit wiring while describing a working circuit OR how to fix a non-working circuit
- Seat the student so there is good visual contact with the teacher and other students.
- Have a limited hearing student seated where good ear is faced toward the call or their group

- Give all instructions through V>A>M (visually, auditorially and modeling)
- Use a laptop computer as a communication alternative
- Consider safety of the student when in contact with warm objects and sharp wires

Learning Disabled

- Modify activity depending on whether the disability is in reading, writing, etc.
- Use step-by-step directions with digital pictures if possible (take the pictures while doing the activity with another class)
- Preview the directions and vocabulary words used in the activity
- Discuss responsibilities and directions with the student before activity
- When assigning cooperative group roles, assign the student to a role that reflects his/her interests and strengths
- Emphasize the importance of drawing and frequently remind the student to draw the circuit
- Frequently ask the student to orally tell you the path of electricity in the drawing
- Ask student to number the contact points and steps in the drawing
- Auditory recordings of class or directions for activity allow student to review or work at own pace
- Graphic organizers, i.e. a T chart or Cliff's Notes
- Color code the ends of D cells and/or clips and/or wires
- Consider safety of the student when in contact with warm objects and sharp wires

ADD/ADHD

- Preview directions and vocabulary words before the activity
- Slow down the pace of the activities
- Discuss with student appropriate behaviors expected during the activity
- Assign group to work in an area with minimal distractions
- Utilize as few pieces of equipment as possible to complete a circuit
- Carefully select cooperative group members and assign the student to a role that reflects his/her interests and strengths
- Emphasize the importance of drawing and frequently remind the student to draw the circuit
- Ask student to number the contact points in the drawing of a circuit
- Color code the ends of D cells and/or clips and/or wires
- Consider safety of the student when in contact with warm objects and sharp wires

Developmentally Delayed

- Preview directions, vocabulary, and hands-on-wiring before the activity
- Slow down the pace of activities
- Provide only the materials necessary to complete each step
- Provide digital pictures with each step of wiring
- Use pneumonic devices to teach vocabulary, i.e. parallel is perfect
- Use cooperative group role assignments
- Implement drawing as often as possible while comparing circuits
- Utilize VAM (visual, auditory, and modeling) when giving directions in class
- Consider safety of the student when in contact with warm objects and sharp wires

Behavior Disordered

- Electricity can be dangerous; be sure to have safety plugs in all outlets in the room
- Preview safety rules before the activity with the student
- Assign a partner that has success working with the student in the past OR allow the student to work with their materials alone
- Assign the student to be your helper for the day –handing out materials and getting materials as needed-helping you to wire circuits that will be used for demonstration and comparison
- Use proximity control as needed or an associate
- Consider safety of the student when in contact with warm objects and sharp wires

Speech and Language

- Utilize cooperative groups
- Show student circuitry silently in a museum walk
- Draw circuits and circuit repairs
- Write sequential steps for circuit comparisons and repairs
- Consider safety of the student when in contact with warm objects and sharp wires

Autism

- Preview the activity and materials with the student
- Pair with a partner that has the ability to redirect the student's attention as needed
- Place the materials within easy reach for the student
- Provide only a few materials at a time or as needed
- Consider safety of the student when in contact with warm objects and sharp wires

Deaf and Blind

- Replace the light bulb in the circuits with a small motor and a flag attachment
- Preview a completed circuit with a working motor/flag for the student to feel
- Use yarn and glue to record the circuit that the student builds
- Consider safety of the student when in contact with warm objects and sharp wires

Traumatic Brain Injury

- Consider safety of the student when in contact with warm objects and sharp wires
- Preview all the materials and vocabulary
- Utilize as many modalities of learning throughout the lesson
- VAM directions (visual, auditory, and model)
- Pacing of lesson
- Utilize alternative means of recording student completed circuits that allows use for students strongest communication means i.e. draw, auditory tape, string, and glue or pantomime the path of a circuit

Other Health Impairments

- Provide gloves and lab coats that protect the skin from contact with all surfaces
- Consider if a light bulb, or motor or buzzer seems the best choice for student to touch
- Consider the use of a computer program that allows drawing of circuits

- Use high contrast colors of working mats and wires for color blindness

Multi-Categorical

- Consider all of the above mentioned adaptations that are suitable for student
- Preview and practice the entire lesson
- Assign the student a cooperative group role that is commensurate with the disability

ELECTRICITY MULTIPLE INTELLIGENCES

Verbal/Linguistic

- Compose a story "A Day in the Life/Path of Electricity" that outlines the path electricity takes on its journey in a small circuit
- Compose and then guess classmates' riddles about a circuit –Is it Parallel or Series Circuit?
- Write a shape poem about light/electricity in the shape of a bulb, lightning bolt, lamp, i.e. any shape that uses light
- Write a formula poem about electricity, diamonte or cinquain or limerick
- Read aloud the children's poetry book by Douglas Florian entitled "Light"
- Try to read a book in the dark and then in the light; discuss the importance of proper lighting when you read and why
- Write a repair manual for a circuit picture that depicts a broken circuit
- Read the biography of Thomas Edison
- Write a newspaper or TV ad for an efficient light bulb
- Conduct a structured controversy debate over the future site of a power plant
- Create a game board that lights up correct vocabulary words and definitions
- Research the use of wind and water electricity sources

Logical/Mathematical

- Count the number of points of contact on a parallel vs. a series circuit
- Identify visual & logical patterns that are evident in all parallel circuits vs. series circuits
- Research and graph the cost of Xmas lights vs. the number of lights and type of circuit
- Research and graph the cost of light bulbs vs. the number of hours of light vs. the type of light vs. the electricity usage
- Connect a portable model electricity meters (available kits from most electric companies) to volt meters and compare the amount of energy used by different energy users
- Take at home readings of electricity meters before & after school and late at night; graph and compare high use times of the day
- Cross compare and graph the electricity usage of a wide variety of appliances and look for the energy hogs
- Cross compare and graph the electricity usage of one country vs. another country
- Create own patterns that are a version of Morse Code and then send messages to classmates utilizing the classroom constructed telegraph
- Visit a wind generator site and count the number of blade spins verses the speed of the wind verses the amount of electricity generated

Visual/Spatial

- Act out the path of a variety of circuit types
- Draw circuits that have been built in the classroom
- Examine and discuss a real home electricity blueprint
- Construct a concept map with the main heading of Electricity
- Use diagrams of circuits and label if it is a working circuit OR if not working; then draw how to fix the circuit
- Visit a power plant
- Take apart a battery and examine the interior and draw what is observed

- While wearing head phones, observe a person sending a telegram with Morse Code and try to tell when a dot and a dash are being sent

Musical/Rhythmic

- Compose a song or rap that utilizes specific vocabulary words
- Compose a song or rap that describes life without electricity
- Listen to a tape of mystery sounds that machines make when using electricity and identify what machine students think it is
- Make a rhythmical song that uses only the sounds of common electrical items
- Research what instruments use electricity and what instruments do not
- Compare the sound of an instrument plugged in and unplugged
- Research OSHA recommendations for sound safety
- Utilize a NASA-designed model (available at nasa.gov) that allows students to plug in any small appliance and convert the movement of the electricity to a specially designed speaker

Body/Kinesthetic

- Utilize hand signals, museum walks, and total physical responses whenever possible during any and all lessons on electricity
- Conduct a relay race to see who can send a model of a pulse of electricity from one end to the other the fastest. (Compare your fastest time to the time it takes the light to reach the light switch)
- Use creative drama to act out famous moments in history that required electricity, i.e. the SOS telegram sent by the Titanic
- Compose and conduct dance movements that communicate the movement of electricity when it is on, off, surged, interrupted, or high/low voltage
- Create a Twister type of game where a foot and hand placed on the correct circles light a bulb (or smaller version with thumb/pinkie circles)
- Use your body to complete a circuit utilizing a small C cell and bulb and wire
- Use classmates to complete a circuit to make a toy buzzer or toy bird activate
- Play "Operations," an electrical game requiring great eye-hand coordination. Ask students to draw what the game board may look like on the inside
- Wear flip-flops or tennis shoes that light up when walked in and ask students to draw what they think the circuit may look like inside the shoe

Intrapersonal

- Draw and record circuits built by self
- Merge daily activities with Day In Life of Electricity story
- Mime the path of electricity in a circuit built by self
- Repair a circuit that is not working by self
- Build a circuit that is self-designed

- Write a story detailing how the student uses electricity from sunrise to bedtime

Interpersonal

- Build a circuit with a partner
- Share own circuit and examine classmate circuits in museum walk
- Repair a circuit with group help
- Write a story outlining how dependent we all are on electricity

- Send a telegraph message across the classroom and listen for classmates to answer the message
- Design a game for your classmates to play that uses a circuit board (tin foil and cardboard) to play the game

Naturalist

- Research synaptic gaps in the animal brain and how the use of electrical and chemical exchanges allow animals to function
- Visit a research lab that utilizes electrical charges to separate and code cells
- Visit ISU plant labs and observe transposable gene therapy and the role it plays in agriculture today

APPENDIX A
The Cascade Model
Management Profile

Assess your classroom management procedures using characteristics of The Cascade Model. Check the column that best describes your classroom. Add the points for each section. Graph the results on the final page.

SCALE: 1 = rarely 2 = occasionally 3 = usually 4 = always

	Rarely 1	Occasionally 2	Usually 3	Always 4
I. ORGANIZING THE CLASSROOM				
1. Classroom furniture and materials are rearranged periodically to accommodate different teaching techniques.	___	___	___	___
2. Supplies and resources are easily accessible without interrupting others.	___	___	___	___
3. It is easy to monitor student activities.	___	___	___	___
4. Bulletin boards are neat and frequently changed.	___	___	___	___
5. Storage areas are orderly and well maintained.	___	___	___	___
6. A private area is located where a student can work without interruption.	___	___	___	___

Total points = ___

II. ROUTINES AND PROCEDURES				
1. Students have a clear understanding of acceptable and unacceptable movement in the classroom.	___	___	___	___
2. The teacher models the same behavior desired of the students.	___	___	___	___

3. Students have been pretrained for fire drills, hallway behaviors, lunchroom procedures, and restroom procedures. ___ ___ ___ ___

4. Students are aware of routines relating to completing assignments, handing in assignments, returning assignments, and the consequences of late assignments. ___ ___ ___ ___

5. Students follow appropriate routines in asking questions, responding to questions, small group work, individual work, and self-monitoring. ___ ___ ___ ___

6. Students effectively use the classroom library, obtain passes for work outside the classroom (if necessary), and leave and enter the classroom unobtrusively during the school day. ___ ___ ___ ___

Total points = ___

III. INSTRUCTION

1. Pretesting is used frequently to ascertain previous student learning. ___ ___ ___ ___

2. Students are provided with advanced organizers and lesson objectives before beginning the lesson. ___ ___ ___ ___

3. Large group lectures are limited to 20 minutes. ___ ___ ___ ___

4. Concrete and semi-concrete resources are used frequently. ___ ___ ___ ___

5. Considerable opportunities are provided for independent and small group learning activities during the class period. ___ ___ ___ ___

6. Homework assignments are appropriate and meaningful. ___ ___ ___ ___

Total points = ___

IV. PERSONALIZED INSTRUCTION

1. Instruction is adapted for individual learners. ___ ___ ___ ___

2. The interests of students are considered when

planning activities. ___ ___ ___ ___

3. The most able students are challenged with meaningful learning experiences. ___ ___ ___ ___

4. All students have opportunities to experience success in the classroom. ___ ___ ___ ___

5. Students and the teacher demonstrate enthusiasm for the lessons and learning. ___ ___ ___ ___

6. Student comments and parental input are positively received and responded to tactfully. ___ ___ ___ ___

Total points = ___

V. TIME ON TASK

1. Materials and assignments are prepared and ready before the students enter the classroom. ___ ___ ___ ___

2. Punctuality is demonstrated in starting and ending classes, meeting appointments, and returning assignments. ___ ___ ___ ___

3. Handing out and implementing the use of materials in the classroom is done quickly and efficiently. ___ ___ ___ ___

4. The teacher moves around the classroom and is involved with assisting students. ___ ___ ___ ___

5. Students are frequently given short assignments and begin working on them at once. ___ ___ ___ ___

6. Class time is used to maximum efficiency. ___ ___ ___ ___

Total points = ___

VI. RECOGNIZING POSITIVE BEHAVIORS

1. Students respect the dignity and worth of others in the classroom. ___ ___ ___ ___

2. Students feel free to communicate ideas without fear or hesitation. ___ ___ ___ ___

3. Students demonstrate self-discipline when not closely monitored. ___ ___ ___ ___

4. Democratic principles are applied in establishing classroom routines and procedures. ___ ___ ___ ___

5. Praise is directed to specific behaviors. ___ ___ ___ ___

6. The teacher reinforcing positive behaviors stimulates improved on-task behavior. ___ ___ ___ ___

Total points = ___

VII. REWARDS

1. Rewards are varied to meet individual differences. ___ ___ ___ ___

2. Concrete and tangible rewards are awarded to students. ___ ___ ___ ___

3. Students are responsive and appreciative of the tangible rewards. ___ ___ ___ ___

4. Reinforcers are given as soon as possible after the desired behavior occurs. ___ ___ ___ ___

5. Activities selected as rewards are arrived at democratically. ___ ___ ___ ___

6. Criteria for receiving rewards is adjusted for individual student abilities. ___ ___ ___ ___

Total points = ___

VIII. QUESTIONS

1. Questions are structured in a manner which allows students to respond. ___ ___ ___ ___

2. There is a wait time of a minimum of 3 seconds before calling on a student. ___ ___ ___ ___

3. The majority of teacher questions provide supportive action and are open-ended. ___ ___ ___ ___

4. Student assignments reflect questions at the application, analysis, synthesis, and evaluation levels rather than knowledge and comprehension. ___ ___ ___ ___

5. Students are encouraged to ask questions. ___ ___ ___ ___

6. Students can ask questions and answer questions without fear or hesitation. ___ ___ ___ ___

Total points = ___

IX. SELF-DISCIPLINE

1. The teacher models self-discipline by using appropriate manners, tone of voice, choice of words, and disposition. ___ ___ ___ ___
2. The teacher shows self-discipline in punctuality, consistency, fairness, and patience. ___ ___ ___ ___
3. The teacher shows self-discipline in advance planning and organization. ___ ___ ___ ___
4. Specific efforts are made to establish positive relationships with the other teachers and principal. ___ ___ ___ ___
5. Specific efforts are made to stimulate personal enthusiasm and generate enthusiasm in students. ___ ___ ___ ___
6. Specific efforts are made to make life outside of school pleasant and rewarding. ___ ___ ___ ___

Total points = ___

X. COMMUNICATION

1. Introductory letters and thank you cards are sent to parents. ___ ___ ___ ___
2. Phone calls are used to communicate with parents in appropriate circumstances. ___ ___ ___ ___
3. Support reports indicating desirable student behaviors are sent home. ___ ___ ___ ___
4. Efforts are made to encourage parent involvement and participation in school activities that reflect participation of their children. ___ ___ ___ ___
5. Support group opportunities for improving parent-student interactions and communication are supported and encouraged by the school. ___ ___ ___ ___

6. Parent suggestions for improving class and teacher relationships with the children are encouraged and positively received. ___ ___ ___ ___

Total points = ___

XI. CONFERENCES

1. Time is taken to talk with students to indicate a desire to be a helpful and supportive adult. ___ ___ ___ ___

2. During conferences, a clear indication is given of one or two behaviors which need to be remediated rather than making references to inadequacies within the individual student. ___ ___ ___ ___

3. During conferences, good qualities are mentioned along with a firm intolerance of specific undesired behaviors. ___ ___ ___ ___

4. While conferencing, modifications which might help the student become more successful are discussed. ___ ___ ___ ___

5. While conferencing, procedures for helping students chart their own progress are provided and discussed. ___ ___ ___ ___

6. When appropriate, parental input and involvement are utilized in preparing an adaptive discipline plan for a student. ___ ___ ___ ___

Total points = ___

XII. FORMULATING RULES

1. A clear articulation is made of classroom behaviors which should be practiced. ___ ___ ___ ___

2. A clear justification can be given for classroom behaviors to be practiced which is acceptable to students, administrators, and parents. ___ ___ ___ ___

3. A clear articulation of unacceptable classroom behaviors is made. ___ ___ ___ ___

4. A clear justification can be given for unacceptable classroom behaviors which is acceptable to students, administrators, and parents. ___ ___ ___ ___

5. A clear articulation of likely consequences for inappropriate behavior is made. ___ ___ ___ ___

6. A clear justification can be given for selecting consequences which is acceptable to students, administrators, and parents. ___ ___ ___ ___

Total points = ___

XIII. IMPLEMENTING RULES

1. Students have a clear understanding of classroom rules. ___ ___ ___ ___

2. The rules are stated in positive terms. ___ ___ ___ ___

3. The total number of rules is less than 10. ___ ___ ___ ___

4. The rules have been evaluated to insure that they produce the desired results. ___ ___ ___ ___

5. All students are familiar with the rules and capable of interpreting them in terms of their own behaviors. ___ ___ ___ ___

6. The rules are reexamined at regular intervals to insure that they are still needed and continue to produce the desired results. ___ ___ ___ ___

Total points = ___

XIV. FORMULATING CONSEQUENCES

1. Logical consequences rather than punishment are used whenever possible. ___ ___ ___ ___

2. Assurance has been made to insure that the consequence is appropriate for the student receiving the restriction. ___ ___ ___ ___

3. A plan for "cooling off" rather than producing confrontation has been formulated. ___ ___ ___ ___

4. A procedure is planned for the student who refuses to comply with an imposed consequence. ___ ___ ___ ___

5. The desired consequence is consistent with school policy and will be supported by the administration of the school. ___ ___ ___ ___

6. Parent involvement and input for correcting

misbehaviors has been encouraged. ___ ___ ___ ___

Total points = ___

XV. IMPLEMENTING CONSEQUENCES

1. Consequences are enforced immediately after the undesired behavior. ___ ___ ___ ___

2. Consequences are implemented in private whenever possible. ___ ___ ___ ___

3. Proximity control, eye contact, and other forms of nonverbal communication are used to alert students to misbehavior. ___ ___ ___ ___

4. Consistent enforcement of rules and imposition of consequences is carried out. ___ ___ ___ ___

5. A plan is in place for refocusing class attention to the directed learning task if several students are involved in misbehavior. ___ ___ ___ ___

6. Consequences for misbehavior respect the dignity and self-worth of the affected students. ___ ___ ___ ___

Total points = ___

XVI. ENVIRONMENTAL MODIFICATIONS

1. Efforts are made to determine if students have any special needs which could be accommodated by classroom arrangement or seating. ___ ___ ___ ___

2. Accommodations are made to allow all students to participate in hands-on activities and laboratory investigations. ___ ___ ___ ___

3. Close collaboration and cooperation occurs between specialists and the regular teacher in addressing the needs of students in the classroom. ___ ___ ___ ___

4. Walkways, placement of supplies, and elements of privacy are modified to allow easy access by all students.___ ___ ___ ___

5. Physical accommodations are made to facilitate and encourage socialization of all students with specific attention to those with special needs. ___ ___ ___ ___

6. Efforts have been made to become aware of technology and software which can be used to extend learning opportunities for students. ___ ___ ___ ___

Total points = ___

XVII. CURRICULUM MODIFICATIONS

1. Alternatives to written work are provided for students who would experience enhanced learning with this adaptation. ___ ___ ___ ___

2. Extra time is provided for assignments and tests when the adaptation would improve student learning and enhance performance. ___ ___ ___ ___

3. Framed outlines or other study help devices are used to assist students in learning. ___ ___ ___ ___

4. Graphic organizers and assistance in study skills are provided to students who need help in organization. ___ ___ ___ ___

5. Mnemonic tools are used to help students who have difficulty assimilating specific facts and concepts. ___ ___ ___ ___

6. Participation guides are provided to help students acquire better interactive skills. ___ ___ ___ ___

Total points = ___

XVIII. INSTRUCTIONAL MODIFICATIONS

1. Efforts are made to expose students to new information through multi-modality and hands-on learning opportunities. ___ ___ ___ ___

2. Efforts are made to examine the learning styles of students and differentiate instruction for different students. ___ ___ ___ ___

3. Additional wait-time is provided for all students to allow more time to think of answers and more opportunity to elaborate on first responses. ___ ___ ___ ___

4. Students receive prompt and supportive feedback on their performance. ___ ___ ___ ___

5. Efforts are made to reduce concept density of the

materials to allow extra time for some students with special needs and opportunities for elaboration by the most able learners. ___ ___ ___ ___

6. Students are able to utilize technology including calculators, word processors, and special software to help them express what they know and what they can do. ___ ___ ___ ___

Total points = ___

XIX. TESTING AND TEXTBOOK MODIFICATIONS

1. Assignments and directions for work are frequently presented to students in written forms. ___ ___ ___ ___
2. Students are given opportunities to work and study together in a collaborative rather than competitive learning atmosphere. ___ ___ ___ ___
3. Students are sometimes provided with a partial outline to help organize thoughts on essay questions. ___ ___ ___ ___
4. Students are sometimes allowed to practice on alternative forms of a test to assist them in learning how to take tests. ___ ___ ___ ___
5. Study guides and study aids such as identifying key words or concepts are used to help students learn the desired information. ___ ___ ___ ___
6. Alternative testing formats are used to allow students to communicate what they have learned. ___ ___ ___ ___

Total points = ___

XX. STUDENT CONTRACTS

1. Student misbehavior is sufficiently targeted to collect data on its frequency of occurrence. ___ ___ ___ ___
2. A reasonable plan for collecting data on student misbehavior has been formulated. ___ ___ ___ ___
3. A thorough study of the data on student misbehavior is conducted to determine if there are patterns to the disruptive behavior. ___ ___ ___ ___
4. A written contract indicating a method of

receiving points for appropriate behavior, a reward for achieving desired behavior, and a time line for meeting noted goals is used to encourage students who have not been successful under general school policies. ___ ___ ___ ___

5. Students using contracts have clear understandings of the reward when the terms of the contract have been obtained. ___ ___ ___ ___

6. In cases of defiant or non-conforming behavior, clear delineation of successive stages for further restriction is communicated to the students. ___ ___ ___ ___

Total points = ___

APPENDIX B

Management Profile Summary

																							XX	Student Contracts	ADAPTIVE
																							XIX	Testing & Textbook Modifications	
																							XVIII	Instructional Modifications	
																							XVII	Curriculum Modifications	
																							XVI	Environmental Modifications	
																							XV	Implementing Consequences	CORRECTIVE
																							XIV	Formulating Consequences	
																							XIII	Implementing Rules	
																							XII	Formulating Rules	
																							XI	Conferences	
																							X	Communication	SUPPORTIVE
																							IX	Self-Discipline	
																							VIII	Questions	
																							VII	Rewards	
																							VI	Recognizing Positive Behaviors	
																							V	Time on Task	PREVENTIVE
																							IV	Personalized Instruction	
																							III	Instruction	
																							II	Routines and Procedures	
																							I	Organizing the Classroom	
24	23	22	21	20	19	18	17	16	15	14	13	12	11	10	9	8	7	6	5	4	3			Category Point Totals	

Appendix C
Skeleton Transparency Master

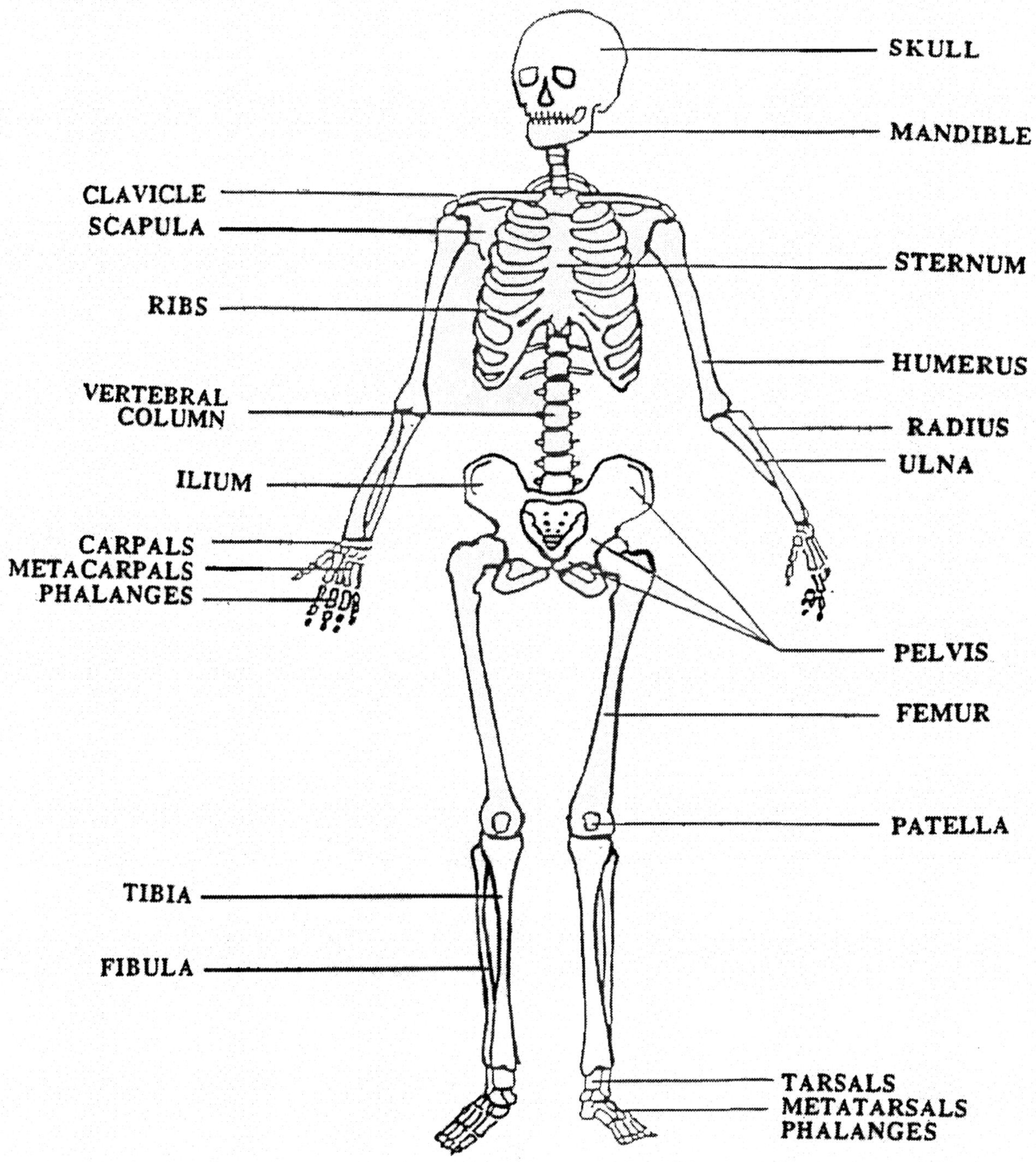

Appendix D
Inquisitive Sketch

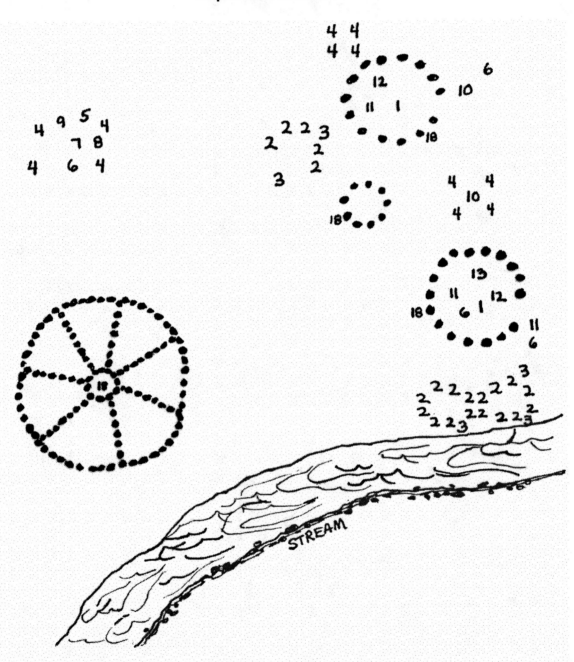

Key:

1. Charred wood
2. 6 inch wooden pegs
3. Sharpened flint, 3" x 5"
4. Post remnant, diameter 4"- 6"
5. Pointed obsidian stone, 3" long
6. Pointed flint, 6" – 8" long
7. Human bones
8. Human skull fragment
9. Hollow carved stone, 4" x 8"
10. Animal skull
11. Flint and obsidian chips
12. Sharpened bone, 4" long
13. Sharpened bone with hole, 3" long
14. Large animal shoulder bone
15. Small animal skull
16. Rounded stone, 6" – 8" diameter
17. Stone, 14" long with 7" depression
18. Stones, 12" – 16" diameter

Appendix E
Inquisitive Sketch

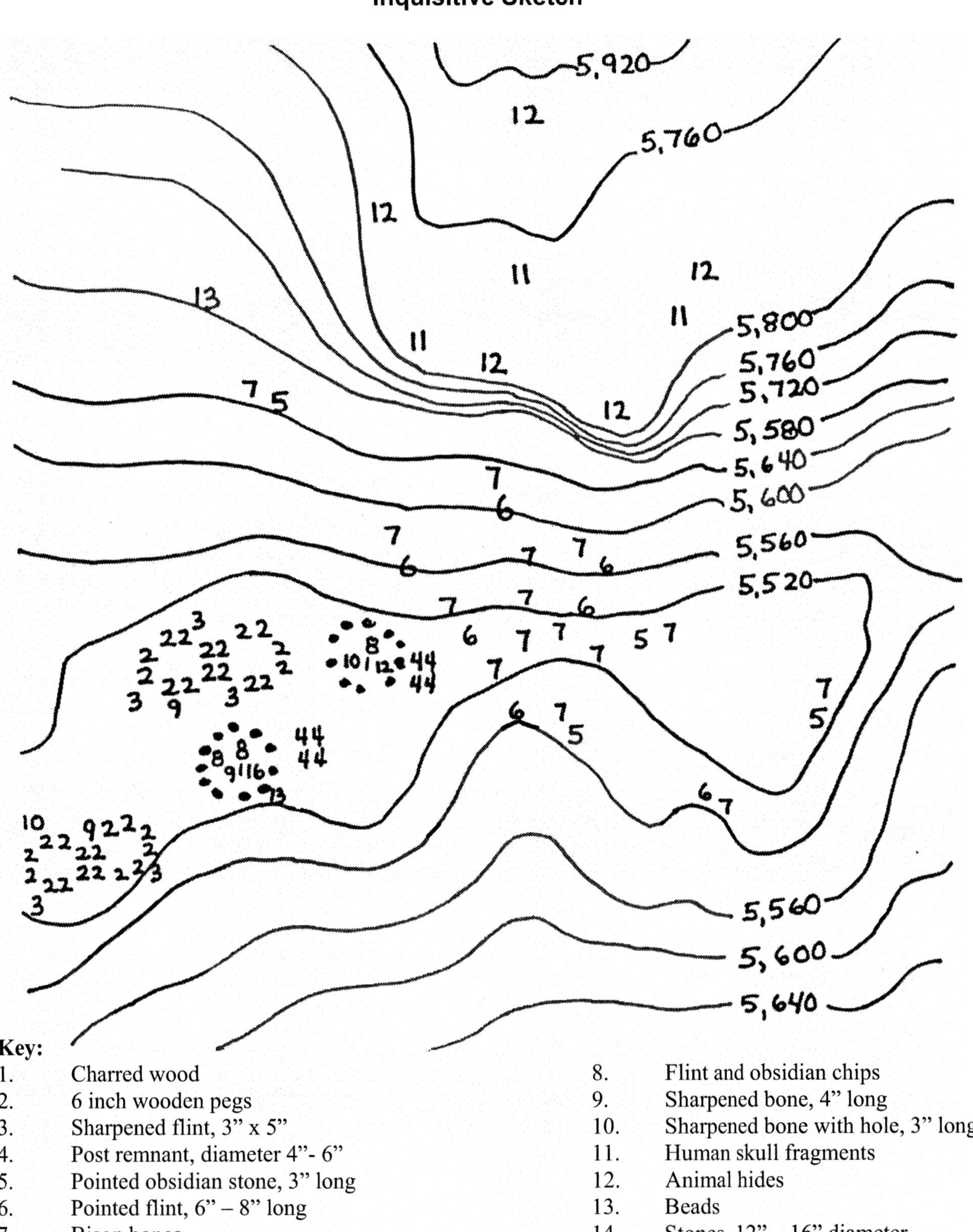

Key:

1. Charred wood
2. 6 inch wooden pegs
3. Sharpened flint, 3” x 5”
4. Post remnant, diameter 4”- 6”
5. Pointed obsidian stone, 3” long
6. Pointed flint, 6” – 8” long
7. Bison bones
8. Flint and obsidian chips
9. Sharpened bone, 4” long
10. Sharpened bone with hole, 3” long
11. Human skull fragments
12. Animal hides
13. Beads
14. Stones, 12” – 16” diameter

Appendix F
Inquisitive Sketch Assessment

Facts	Inferences	Evaluation of Inferences

Solution Finding

Acceptance Finding:

Appendix G
Shake, Rattle, and Roll

SHAKE, RATTLE, AND ROLL

Materials Needed
one die
a crayon

Directions

1. A player must first throw the number *in order to color in the skull.*
2. After that, the player can throw any number. *BUT* the parts in capital letters must be filled in *first*. All the parts written in capital letters must be filled in before players can start on the parts written in lower-case letters.
3. Players cross out the name of the bones they have colored in as they go.
4. The player finishing first is the winner! Have fun!

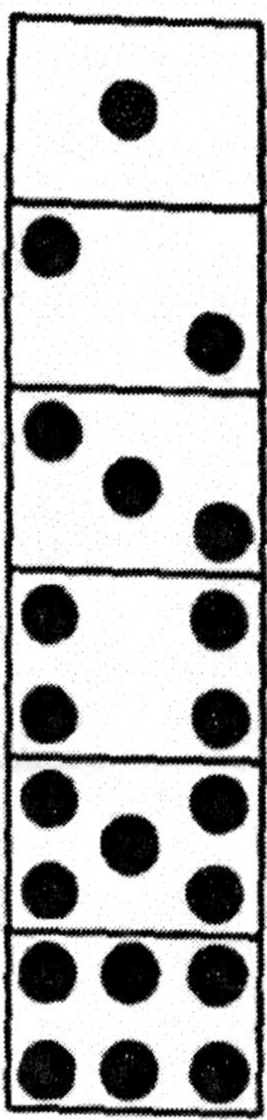

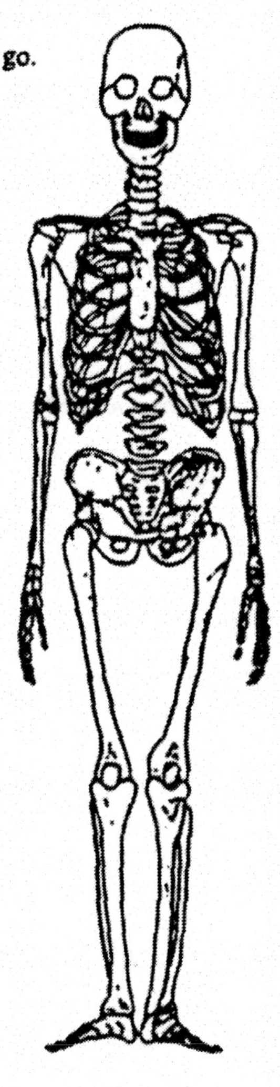

Appendix H
Temperature Change as Evidence of Energy Transfer

Concept

Measuring temperature in a system using a thermometer, measuring the amounts of transferred energy as indicated by changes of temperature, and predicting temperatures of equal mixtures of warm and cold water are targeted concepts of this activity.

Thermometers: The type of thermometer used in the activity is a bi-metal strip in a coil. Conventional thermometer scales are based on the freezing and boiling temperatures of pure water at sea level. There are two standard scales; the Fahrenheit scale and the Celsius scale.

1. The Fahrenheit scale registers 32 degrees when it is interacting with freezing water and 212 degrees when it is interacting with rapidly boiling water.

2. The Celsius scale's corresponding temperatures are 0 degrees when interacting with freezing water and 100 degrees when interacting with rapidly boiling water.

The intermediate temperatures are marked by dividing the interval between freezing and boiling water into equal parts. The temperature indicated by a thermometer is actually the temperature of the liquid in the bulb.

Thermal Energy (heat): Energy is gained by water or other objects when they are heated, and the energy is given off by objects when they are cooled. This form of energy is called *thermal energy*, or *heat.* For example: A cold cup is warmed by the hot coffee poured into it, and the coffee's temperature is lowered by the cold cup.

The system that is initially at the higher temperature always acts as an *energy source* and gives off heat, while the system initially at the lower temperature always acts as an *energy receiver* and gains thermal energy.

Exploration

Allow students to become familiar with the thermometer by placing it in cups with water of different temperatures.

Introduce the concept of looking at temperature chances through the use of a "double boiler" to protect the thermometer from contamination. (Figure __)

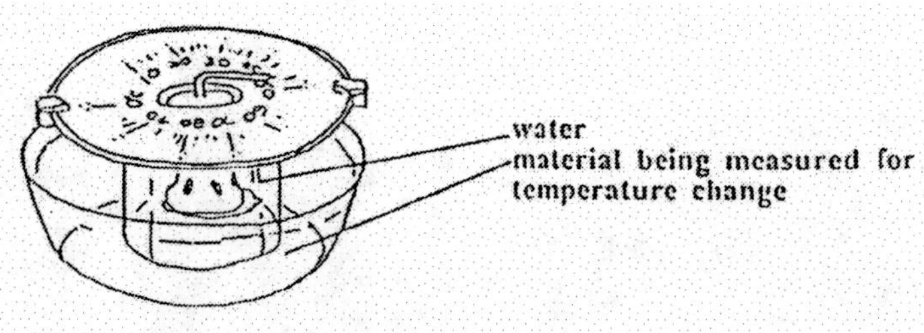

Appendix I
Model Plane Construction

Materials

1 propeller
1 hook
1 jumbo straw
1 super jumbo straw
1 rubber band, #33
2 popsicle sticks

Tools

1 hole punch
1 pair of scissors
1 stapler
1 sandpaper piece

Directions

1. Use sandpaper to taper *both* ends of both popsicle sticks on one side.

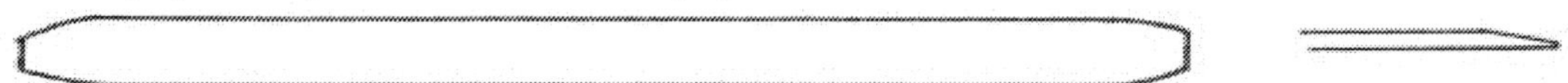

2. Cut the *super jumbo* straw in half. Punch one hole near one end of each piece. Slide the smaller *jumbo* straw through the holes.

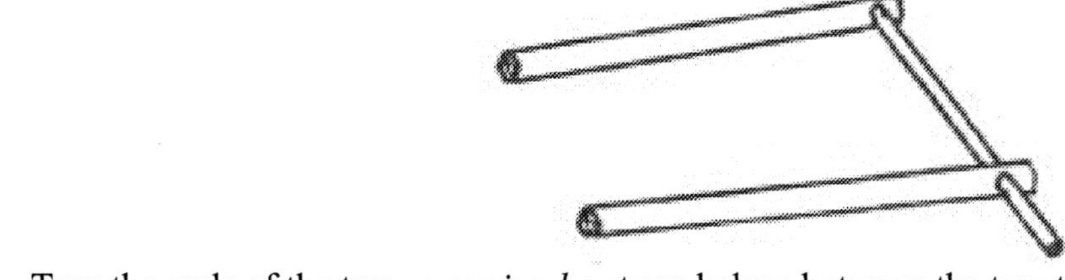

3. Trap the ends of the two *super jumbo* straw halves between the two tapered *popsicle sticks* with the tapered sides of the sticks on the outside. Allow about one inch of the smaller *jumbo straw* to protrude to the outside ends of the two larger *super jumbo straw* halves. Staple through the popsicle sticks at the intersections with the two larger *super jumbo straws.* Be sure you catch the straw ends with at least one leg of the staple.

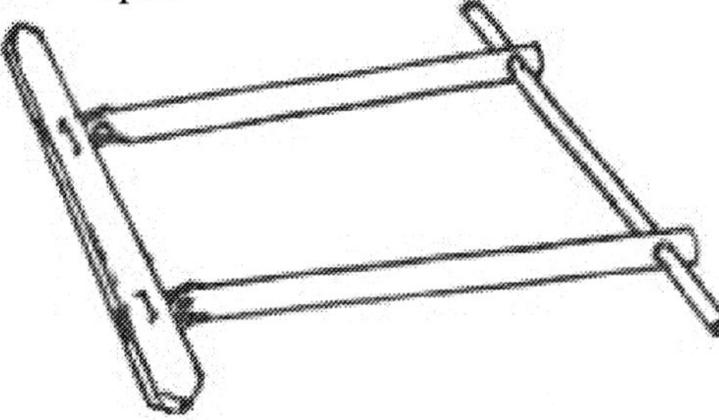

4. Slide the *propeller* onto one end of the popsicle stick, stick the *hook* onto the other end. Catch one end of the *rubber band* onto the hook and the other end onto the propeller. You are ready to fly!

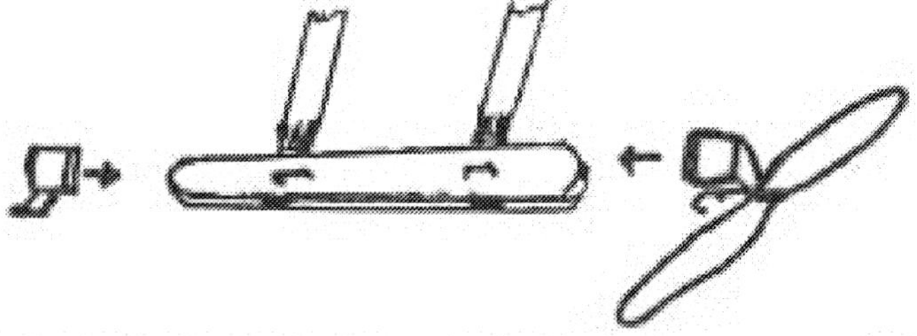

Appendix J
Footprint Puzzle

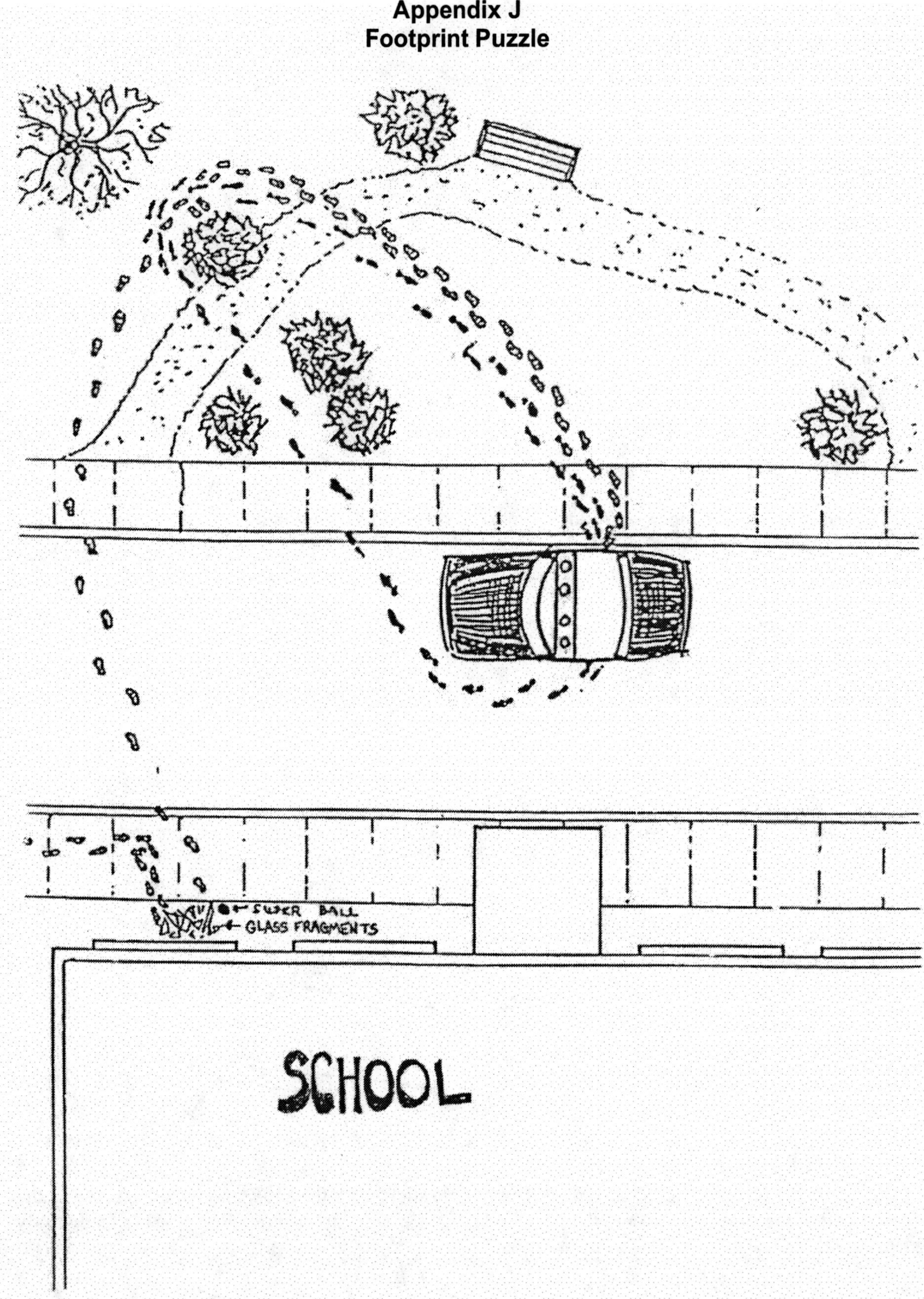

Appendix K
Footprint Puzzle

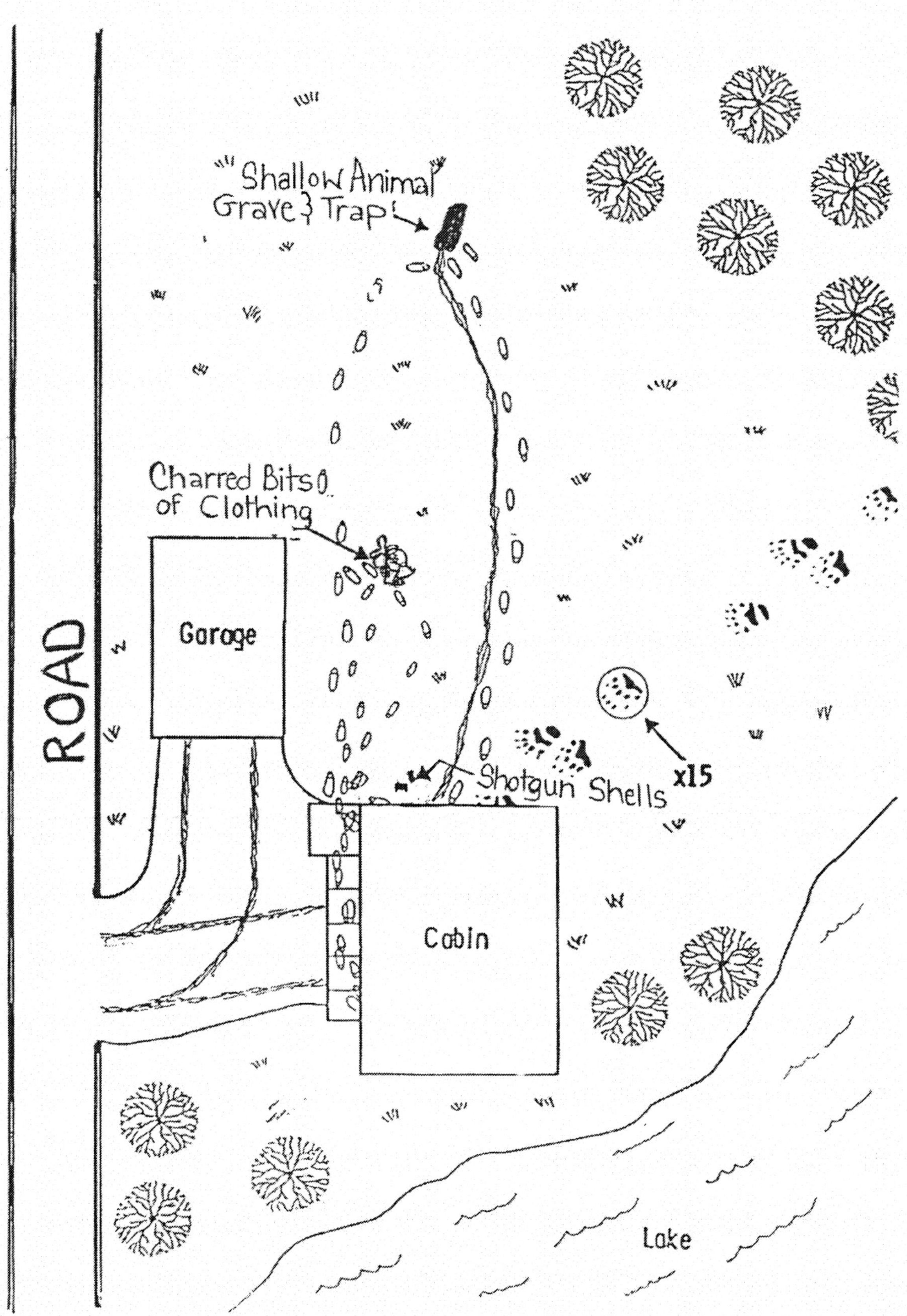

Appendix L

Lesson 1: Observing the *Puzzling Powders*		
Powder Number	**What I Think It Is**	**Why I Think So**
1		
2		
3		
4		
5		

Appendix M

Lesson 2: Mixing With Water	
Powder Name	**What Happens With Water**

Appendix N

Lesson 3: Heat Test	
Powder Number	**What Happens with Heat**

Appendix O

Lesson 4: Filter Test	
Powder Name	**What Does the Filter Paper Look Like**

Appendix P

Lesson 5: Iodine Test	
Powder Name	**What Happens With Water**

Appendix Q

Lesson 6: Vinegar Test	
Powder Name	**What Happens with Vinegar**

Appendix R

<table>
<tr><th colspan="4">Lesson 7: Puzzling Powder Mixtures</th></tr>
<tr><th colspan="2">Powder Name</th><th colspan="2">What Happens with Vinegar</th></tr>
<tr><th>What you did</th><th>What happened</th><th>Powders it Probably Does Not Contain</th><th>Powders it Probably Does Contain</th></tr>
<tr><td></td><td></td><td></td><td></td></tr>
<tr><td></td><td></td><td></td><td></td></tr>
<tr><td></td><td></td><td></td><td></td></tr>
<tr><td></td><td></td><td></td><td></td></tr>
<tr><td></td><td></td><td></td><td></td></tr>
</table>

References

Albert, L. (1996). *Cooperative discipline.* Circle Pines, Minnesota: American Guidance Service, Inc.

American Association for the Advancement of Science. (1991a). *Access in word and deed.* Washington, DC: Author.

American Association for the Advancement of Science. (1991b). *Access to science literacy.* Washington, DC: Author.

American Association for the Advancement of Science. (1991c). *Laboratories and classrooms in science and engineering.* Washington, DC: Author.

American Association for the Advancement of Science. (1991d). *Workshops and conferences for scientists and engineers.* Washington, DC: Author.

Anderson, A. & Stokes, S. (1984). Social and institutional influences on the development and practices of literacy. In H. Goelman, A. Goelman, A. Oberg, & F. Smith (Eds.), *Awakening to literacy* (pp. 24-37). Exeter, NH: Heinemann Educational Books.

Apple, M. (1993). Controlling the work of teachers. In H.S. Shapiro & D.E. Purpel (Eds.), *Critical social issues in American education: Toward the 21st century* (pp. 255-271). White Plains, NY: Longman Publishing Group.

Armstrong, T. (1996). ADD: Does it really exist? *Phi Delta Kappan, 77*(6), 424-428.

Autism Society of America. (2006). *Facts and statistics.* Retrieved 13 October 2006, from http://www.autism-society.org/site/PageServer?pagename=FactsStats.

Ausubel, D. P. (1968). *Educational psychology: A cognitive view.* New York: Holt, Rinehart & Winston.

Bailey, L. (2005, November). Understand Chris to teach him more effectively. *Middle School Journal 37*(2), 37-46.

Bailey, N. J. (2005, November). Let us not forget to support LGBT youth in the middle school years. *Middle School Journal, 37*(2), 31-35.

Bailey, S., Burbidge, L., Campbell, P., Jackson, B., Marx, F., & McIntosh, P. (1992). *The AAUW report: How schools shortchange girls.* Washington, D.C.: AAUW Educational Foundation.

Baker, E., Wang, M., & Walberg, H. (1994). The effects of inclusion on learning. *Educational Leadership, 52*(4), 33-35.

Banton, M., & Singh, G. (2004). 'Race', disability and oppression. In J. Swain, S. French, C. Barnes, & C. Thomas (Eds.), *Disabling barriers, enabling environment* (pp. 111-117). Buckingham: Open University Press.

Barkly, R. A. (1990). *Attention deficit hyperactivity disorder: A handbook for diagnosis and treatment.* New York: Guilford.

Bartz, D. (1991). *Twelve teaching methods to enhance student learning: What research says to the teacher.* Washington, DC: National Education Association. (ERIC Document Reproduction Service No. ED 340 686)

Bauwens, J., Hourcade, J. J., & Friend, M. (1989) Cooperative teaching: A model for general and special education integration. *Remedial and Special Education, 10*(2), 17-22.

Beane, D.B. (1985, reprinted in 1988). *Mathematics and science: Critical filters for the future of minority students.* Washington, D.C.: The Mid-Atlantic Equity Center, The American University.

Benedict, R. R., Snell, R., & Miller, D. (1987). Enterprise high: Helping school dropouts become self-supporting adults. *Educational Leadership, 44,* 75-78.

Bentley, M., Ebert, C., & Ebert, E. (2000). *The natural investigator: A constructivist approach to teaching elementary and middle school science.* Belmont, CA: Wadsworth.

Best, G. A. (1992). Physical and health problems. In L. M. Bullock (Ed.), *Exceptionalities in children and youth* (pp. 392-419). Needham Heights, MA: Allyn and Bacon.

Biklen, D. (1992). *Schooling without labels.* Philadelphia: Temple University Press.

Biological Sciences Curriculum Study. (1990). *Science for life and living: Integrating science, technology, and health.* Sneak preview. Dubuque, IA: Kendall/Hunt.

Birch, J. W. (1975). *Hearing impaired children in the mainstream.* St. Paul: University of Minnesota, Leadership Training Institute/Special Education.

Blackorby, J., Chorost, M., Garza, N., & Guzman, A. (2003). The academic performance of secondary school students with disabilities. In M. Wagner., C. Marder, J. Blackorby, R. Camato, P. Newman, P. Levine, E. Davies-Mercier, et al., *The achievements of youth with disabilities during secondary school. A report from the National Longitudinal Transition Studies-2 (NLTS2).* Menlo Park, CA: SRI International. Available at http://www.nlts2.org/pdfs/achievements_ch4.pdf .

Blomgren, R. (1992). Special education and the quest for human dignity. In H.S. Shapiro & D.E. Purpel (Eds.), *Critical social issues in American education: Toward the 21st century* (pp. 230-235). White Plains, NY: Longman Publishing Group.

Bloom, B. S. (1976). *Human characteristics and student learning.* New York: McGraw-Hill.

Blumenkopf, T. A., Stern, V., Swanson, A. B., & Wohlers, H. D. (1996). *Working chemists with disabilities: Expanding opportunities in science.* Washington, D.C.: American Chemical Society.

Borich, G. D., & Tombari, M. L. (1997). *Educational psychology: A contemporary approach.* New York: Addison-Wesley.

Brantlinger, E. (2004). Confounding the needs and confronting the norms: An extension of Reid and Valle's essay. *Journal of Learning Disabilities, 37*(6), 490-499.

Bruner, J. (1961). The act of discovery. *Harvard Educational Review, 31*, 21-32.

Bruner, J. (1963). *The process of education.* New York: Vintage Books.

Bynner, W. (1944). *The way of life according to Laotzu.* New York: John Day.

Boston Public Schools. (1998, March 9). *High school restructuring.* Boston: Author.

Boyer, E. L. (1995). *The basic school: A community for learning.* San Francisco, CA: Jossey-Bass Inc., Publishers.

Brookover, W., & Lezotte, L. (1979). *Changes in school characteristics coincident with changes in student achievement.* East Lansing: Institute for Research on Teaching, College of Education, Michigan State University.

Brophy, J. E., & Good, T. (1986). Teacher behavior and student achievement. In M. Wittrock (Ed.), *Handbook of research on teaching* (3rd ed., pp. 328-375). New York: Macmillan.

Bullock, L. M. (1992). Behavioral disorders. In L. M. Bullock (Ed.), *Exceptionalities in children and youth* (pp. 124-167, 254-287). Needham Heights, MA: Allyn and Bacon.

Butkowsky, I. S., & Willows, D. M. (1980). Cognitive-motivational characteristics of children varying in reading ability: Evidence for learned helplessness in poor readers. *Journal of Educational Psychology, 72*, 408-422.

Cajete, G. (1999). *Igniting the sparkle: An indigenous science education model.* Skyland, NC: Kivaki Press.

Campbell, P. (1997). Utility is not enough. In N. Kreinberg & E. Wahl (Eds.), *Thoughts and deeds. Equity in mathematics and science education.* Washington, D.C.: Collaboration for Equity, American Association for the Advancement of Science.

Campbell, P., Kibler, T., & Campbell-Kibler, K. (1991). Taking the SAT at twelve: One family's view of talent search. *College Prep, 7*, 8-10.

Carin, A. (1997). *Teaching science through discovery.* Upper Saddle River, NJ: Merrill/Prentice Hall.

Carpenter, K., & Craig, J. L. (1991). *Effective discipline.* Mangilao, GU: University of Guam Printing.

Cartwright, G. P., Cartwright, C. A., & Ward, M. E. (1995). *Educating special learners.* Belmont, CA: Wadsworth Publishing.

Cawley, J. F. (1994). Science for students with disabilities. *Remedial and Special Education, 15*(2), 67-71.

Cawley, J. F., Kahn, H., & Tedesco, A. (1989). Vocational education and students with learning disabilities. *Journal of Learning Disabilities, 22,* 630-634.

Cheney, C. (1989). The systematic adaptation of instructional materials and techniques of problem learners. *Academic Therapy, 25*(1), 25-30.

Cole, D. A., & Meyer, L. H. (1991). Social integration and severe disabilities: A longitudinal analysis of child outcomes. *The Journal of Special Education, 25,* 340-351.

Collins, A., Brown, J.S., & Newman, S.E. (1989). Cognitive apprenticeship: Teaching the crafts of reading, writing and mathematics. In L.B. Resnick (Ed.), *Knowing, learning, and instruction: Essays in honor of Robert Glaser* (pp. 453-494). Hillsdale, N.J.: Lawrence Erlbaum.

Collins, P.H. (2000). *Black feminist thought.* New York: Routledge.

Columbia Falls v. State. (16 April 2004). Montana 1st District Court.

Conners, C. K. (1989). *Conners' parent rating scales.* North Tonawanda, NY: Multi-Health Systems.

Cooper, M. (2005). *Bound and determined to help children with learning disabilities succeed.* United States: Learning Disabilities Worldwide.

Costello, C. (1991). *A comparison of student cognitive and social achievement for handicapped and regular education students who are educated in integrated versus a substantially separate classroom.* Unpublished doctoral dissertation, University of Massachusetts, Amherst.

Cox, J. W. (1970). *Laboratory experiences for use in a college course for non-science majors.* Unpublished manuscript, University of Montana at Missoula.

Curtin, E.M. (2006, January). *Lessons on effective teaching from middle school ESL students. Middle School Journal 37*(3), 38-45.

Davison, J. (2001). *Attention deficit/hyperactivity disorder: Perspectives of participants involved in the identification and treatment process.* Journal of Educational Thought, 35, 227-247.

Delpit, L. (1995). *Other people's children: Cultural conflict in the classroom.* New York: New York Press.

Devine, T., Seuk, J., & Wilson, A. (Eds.). (2001). *Cultivating heart and character: Educating for life's most essential goals.* Chapel Hill, NC: Character Development Publishing.

Dewey, J. (1910). *How we think.* New York: D. C. Heath.

Diamond, J.B., Randolph, A. & Spillane, J.P. (2004). Teachers' expectations and sense of responsibility for student learning: The importance of race, culture, and organizational habitus. *Anthropology and Educational Quarterly, 35*(1), 75-98.

Dobson, J. (1977). *Dare to discipline.* Farmington Hills, MI: Tyndale Press.

Dodd, J. E., & Himmelstein, J. (1996). *Science education: A constructivist paradigm for students who are deaf and hard-of-hearing.* Paper presented at the Working Conference on Science for Persons with Disabilities, St. Louis.

Donahoe, K., & Zigmond, N. (1988). *High school grades of urban LD students and low-achieving peers.* Paper presented at the annual meeting of the American Educational Research Association, San Francisco.

Downing, R.A., & Crosby, F.J. (2005, December). The perceived importance of developmental relationships on women undergraduates' pursuit of science. *Psychology of Women Quarterly, 29*(4), 419-426.

Driver, R., & Oldham, V. (1986). A constructivist approach to curriculum development in science. *Studies in Science Education, 13*(2), 105-122.

Driver, R., Asoko, H., Leach, J., Mortimer, E., & Scott, P. (1994). A constructivist approach to curriculum development in science. *Educational Researcher, 23*, 7-20.

Drug and Chemical Evaluation Section. (1995, October). *Methylphenidate: A background paper.* Washington, DC: U.S. Department of Justice, Drug Enforcement Administration, Office of Diversion Control.

Dweck, C. S. (1975). The role of expectations and attributions in the alleviation of learned helplessness. *Journal of Personality and Social Psychology, 31,* 674-685.

Dykstra, D., Boyle, F., & Monarch, I. (1992). Studying conceptual change in learning physics. *Science Education, 76* (6), 615-652.

Earle, J. (1990). Counselor advocates: Changing the system, a low-cost option solves a lot of problems. *Public Welfare, 48,* 61-22.

Eccles, J.S., & Harold, R.D. (1996). Parent-school involvement during the early year. *Teachers College Record, 94*, 568-587.

Eggen, B. (2002, February). *Administrative accountability and the novice teacher.* Paper presented at the Annual Meeting of the American Association of Colleges for Teacher Education, New York City. (ERIC Document Reproduction Service No. ED 464 050).

Einstein, A., & Enfield, L. (1966*). The evolution of ideas in physics from early concepts to relativity and quanta.* New York: Simon and Schuster.

Elementary Science Study. (1967). *Bones teachers guide.* St. Louis: McGraw-Hill, Webster Division.

Elementary Science Study. (1967). *Bones picture book.* St. Louis: McGraw-Hill, Webster Division.

Elementary Science Study. (1967). *How to make a chicken skeleton.* St. Louis: McGraw-Hill, Webster Division.

Elementary Science Study. (1967). *Bones teachers guide.* St. Louis: McGraw-Hill, Webster Division.

Elementary Science Study. (1967). *Bones picture book.* St. Louis: McGraw-Hill, Webster Division.

Elementary Science Study. (1967). *How to make a chicken skeleton.* St. Louis: McGraw-Hill, Webster Division: Author.

Elementary Science Study. (1967). *Mystery powders teachers guide.* St. Louis: McGraw-Hill, Webster Division.

Emmer, E. T., Everston, C., Sanford, J., Clements, B., & Worsham, M. (1980). *Organizing and managing the junior high classroom.* Austin: University of Texas-Austin, Research and Development Center for Teacher Education.

Energy sources teacher guide, science curriculum improvement study. (1970). Chicago: Rand-McNally.

Englemann, S., Becker W. C., & Carnine, D. (1993). *Direct instruction.* In Educational approaches and program options for integrating students with disabilities: A decision tool. Longmont, CO: Sopris West. (ERIC Document Reproduction Service No. ED 367 071)

Evertson, C. M., Emmer, E. T., Clements, B. S., Sanford, J. B., & Worsham, M. E. (1981). *Organizing and managing the elementary school classroom.* Austin: University of Texas, Research and Development Center for Teacher Education.

Farka, G. (1996). *Human capital or cultural capital? Ethnicity and poverty group in an urban district.* New York: Aldine de Gruyter.

Ferguson, P., & Asch, A. (1989). Lessons from life: Personal and parental perspectives on school, childhood, and disability. In D. Bicklen, A. Ford, & D. Ferguson (Eds.), *Disability and Society* (pp. 108-140). Chicago: National Society for the Study of Education.

Fleming, W. C. (2006, November). Myths and stereotypes about Native Americans. *Phi Delta Kappan, 88*(3), 213-217.

Flick, L. (1995, April) *Complex instruction in complex classrooms: A synthesis of research on inquiry teaching methods and explicit teaching strategies.* Paper presented at the annual meeting of the National Association of Research in Science Teaching, San Francisco. (ERIC Document Reproduction Service No. ED 383 563)

Fogarty, K. (2000). Professional clinical resources. *The educational process: Information to help parents,* St. Louis: St. Louis Learning Disabilities Association.

Fowler, J. W., & Peterson, P. (1981). Increasing reading persistence and altering attributional style of learned helpless children. *Journal of Educational Psychology, 73,* 251-260.

Frederick, J. D. & Nicholson, H.J. (1986). *The explorer's pass: A report on case studies of girls and math, science, and technology.* Indianapolis: Girls Incorporated.

Friedl, A., & Koontz, T. Y. (2001). *Teaching science to children: An inquiry approach.* Boston: McGraw-Hill.

Gagne, R. (1974). *Essentials of learning for instruction.* Hinsdale, IL: Dryden Press.

Gagne, R., & Briggs L. (1979). *Principles of instructional design.* New York: Holt, Rinehart & Winston.

Gardner, H. (1993). *Multiple intelligences: The theory in practice.* New York: Basic Books.

Gallagher, D. J. (1995). In search of the rightful role of method: Reflections on conducting a qualitative dissertation. In T. Tiller & A. Sparkes & F. Dowling-Naess (Eds.), *The qualitative challenge: Reflections on educational research* (pp. 17-35). Norway: Caspar Forlag A/S.

Gallagher, D. J. (2001). Neutrality as a moral standpoint, conceptual confusion and the full inclusion debate. *Disability & Society, 16*(5), 637-654.

Garland-Thompson, R. (1997). Feminist theory, the body, and the disabled figure. In L. Davis (Ed.), *The disability studies reader* (pp. 279-292). New York: Routledge.

Gartner, A., & Lipsky, D. K. (1987). Beyond special education: Toward a quality system for all students. *Harvard Educational Review 57*(4), 367-395.

Geiger, W. L., & Ringlaben, R. P. (1992). Children and youth with mental retardation. In L. M. Bullock (Ed.), *Exceptionalities in children and youth* (pp. 254-287). Needham Heights, MA: Allyn and Bacon.

Gentile, J. R., & Monaco, N. M. (1986). Learned helplessness in mathematics: What educators should know. *Journal of Mathematical Behavior, 5*(2), 159-178.

Gentile, J. R., & Monaco, N. M. (1988). A learned helplessness analysis of perceived failure in mathematics. *Focus on Learning Problems in Mathematics, 10*, 15-28.

Gibbons, B. A. (2003). Supporting elementary science education for English learners: A constructivist evaluation instrument. *The Journal of Educational Research, 96*(6), 371-380.

Gibson, L. (2006, November). Preparing educators to meet the challenge of Indian education for all. *Phi Delta Kappan, 88*(3), 204-207.

Gilliland, H. (1999). *Teaching the Native American* (4th ed). Dubuque, IA: Kendall Hunt.

Ginott, H. (1972). *Teacher and child.* New York: Macmillan.

Goleman, D. (1995). *Emotional intelligence: Why it can matter more than IQ.* New York: Butnam Books.

Good, T. L., & Brophy, J. E. (1994). *Looking in classrooms* (6th ed.). New York: Harper-Collins.

Gough, E. R. (1981). Some psychological considerations in the education of blind students. In M. E. Corrick, Jr. (Ed.), *Teaching handicapped students science* (pp. 79-82). Washington, DC: National Education Association of the United States.

Granger, L., & Granger, L. (1986). *The magic feather.* New York: E.P. Dutton.

Guskey, T. R., Passaro, P. D., & Wheeler, W. (1995, Winter). Mastery learning in the regular classroom: Help for at-risk students with learning disabilities. *Teaching Exceptional Children,* pp.15-18.

Hadzigeorgiou, Y. (1999). On problem situations and science learning. *School Science Review, 81*, 43-49.

Hadzigeorgiou, Y., & Stefanich, G. (In press). Imagination in science education. *Contemporary Education.*

Hale, J. E. (2001). *Learning while black: Creating educational excellence for African American children.* Baltimore: Johns Hopkins University Press.

Hansen, L. (2006, January). Strategies for ELL success. *Science & Children 43*(4), 22-25.

Haury, D. L. (1993). *Teaching science through inquiry.* ERIC/CSMEE Digest (Report No. EDO-SE-93-4). Washington, DC: Office of Educational Research and Improvement. (ERIC Document Reproduction Service No. ED 359 048)

Haycock, K. (2002, December). Toward a fair distribution of teacher talent. *Educational Leadership 60*(4), 11-15.

Haycock, K. (2001, March). Closing the achievement gap. *Educational Leadership, 58*(6), 6-11.

Heshusius, L. (2004). Special education knowledges: The inevitable struggle with the "self." In D.J. Gallagher, L. Heshusius, R. P. Iano, & T. Skrtic (Eds.), *Challenging orthodoxy in special education: Dissenting voices.* Denver, CO: Love Publishing.

Hilberg, R. S., & Tharp, R. (2002). Theoretical perspectives, research findings, and classroom implications of the learning styles of American Indian and Alaska native students. *ERIC Digest, ED,* 468-000.

Hollowood, T., Salisbury, C, Rainforth, B., & Palombaro, M. (1995). Use of instructional time in classrooms serving students with and without severe disabilities. *Exceptional Children 61*(3), 242-253.

Hoover, J. J. (1990). Curriculum adaptation: A five-step process for classroom implementation. *Academic Therapy, 25*(4), 407-416.

Hopkins, W. (2006, November). The promise of IEFA. *Phi Delta Kappan, 88*(3), 207.

Howe, A., & Jones, L. (1993). *Engaging children in science.* New York: Macmillan.

Hunter, M. (1982). *Mastery teaching.* El Segundo, CA: TIP Publications.

Hutchins, C. L. (1970). *Inquiry development program in the physical sciences: Program report.* Berkeley, CA: Far West Laboratory for Educational Research and Development.

Individuals with Disabilities Education Act of 1990. 20 U.S.C. 1400-1485.

Individuals with Disabilities Education Act Amendments of 1997, PL 105-17, 20 U.S.C. 1400-et seq., 105th Congress, 1st session.

Iowa Department of Education (1998). *Iowa IEP guidebook: Their future . . . our guidance*: Iowa IEP handbook. Des Moines: Author.

Jenkins, E. (1989). Processes in science education: An historical perspective. In J. Wellington (Ed.), *Skills and processes in science education: A critical analysis.* London: Routledge.

Johnson, C. C. (2005). Making instruction relevant to language minority students at the middle level. *Middle School Journal, 37*(2), 10-14.

Jones, C. J. (1992). *Enhancing self-concepts and achievement of mildly handicapped students.* Springfield, IL: Charles C. Thomas.

Juneau, D., & Broaddus, M. S. (2006, November). And still the waters flow: The legacy of Indian education in Montana. *Phi Delta Kappan, 88*(3), 193-197.

Kamii, C., & DeVries, R. (1993). *Physical knowledge in preschool education: Implications of Piaget's theory.* New York: Teachers College Press.

Kaplan, S. (2003) Is there a gifted-child pedagogy? *Roeper Review, 35*(4), 165.

Kaskinen-Chapman, A. (1992). Saline area schools and inclusive community concepts. In R.Villa, J. Thousand, W. Stainback, & S. Stainback (Eds.), *Restructuring for caring and effective education: An administrative guide to creating heterogeneous schools.* Baltimore: Paul H. Brookes.

Keller, E.C. (2007). (Webmaster). *Strategies on teaching science to students with disabilities.* Retrieved January 15, 2007, from http://www.as.wvu.edu/~scidis

Kelly, D. (1992). Introduction. In T. Neary, A. Halvorsen, R. Kronberg, & D. Kelly (Eds.), *Curricular adaptations for inclusive classrooms.* San Francisco: California Research for the Integration of Students with Severe Disabilities, San Francisco State University.

Kliewer, C. M., & Biklen, D. (1996). Labeling: Who wants to be called retarded? In W. Stainback & S. Stainback (Eds.), *Controversial issues confronting special education: Divergent perspectives* (2nd ed., pp. 83-95). Boston: Allyn & Bacon.

Kozol, J. (2005). *The shame of the nation: The restoration of apartheid schooling in America.* New York: Crown Publishers.

Kramer, P. D. (1993). *Listening to prozac: A psychiatrist explores antidepressant drugs and the remaking of the self.* New York: Penguin Books.

Krashen, S. (1994) Bilingual education and second language acquisition theory. In C. F. Leyba (Ed.), *Schooling and language minority students* (pp. 61-63). Los Angeles, CA: California State University, Los Angeles.

Lacey, R. A. (1991). I have a dream for dropout prevention. *Education Digest, 56,* 20-23.

Lambert, N., Hartsough, C., & Sandoval, J. (1990). *Children's attention and adjustment survey.* Circle Pines, MN: American Guidance Service.

Lang, H. G. (1994). Silence of the spheres: The deaf experience in the history of science. Westport, CT: Bergan and Garvey.

Lawrence, P. A. (1988). Basic strategies for mainstreaming integration. *Academic Therapy, 23*(4), 335-349.

Lee, O. (2004). Teacher change in beliefs and practices in science and literacy instruction with English Language Learners. *Journal of Research in Science Teaching, 41*(1), 65-93.

Lee, O., & Fradd, S. H. (2001). Instructional congruence to promote science learning and literacy development for linguistically diverse students. In D. R. Lavoie & W. M. Roth (Eds.), *Models of science teacher preparation* (pp. 109-126). AA Dordrecht, The Netherlands: Kluwer Academic Publishers.

Levine, M. (2002). *A mind at a time.* New York: Simon & Schuster.

Linek, W. M., Rasinski, T. V., & Harkins, D. M. (1997). Teacher perceptions of parent involvement in literacy education. *Reading Horizon, 38*(2), 90-107.

Lipsky, D., & Gartner, A. (1989). *Beyond separate education: Quality education for all.* Baltimore: Paul H. Brookes.

Loucks-Horsley, S., Hewson, P., Love, N., & Stiles, K. (1998). *Designing professional development for teachers of mathematics and science.* Thousand Oaks, CA: Corwin Press.

Lovitt, T. C., & Horton, S. V. (1994, March). Strategies for adapting science textbooks for youth with learning disabilities. *Remedial and Special Education, 15*(2), 105-116.

Mack, P. (2000). Personalized teaching and learning: Inquiry-based instruction. *Teaching and Learning, 14*, 23-32.

Mantsios, G. (2000). Media magic: Making class invisible. In T. E. Ore (Ed.), *The social construction of difference and inequality: Race, class, gender, and sexuality* (pp. 71-79). London: Mayfield Publishing Company.

Marek, E. A., Eubanks, C., & Gallaher, T. H. (1990). Teachers' understanding and the use of the learning cycle. *Journal of Research in Science Teaching, 27*(9), 821-834.

Martin, D. (1997). *Elementary science methods: A constructivist approach.* Albany, NY: Delmar.

Martin, R., Sexton, C., Wagner, K., & Gerlovich, J. (1997). *Teaching science for all children* (2nd ed.). Boston: Allyn & Bacon.

Mastropieri, M. A., & Scruggs, T. E. (1993). *A practical guide for teaching science to students with special needs in inclusive settings.* West Lafayette, IN: Purdue Research Foundation.

McCarty, T. L., & Watahomigie, L. J. (1999). Community-based indigenous language education in the USA. In S. May (Ed.), *Indigenous Community-Based Education.* Clevedon, England: Multilingual Matters.

McDonald, F. F., & Elias, P. (1976). *Beginning teacher evaluation studies, phase II 1973-74* (Executive Summary Report). Princeton: Educational Testing Service.

McGuinness, D. (1989). Attention deficit disorder: The emperor's clothes, animal "pharm," and other fiction. In S. Fisher & R. P. Greenberg (Eds.), *The limits of biological treatments for psychological distress: Comparisons with psychotherapy and placebo* (pp. 151-187). Hillsdale, NJ: Lawrence Erlbaum.

Meek, C. (2006, December). From the inside out: A look at testing special education students. *Phi Delta Kappan, 88*(4), 293-297.

Mongillo, J. (Ed.). (1983). *Gateways to science laboratory program.* New York: McGraw-Hill, Webster Division.

Moos, R. H., & Moos, B. S. (1978). Classroom social climate and student absences and grades. *Journal of Educational Psychology, 70*, 263-269.

Mostakas, C. E. (1967). *Creativity and conformity*. Princeton, NJ: D. Van Discrepant.

Msengi, S. G. (2006). *Family, child, teacher perceptions of what African American adult family members think and do to assist their elementary school-aged children to become better readers*. Unpublished doctoral dissertation, University of Northern Iowa, Cedar Falls.

Murnane, R. J., & Raizen, S. A. (Eds.) (1988) *Improving indicators of the quality of science and mathematics education in grades K-12*, Committee on Indicators of Precollege Science and Mathematics Education, Commission on Behavioral and Social Sciences and Education, National Research Council. Washington, DC: National Academy Press.

National Association of Elementary School Principals. (1983). *School discipline and public law 94-142*. Reston, VA: Author.

National Center on the Economy. (1997). *New Standards Performance Standards, Volume 2 Middle School.* Pittsburgh, National Center on Education and the Economy and the University of Pittsburgh: Author.

National Center on Education and the Economy/University of Pittsburg. (1997). *Performance standards: Vol. 1, Elementary school*. Pittsburg: Author.

National Center on Education and the Economy/University of Pittsburg. (1997). *Performance standards: Vol. 2, Middle school*. Pittsburgh: Author.

National Science Foundation. (1997). *Foundations: The challenge and promise of K-8 science education reform*. Arlington, VA: Author.

National Science Foundation (NSF). (1999). *Women, minorities, and persons with disabilities in science and engineering.* Arlington, VA: National Science Foundation.

Neuman, S. B., Hagedorn, T., Celano, D., & Daly, P. (1995). Toward a collaborative approach to parent involvement in early education: A study of teenage mothers. In an African-American community. *American Educational Research Journal, 32*, 801-827.

Ngai, P., & Allen K. (2006, November). IEFA in an urban public school. *Phi Delta Kappan, 88*(3), 211.

Oakes, J. (1985). *Keeping track: How schools structure inequality*. New Haven: Yale University Press.

Olarewaju, A. D. (1988). Instructional objectives: What effects do they have on students' attitudes towards integrated science? *Journal of Research in Science Teaching, 25*(4), 283-291.

Orlich, D., Harder, R., Callahan, R., & Gibson, H. (2001). *Teaching strategies. A guide to better instruction* (6th ed.). New York: Houghton Mifflin.

Orr, E. W. (1987). *Twice as less: Black English and the performance of black students in mathematics and science*. New York: W.W. Norton.

Otto, P. (1991). Modeling problem-solving inquiry processes. *Journal of Science Teacher Education*,

2(2), 37-39.

Overmier, J. B. and Seligman, M.E.P. (1967). Effects of inescapable shock upon subsequent escape and avoidance responding. *Journal of Comparative and Physiological Psychology*, 63, 28-33.

Patton, J., Polloway, E., & Cronin, M. (1990). *A survey of special education teachers relative to science for the handicapped.* Unpublished manuscript, University of Hawaii, Honolulu.

Paulson, F. L., Paulson, P. R., & Meyer, C. A. (1991). What makes a portfolio a portfolio? *Educational Leadership, 48*(5), 60-63.

Petersen, A. (2006). *Exploring intersectionality in education: The intersection of gender, race, disability, and class.* Unpublished doctoral dissertation. University of Northern Iowa, Cedar Falls.

Pettit, S. (2006). *There are no winners here: Teacher thinking and student underachievement in the 6th grade.* Unpublished doctoral dissertation, University of Northern Iowa, Cedar Falls.

Pewewardy, C., & Hammer, P. (2003). Culturally responsive teaching for American Indian students. *ERIC Digest, ED*, 482-325.

Phillips, D. A. (1987). Socialization of perceived academic competence among highly competent children. *Child Development, 58*, 1308-1320.

Piaget, J. (1970). *Genetic epistemology*. New York: Viking.

Piaget, J. (1971). *The science of education and the psychology of the child.* New York: Viking.

Piaget, J. (1973). *To understand is to invent.* New York: Grossman.

Piltz, A., & Sund, R. (1974). *Creative teaching of science in the elementary school.* Boston: Allyn and Bacon.

Polloway, E. A. (1997). *Strategies for teaching learners with special needs*. Upper Saddle River, NJ: Merrill.

Posner, G., Strike, K., Hewson, P., & Gertzog, W. (1982). Accommodation of a scientific conception: Toward a theory of conceptual change. *Science Education, 66*(2), 211-222.

Pretzlik, U., & Chan, L. (2004). Children's self-perception as readers. In T. Nunes & P. Bryant (Eds.), *Handbook of children's literacy,* (pp. 119-146). Dordrecht: The Netherlands: Kluwer Academic Publishers.

Quinn, T. (1991). The influence of school policies and practices on dropout rates. *NASSP Bulletin, 75,* 73-83.

Recht, D. R., & Leslie, L. (1988). Effect of prior knowledge on good and poor readers' memory of text. *Journal of Educational Psychology, 80,* 16-20.

Reese, L., Kroesen, K., & Gallimore, C. (2000). Agency and school performance among urban Latino youth. In R. Taylor & M. Wang (Eds.), *Resilience across contexts: Family, work, culture and community* (pp. 295-332). Mahwah, NJ: Lawrence Erlbaum Associates.

Rehwoldt, R. E., & Samoff, J. H. (1978). Some considerations in the development of programs for the science education of the handicapped. *Proceedings of the Working Conference on Science Education for Handicapped Students* (pp. 14-16). Washington, DC: National Science Teachers Association.

Reif, F., & Larkin, J. (1991). Cognition in scientific and everyday domains: Comparison and learning implications. *Journal of Research in Science Teaching, 28*(9), 733-760.

Reitz, V. (2005, October 6). More women received Ph.D.s, but female senior faculty are still rare. *Machine Design, 77*(19), 66.

Resnick, L. (1983). Mathematics and science learning: A new conception. *Science, 220*, 477-478.

Rhodes, R. (1994). *Nurturing learning in Native American students.* Hotevilla, AZ: Sonwai Books.

Rich, D. (1992). *Megaskills.* (Rev. ed.). New York: Houghton Mills.

Riding, R.J., & Rayner, S. (Eds.). (1998). *Cognitive styles and learning strategies: Understanding style differences in learning and behavior.* London: David Fulton.

Roberts, R., & Bazler, J. A. (1993, January). Adapting for disabilities. *The Science Teacher, 60*(1), 22-25.

Rosenshine, B. (1983). Teaching functions in educational programs. *The Elementary School Journal, 83*, 335-351.

Rosenshine, B. (1986). Synthesis of research on explicit teaching. *Educational Leadership, 43*(7), 60-69.

Rosenshine, B. (1979). Content, time, and direct instruction. In P. Peterson & H. Walberg (Eds.), *Research on teaching: Concepts, findings, and implications.* Berkeley, CA: McCutchan.

Rosenshine, B., & Stevens, R. (1986). Teaching functions. In M. Wittrock (Ed.), *Handbook of research on teaching* (3rd ed., pp. 376-391). New York: Macmillan.

Rowe, M. B. (1973). *Teaching science as a continuous inquiry.* New York: McGraw-Hill.

Sadker, M., & Sadker, D. (1994). *Failing at fairness: How America's schools cheat girls.* New York: C. Scribner's Sons.

Sanders, W., & Rivers, J. (1996). *Cumulative and residual effects of teachers on future student academic achievement.* Knoxville, TN: University of Tennessee Value-Added Research and Assessment Center.

Sandstrom, K., Martin, D. D., & Fine, G. A. (2001). Symbolic interactionism at the end of the century. In G. Ritzer & B. Smart (eds.), *Handbook of Social Theory* (pp. 216-231). London: Sage.

Schlossberg, N. (1989). Marginality and mattering: Key issues in building community. In D.C. Roberts (Ed.), *Designing campus activities to foster a senses of community* (pp. 5-15). San Francisco: Student Services.

Scientific reasoning teachers guide, SAVI/SELPH (1981). Berkley, CA: Center for Multisensory Learning, Lawrence Hall of Science.

Scruggs, T. E., Mastropieri, M. A., Bakken, J. P., & Brigham, F. J. (1993). Reading vs. doing: The relative effects of textbook-based and inquiry-oriented approaches to science education in special education classrooms. *The Journal of Special Education, 27,* 1-15.

Seligman, M. E. P., & Maier, S. E (1967). Failure to escape traumatic shock. *Journal of Experimental Psychology, 74*, 1-9.

Semmel, M. I., Abernathy, T. V., Butera, G., & Lesar, S. (1991). Teacher perceptions of the regular education initiative. *Exceptional Children, 58*, 9-24.

Serpell, R., Baker, L., & Sonnenschein, S. (2005). *Becoming literate in the city: The Baltimore early childhood project.* New York: Cambridge University Press.

Settles, I. H., Cortina, L. M., Malley, J., & Stewart, A. J. (2006, March). The climate for women in academic science: The good, the bad, and the changeable. *Psychology of Women Quarterly, 30*(1), 47-58.

Shields, P. H., Gordon, J. G., & Dupree, D. (1983). Influence of parental practice upon the reading achievement of good and poor readers. *Journal of Negro Education, 52*(4), 436-445.

Shostak, R. (1990). Lesson presentation skills. In J. M. Cooper (Ed.), *Classroom teaching skills* (4th ed.). Lexington, MA: Heath.

Simmons, J. (1991) *Learning controversy: A situational perspective.* (ERIC Document Reproduction Service No. ED 337 759)

Simpson, L. (2002). Stories, dreams, and ceremonies: Anishnaabe ways of learning. *Tribal College: Journal of American Indian Higher Education, 11*(4), 26-29.

Simpson, R. L. (1992). Children and youth with autism. In L. M. Bullock (Ed.), *Exceptionalities in children and youth* (pp. 168-195). Needham Heights, MA: Allyn and Bacon.

Sims, M. (2003, December 8). *Release of 2003 National School Climate Survey sheds new light on the experiences of LGBT students in America's schools*. Retrieved July 17, 2004, from http://www.glsen.org/cgi-bin/iowa/all/news/record/1413.html.

Slavin, R. E. (1989). Students at risk of school failure: The problem and its dimensions. In R. E. Slavin, N. L. Karweit, & N. A. Madden (Eds.), *Effective programs for students at risk* (pp. 3-19). Boston: Allyn and Bacon.

Slavin, R. E., Karweit, N. L., & Madden, N. A. (Eds.) (1989). *Effective programs for students at risk.* Boston: Allyn and Bacon.

Smith, D. D. (1998). *Introduction to special education: Teaching in an age of children.* Needham Heights, MA: Allyn and Bacon.

Smith, D. D., & Luckason, R. (1995). *Introduction to special education: Teaching in an age of children.* Needham Heights, MA: Allyn and Bacon.

Smith, E., & Tyler, R. (1942). *Appraising and recording student progress.* New York: Harper & Row.

Sonnenschein, S., & Schmidt, D. (2000). Fostering home and community connections to support children's reading. In L. Baker, M.J. Dreher, & J.T. Guthrie (Eds.), *Engaging Young Readers: Promoting achievement and motivation* (pp. 264-284). New York: Guilford.

Starnes, B. A. (2006). What we don't know can hurt them: White teachers, Indian children. *Phi Delta Kappan, 87*(5), 384-392.

Sternberg, R. (1990). *Metaphors of mind: Conceptions of the nature of intelligence.* Cambridge and New York: Cambridge University Press.

Stiker, H. J. (1997). *A history of disability.* Ann Arbor: University of Michigan Press.

Stainback, W., & Stainback, S. (1989). Practical organizational strategies. In S. Stainback, W. Stainback, & M. Forest (Eds.), *Educating all students in the mainstream of regular education,* (pp. 3-14). Baltimore, MD: Brookes.

Stainback, W., Stainback, S., & Bunch, G. (1989). Introduction and historical background. In S. Stainback, W. Stainback, & M. Forest (Eds.), *Educating all students in the mainstream of regular education,* (pp. 3-14). Baltimore, MD: Brookes.

Stefanich, G. P. (dir.). (1994). *A futures agenda: Proceedings of a working conference on science for persons with disabilities.* Cedar Falls, Iowa: University of Northern Iowa.

Stefanich, G. P. (Ed.). (2001). *Science Teaching in Inclusive Classrooms: Theory & Foundations.* Cedar Falls, IA: Wolverton.

Stefanich, G., & Bell, L. (1987). *The cascade model: A dynamic approach to classroom discipline.* Dubuque, IA: Kendall/Hunt.

Strain, P. (1983). Generalization of autistic children's social behavior change: Effects of developmentally integrated and segregated settings. *Analysis and Intervention in Developmental Disabilities, 3*(1), 23-34.

Straub, D., & Peck, C. (1994). What are the outcomes for nondisabled students? *Educational Leadership, 52*(4), 36-40.

Suchman, J. R. (1966). *Teachers guide: Inquiry development program in physical science.* Chicago: Science Research Associates.

Suffocating candle teachers guide, science: A process approach, part D. (1968). Washington, DC: American Association for the Advancement of Science.

Takes, M. J. (1993). *Cooperative teaching as a method of collaboration between regular and special educators in an integrated setting.* Unpublished Doctoral Dissertation, University of Northern Iowa, Cedar Falls.

Taylor, B. M., Pearson, P. D., Clark, K., & Walpole, S. (2000). Effective schools and accomplished teachers: Lessons about primary-grade reading instruction in low-income schools. *The Elementary School Journal, 101*(2), 121-166.

Trickett, E., & Moos, R. (1974). Personal correlates of contrasting environments: Student satisfaction with high school classrooms. *American Journal of Community Psychology, 2*, 1-12.

Tyrrell, R. (1990). What teachers say about cooperative learning. *Middle School Journal, 21*(3), 16–19.

Ullman, R. K., Sleator, E. K., & Sprague, R. L. (1991). *ADD-H comprehensive teacher's rating scale.* Champaign, IL: Metritech.

U.S. Department of Education. (1991). *A clarification of ADD: U.S. Department of Education clarifies continuing responsibility of schools toward children with ADD.* (Publication Section 504). Washington, DC: Author.

U.S. Department of Education. (1996). *Eighteenth annual report to Congress on the implementation of the Individuals with Disabilities Education Act, Appendix A.* Washington, DC: Author.

United States Department of Education. (2004). *Annual Report to Congress on the Implementation of the Individuals with Disabilities Act*, National Center for Educational Statistics. Washington, DC: Author.

VanLeuvan, P. (2004, May/June). Young women's science/mathematics career goals from seventh grade to high school graduation. *The Journal of Educational Research, 97*(5), 248-267.

Vaughn, S., Bos, C., & Schumm, J. S. (1997). *Teaching mainstreamed, diverse, and at-risk students in the general education classroom.* Needham Heights, MA: Allyn and Bacon.

Vernon, A. (1999). *The dialectics of multiple identities and the disabled people's movement, 14*(3), 385-398.

Vetter, B. (1996). Myths and realities of women's progress in the sciences, mathematics, and engineering. In C. Davis, A. Ginorio, C. Hollenshead, B. Lazarus, & P. Rayman (Eds.), *The equity equation: Fostering the advancement of women in the sciences, mathematics, and engineering* (pp. 29-56). San Francisco: Jossey-Bass.

Victor, E., & Kellough, R. D. (1997). *Science for the elementary and middle school* (8th ed.). Upper Saddle River, NJ: Merrill/Prentice-Hall.

Vidal, A. (2002). Methods for retention of undergraduate women in science majors. *Geological Society of America, 34*(6), 121.

Villa, R. A., & Thousand, J. S. (1988). Enhancing success in heterogeneous classrooms and schools: The power of partnership. *Teacher Education and Special Education, 11*(4), 144-154.

Villa, R., Thousand, J., Stainback, W., & Stainback, S. (1992). *Restructuring for caring and effective education: An administrative guide to creating heterogeneous schools.* Baltimore: Paul H. Brookes.

Wahl, E. (2001). Can she really do science? Gender disparities in math and science education. In H. Rousso & M.L. Wehmeyer (Eds.), *Double jeopardy: Addressing gender equity in special education* (pp. 133-153). Albany: State University of New York Press.

Wang, M. C., & Wahlberg, H. J. (1988). Four fallacies of segregationalism. *Exceptional Children, 48,* 106-114.

Wang, M. C., Walberg, H., & Reynolds, M. C. (1992). A scenario for better – not separate – special education. *Educational Leadership, 50*(2), 35-38.

Ward, M. E. (1986). The visual system. In G. T. Scholl (Ed.), *Foundations of education for blind and visually handicapped students: Theory and Practice* (pp. 35-64). New York: American Foundation for the Blind.

Warren, W. Z. (2006, November). One teacher's story: Creating a new future or living up to our own history? *Phi Delta Kappan, 88*(3), 198-203.

Wasta, M. J. (2006, December). No child left behind: The death of special education? *Phi Delta Kappan, 88*(4), 298-299.

Watters, J. J., & Dizemann, C.M. (2003). The gifted student in science: Fulfilling potential. *Australian Science Teachers Journal, 49*(3), 46-53.

Watts, J. (2003). *Native American students.* Teaching Learning Committee, Montana State University. Bozeman, MT. Retrieved from http://www.montana.edu/teacherlearn/Papers.

Weigel, D. J., Martin, S. S., & Bennett, K.K. (2005). Ecological Influences of the home and child-care center on pre-school-age children's literacy development. *Reading Research Quarterly, 40*(2), 204-233.

Weld, J. D. (1990, November). Making science accessible: Special students, special needs. *The Science Teacher*, 57(8), 34-37.

Wolfensberger, W., & Thomas, S. (1983). *Program analysis of service system's implementation of normalization goals.* Toronto, Canada: National Institute on Mental Retardation.

Wolfinger, D. (2000). *Science in the elementary and middle school.* New York: Addison-Wesley Longman.

Wood, J. E. (1998). *Adapting instruction to accommodate students in inclusive settings.* Upper Saddle River, NJ: Prentice Hall.

Wood, J. W., & Reeves, C. K. (1989). Mainstreaming: An overview. In J.W. Wood (Ed.), *Mainstreaming: A practical approach for teachers.* Columbus, OH: Merrill.

Wood, K. (1990). Meaningful approaches to vocabulary development. *Middle School Journal, 21*(4), 22-24.

Wood, K. D., & Tinajero, J. (2002). Using picture storybooks to teach content to second language learners. *Middle School Journal, 33*(5), 47-51.

Woodward, J. (1994). The role of models in secondary science instruction. *Remedial and Special*

Education, 15(2), 94-104.

Wright, B. (1993). *An investigation of the practices and perceptions of three regular elementary teachers regarding the integration of students with severe disabilities.* Unpublished doctoral dissertation, University of Northern Iowa, Cedar Falls.

Ysseldyke, J., Thurlow, M., Christenson, S., & Weiss, J. (1987). Time allocated to instruction of mentally retarded, learning disabled, emotionally disturbed and non-handicapped elementary students. *The Journal of Special Education, 21,* 23-42.

Zeichner, K. (1996). Educating teachers for cultural diversity. In K. Zeichner, S. Melnick, & M.L. Gomez (Eds.), *Currents of reform in preservice teacher education* (pp. 133-175). New York: Teachers College Press.

Zinn, H. (2003). *A people's history of the United States: 1492-present.* New York: Harper Collins Publishers.

Zorfass, J. (1991). *Evaluation of the integration of technology for instructing handicapped children (middle school level). Final report of phase II.* Washington, DC: Special Education Programs (ED/OSERS). (ERIC Reproduction Service No. ED 342 160).

Zorfass, J., Remz, A., & Persky, S. E. (1991). *Evaluation of the integration of technology for instructing handicapped children (middle school level).* Final report of phase II. Washington, DC: Special Education Programs (ED/OSERS). (ERIC Reproduction Service No. ED 342 160)

Index